D1268366

GRAPHIC ARTISTS GUILD'S

DIRECTORY OF ILLUSTRATION

No. 22

WWW.DIRECTORYOFILLUSTRATION.COM

800 / 876 / 6425

COLLABORATE TO

GENERATE GREAT FORTUNE

No. 22

CREATIVE TALENT FOR DAILY INSPIRATION

FEATURED HERE

GRAPHIC ARTISTS GUILD'S

DIRECTORY OF ILLUSTRATION

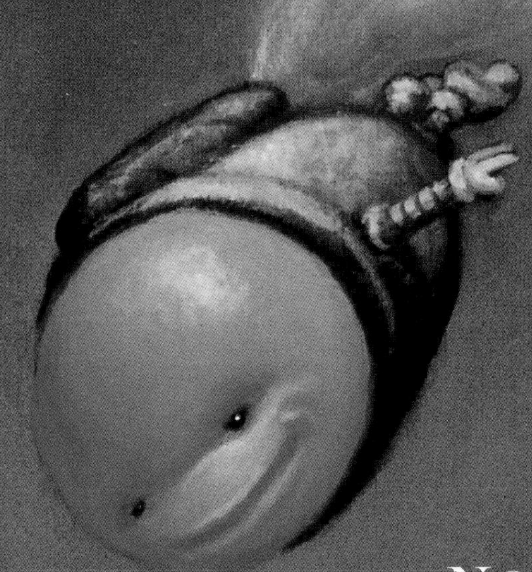

No. 22

WORK HARD. DEVELOP RELATIONSHIPS.

CREATIVELY EXCHANGE

PUBLISHER : EDITOR
Glen R. Serbin

VICE PRESIDENT : SOURCE BOOK DIRECTOR
Elizabeth Nebb Owen

CONTROLLER
Radana Khadilkar

MARKETING REPRESENTATIVES
Ellie Altomare
Jim Christen
Jo Ann Miller
Beth Pierson

MARKETING ASSISTANTS
Vicky Kearney
John Peale

DIRECTOR OF PRODUCTION
Tamra Dempsey

PRODUCTION MANAGER
Barbara Kuhn

PRODUCTION STAFF
Marguerite Freeman

PAGE DESIGN SERVICES
Theil Shelton

DISTRIBUTION COORDINATOR
Kim Harvey

EDITORIAL PROOFING
Karen Bridgers
Julie Simpson

ACCOUNTING ASSISTANT
Johanna Wagner

MANAGING EDITOR : MAGAZINE DIVISION
Julie Simpson

MANAGER : SITEDESIGNWORKS DIVISION
Christina Henson

ADMINISTRATIVE SUPPORT
Kim Taylor

COMPUTER DATABASE COORDINATOR
Debbie Mahterian

GRAPHIC ARTISTS GUILD LIAISON : ADMINISTRATIVE DIRECTOR
Patricia McKiernan

ACCOUNTING FIRM
Damitz, Brooks, Nightingale,
Turner & Morrisset

PRINTER
Toppan Printing Co., Ltd., Tokyo

SHIPPING & MAILING
Express Logistics, Inc.

COVER ILLUSTRATION
Bob Dob
www.bobdob.com
see pages 224-225

BOOK DESIGN
Mark Murphy : Murphy Design Inc.
www.murphydesign.com

PUBLISHED BY
Serbin Communications, Inc.
813 Reddick Street
Santa Barbara / California / 93103
805-963-0439
www.serbin.com / admin@serbin.com

Graphic Artists Guild
90 John Street / Suite 403
New York / New York / 10038
212-791-3400
www.gag.org / admin@gag.org

COVER CONCEPT
"Good Fortune" by Bob Dob is an original commission created for *DI No. 22*.

Printed in Japan ISBN-1-888318-39-2

NO. 22

GRAPHIC ARTISTS GUILD'S DIRECTORY OF ILLUSTRATION 22

www.DIRECTORYOFILLUSTRATION.com

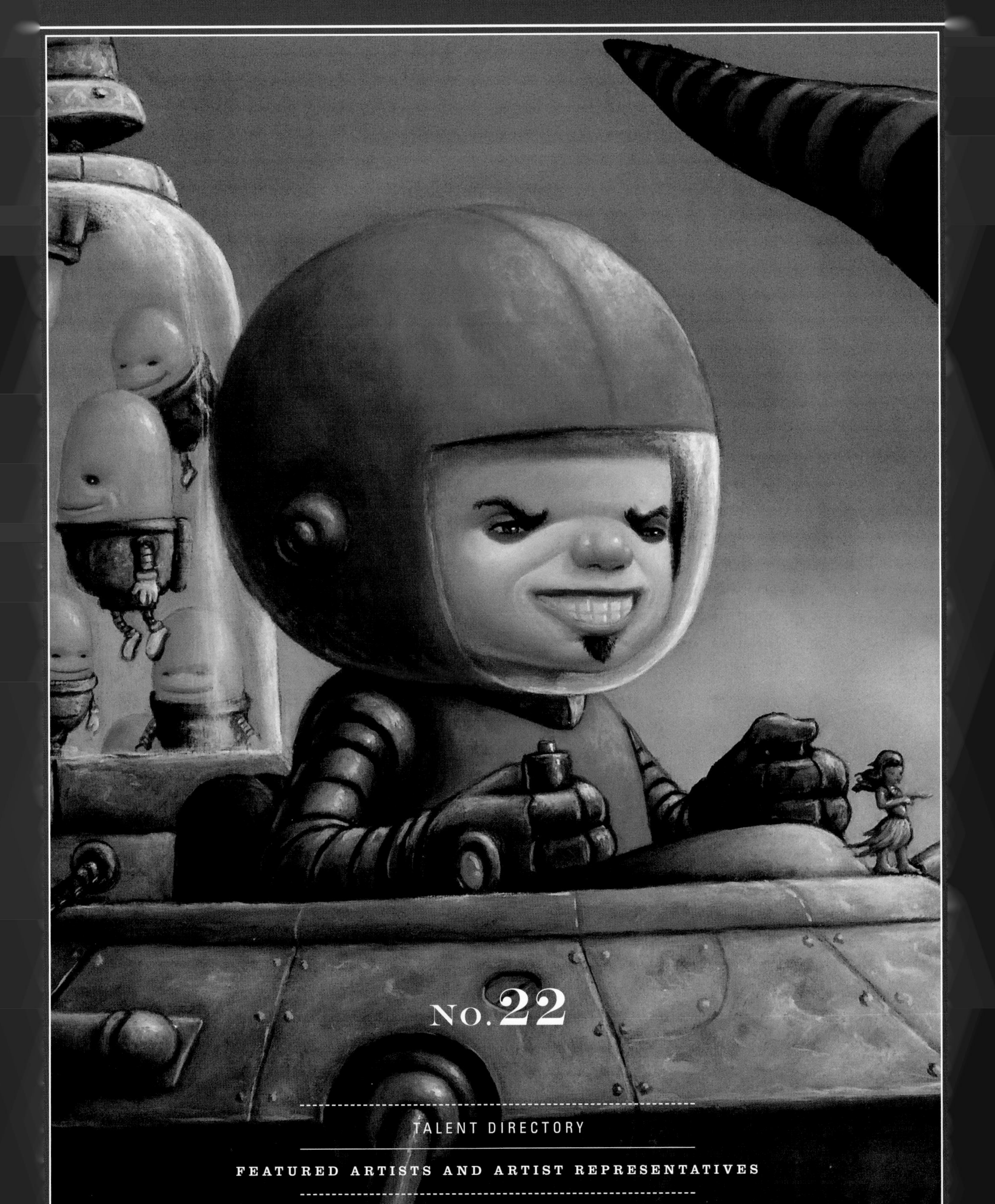

No. 22

TALENT DIRECTORY

FEATURED ARTISTS AND ARTIST REPRESENTATIVES

Dd

Ee

Ff

Gg

Mm

Nn

Oo

Pp

Qq

Rr

Ss

Tt

Vv

Ww

Xx

Yy

Zz

ORIGINAL IDEAS START WITH YOU AND COME TO LIFE WITH THE ORIGINAL ART IN THIS BOOK.

ART IS THE ELEMENT THAT GIVES POWERFUL VISUAL REPRESENTATION TO AN IDEA OR MESSAGE. ART HAS THE ABILITY TO CREATE MOOD, DRAMA, EXCITEMENT, DESIRE, AND TO PROVOKE POWERFUL EMOTIONS. THAT IS WHY CHOOSING THE RIGHT VISUAL IMAGE TO REACH YOUR TARGET AUDIENCE IS CRITICAL TO YOUR PROJECT'S SUCCESS.

In this Directory, you will find thousands of exciting, original artworks created by hundreds of the top illustrators in the United States. These beautiful works can be used for any art application: print, web, animation, and much more. Creating powerful, memorable messages that will reach your targeted audience is easy. All it takes is a collaborative effort that begins when you call a talented illustrator and turn him or her loose with your ideas. Original project ideas may start with you, but to make your messages sing, you need the unique, visual voice of a talented illustrator.

While it is true that you can locate original artworks on the Internet, it can be a very tedious task unless you know the name of a particular illustrator and are already familiar with the artist's work. Even then, you must click through numerous thumbnail images, and viewing original artwork online does not allow you to see how an image works on a page, nor do you see the subtle nuances that are often diminished when viewed on a 72 dpi monitor. That is why we have created this directory.

The Graphic Artists Guild's Directory of Illustration is designed to help you, easily and quickly, find original artwork that is perfect for your projects. All you have to do is find a comfortable chair and turn the pages of this book. Mark all the pages that speak to you with a sticky note and explore styles that offer the look and feel that you are after. Let the images fuel your imagination. When an image catches your eye, think of how the artist could bring your idea to life–and catch the eye of your specific audience.

Contact information is provided for each artist contributor, so your business is always connected to an endless supply of professional artists whose original, creative efforts will give you and your business the competitive edge.

We know that the beautiful images in this directory will enhance your viewers' experiences, and at the same time, they will provide your business with powerful tools for success

John P. Schmelzer

President // Graphic Artists Guild

GRAPHIC ARTISTS
GUILD

PROTECTION

STANDARDS

ETHICS

ADVOCACY

INFLUENCE

PEER NETWORK

UNION CLOUT

KNOWLEDGE

RESPECT

SUPPORT

JUST A FEW OF THE BIG DIVIDENDS

FROM A SMALL INVESTMENT IN YOUR FUTURE.

JOIN US AND REAP THE REWARDS ON-LINE AT WWW.GAG.ORG

THE GRAPHIC ARTISTS GUILD

GRAPHIC ARTISTS
GUILD

ACCESS GOOD FORTUNE ONLINE

WWW.DIRECTORYOFILLUSTRATION.COM

MARCOS CHIN

DISCOVER HUNDREDS OF UNIQUE ARTIST PORTFOLIOS

ACCESS 365 DAYS A YEAR

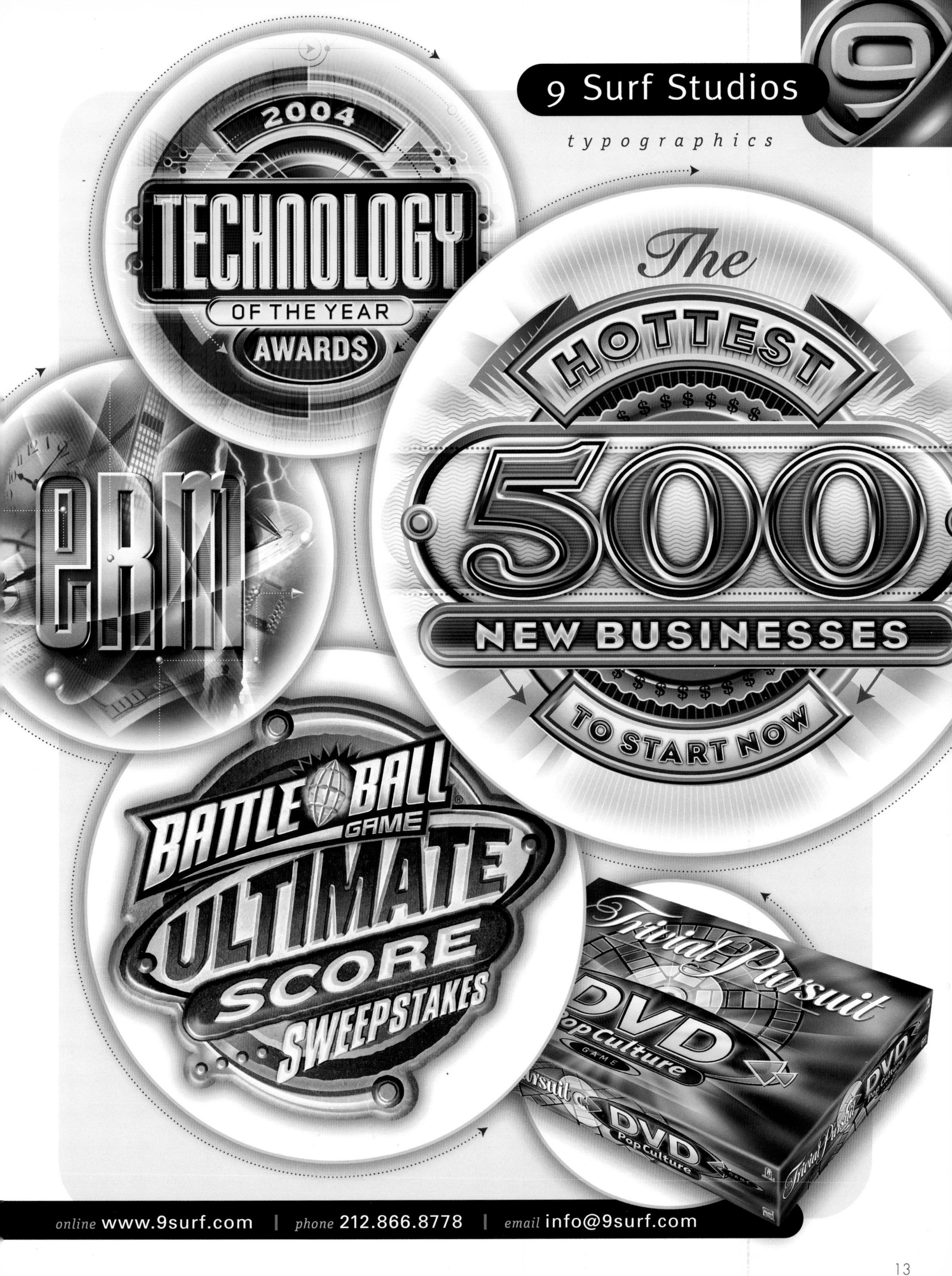
9 Surf Studios
typographics
2004
TECHNOLOGY
OF THE YEAR
AWARDS
The
HOTTEST
500
NEW BUSINESSES
TO START NOW
BATTLE BALL
GAME
ULTIMATE
SCORE
SWEEPSTAKES
Trivial Pursuit
DVD
Pop Culture
GAME
online www.9surf.com | phone 212.866.8778 | email info@9surf.com

Barbie
LANG & REED
Trefethen
TWISTA
Cabernet Sauvignon

Niebaum-Coppola

RUTHERFORD

AZUMAYA

LETTERING XXXXXXXXXXXXXXXXXXXXXXXXXXXXXXXXXXXXXXXXXX

Shimmer
Fruit Co

CITY HALL

AVENUE P

photo
gram

CAFFE GRECO DESIGN

Dolphin
RECORDING

uPns

LOGOS XXXXXXXXXXXXXXXXXXXXXXXXXXXXXXXXXXXXXXXXXXXXXX

FRANCIS
COPPOLA
PRESENTS
1995
ROSSO
CALIFORNIA RED WINE

SOFIA
Blanc de Blancs
CALIFORNIA
1998
FRANCIS COPPOLA

PACKAGING XXXXXXXXXXXXXXXXXXXXXXXXXXXXXXXXXXXXXXXXX

TRIPLE PLAY
DESIGN COMPANY

Eric Kittelberger — Illustrator
1728 Sedwick Avenue NW, Massillon, Ohio 44646
www.TriplePlayDesign.com
v 330 830-0893 f 330 830-0879
eric@TriplePlayDesign.com

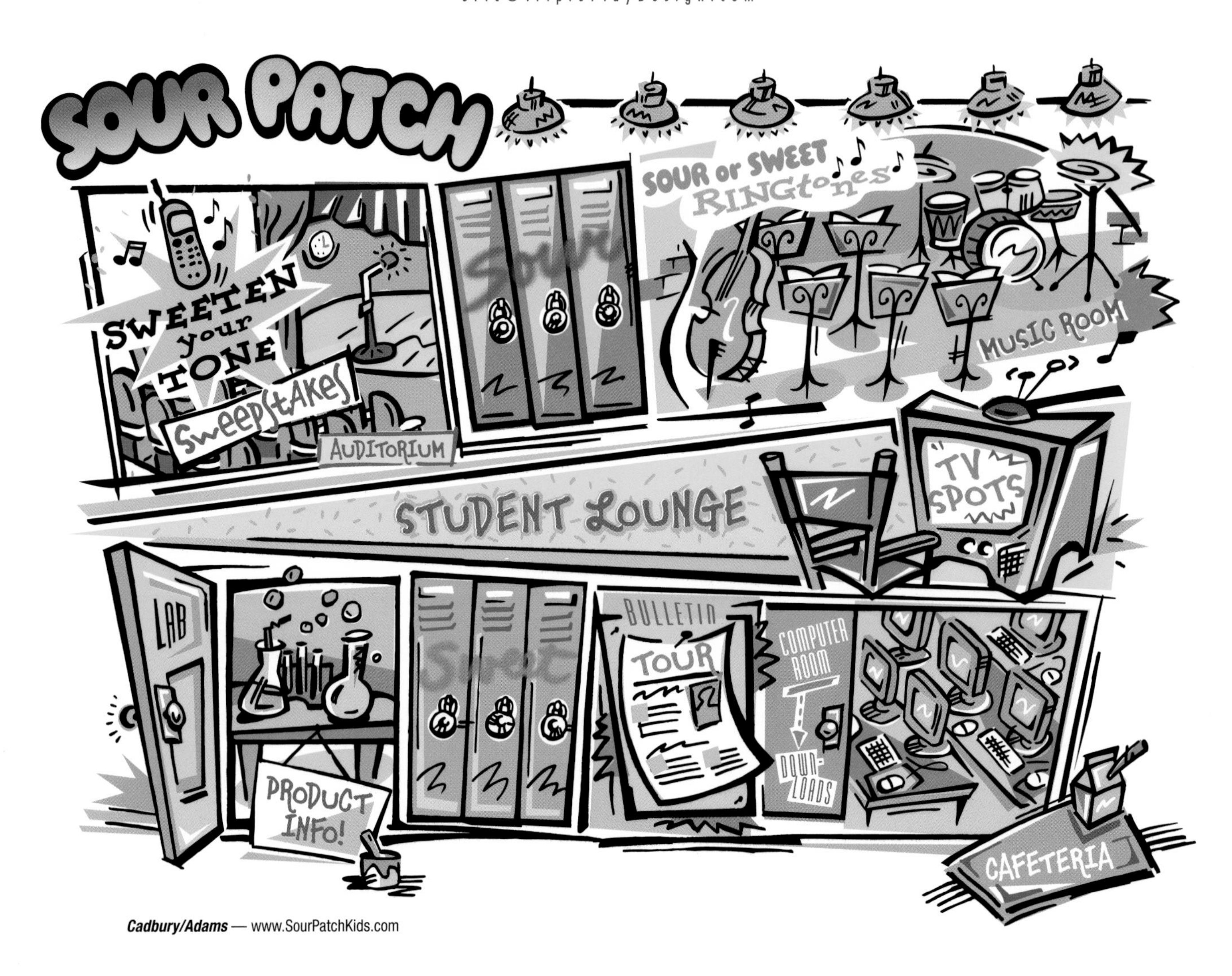
SOUR PATCH
SWEETEN your TONE
Sweepstakes
AUDITORIUM
SOUR or SWEET RINGtones
MUSIC ROOM
STUDENT LOUNGE
TV SPOTS
LAB
PRODUCT INFO!
BULLETIN
TOUR
COMPUTER ROOM
DOWN-LOADS
CAFETERIA

Cadbury/Adams — www.SourPatchKids.com

The scoop on poop.
Over 7,000 dung beetles have been found in one pad of elephant dung. That's enough beetles to fill almost half of a bath tub. The beetles remove dung left by elephants and use it as food.
A hyena leaves its den to poop in a specific location called a latrine. Doing so, keeps predators away from the hyena den.
Before some African plant seeds can germinate, or grow, they must pass through the intestines of an elephant.

Simple facts about poo.
Elephants poop almost 80 pounds per day, enough to fill the trunk of a car.
A male Nile hippo defends its territory by facing backside to neckside with other males and showers them with urine and poop.
A dik dik (small African antelope) marks its territory by dropping poop on other animal's dung.
Scientists study fossilized poop, called coprolite, to determine what ancient animals ate.

Cleveland Metroparks Zoo

DUBLIN'S JOURNEY
Sugardaddy's Sumptuous Sweeties — it's not your everyday brownie!™
Psst... Wanna know a secret?
GET IN ON THE SECRET!
sugardaddys.com
THE PONTIFICAL COLLEGE JOSEPHINUM
BUILDING SPIRITUAL BRIDGES
TIME WARNER CABLE
Put TIME on Your Side
DIGITAL PHONE
HIGH-SPEED ONLINE
CABLE

Sugardaddy's
sumptuous sweeties

FIRSTLINK
HELPING PEOPLE CONNECT

Costume Specialists

DELAWARE AREA
CHAMBER OF COMMERCE

NATIONAL BOARD & ASME
SAFETY BY DESIGN
NOT BY DEFAULT
COLORADO SPRINGS

Brian
Hunter

- Illustration
- Graphic Design
- Photo Editing

1421 Setzer Road
Stroudsburg, PA 18360
tel: 570.620.0822
email: bhunter@huntergrafx.net
web: www.huntergrafx.net

NorthCell
PHARMACEUTICAL

THE
AMMERMAN Co.
Painting & Home Improvements

A QUALITY CRAFTED PRODUCT
Mary's Country Kitchen
Mango Madness
Harper's Country Candles
Raton Rd
Distributed by Harper's Country Candles
Sommersville, NC

Raccoon Ridge
Sheba Chardonnay

super-scented candles
Teaberry
AMERICAN CANDLE
Rte. 611 • BARTONSVILLE, PA 18321 570-629-3388

super-scented candles
Mountain
Forest
AMERICAN CANDLE
Rte. 611 • BARTONSVILLE, PA 18321 570-629-3388

American
Candle
Fund Raiser
Route 611 • Bartonsville • Pennsylvania • 18321
570-629-3388
Jar Candle
Toppers $20.00
Wrought Iron
Holder $16.00
Candle Warmer
$15.00
Wick Trimmer
$4.00
Super-Scented and Triple Fragrances

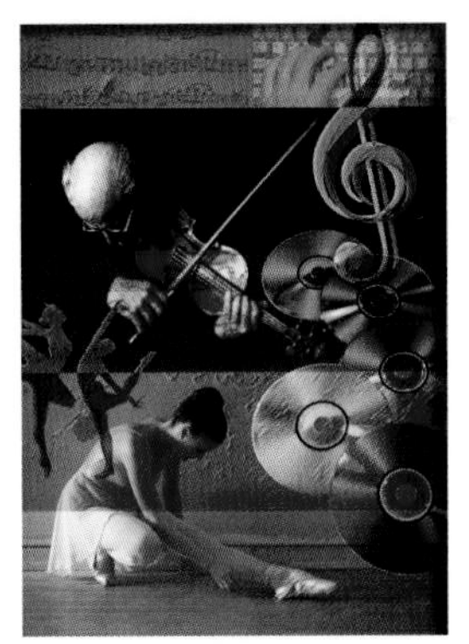

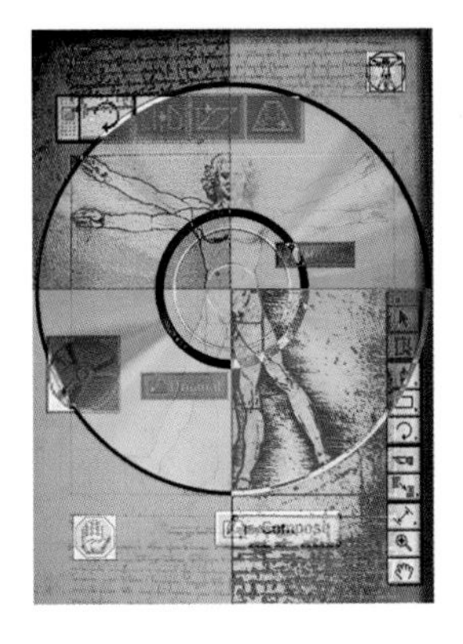

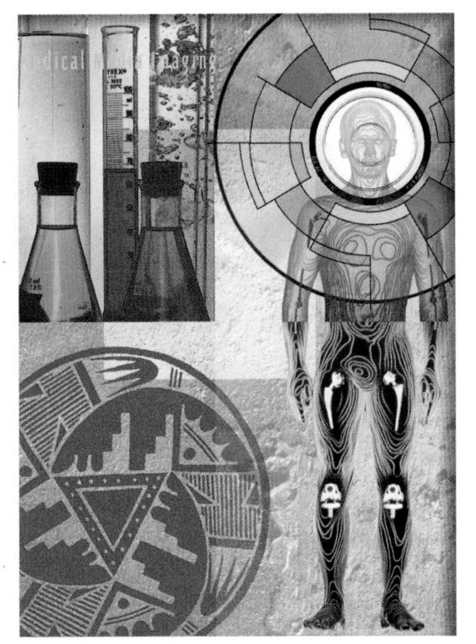

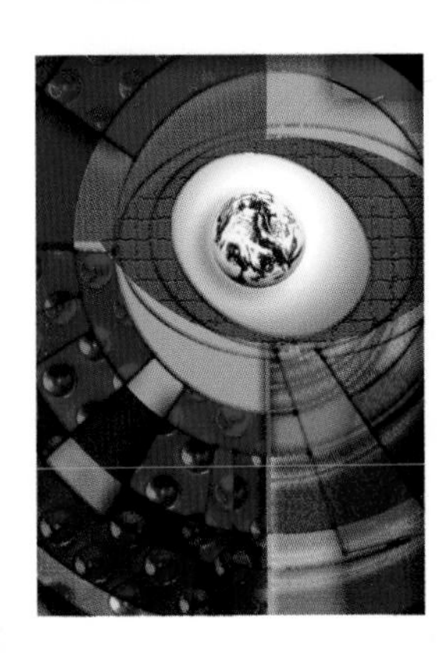

TYCO R/C
JACKED
THE LORD OF THE RINGS
THE FELLOWSHIP OF THE RING
THE LORD OF THE RINGS
THE RETURN OF THE KING
SUPER POSEABLE PELENNOR FIELDS ARAGORN
THE LORD OF THE RINGS
THE TWO TOW
Microwavable
RAGÚ®
Express!™
Pasta Snacks
Classic Meat flavor
ENLARGED TO SHOW DETAIL
Spiral Pasta
Real Sauce
6 Single Servings of Pasta & Sauce
NET WT 1 LB. 8.7 OZ (703g)
Directions:
NBA VIDEO
NATIONAL CHAMPIONSHIP
SUPER BOWL XXXVI CHAMPIONS
Patriots
NFL
OFFICIAL ENHANCED DVD EDI
Design Force, Inc. is a design consultancy specializing in the development of brand, package and promotion design for the global brand leaders in the toy, entertainment, food and beverage industries. Over the past 15 years, we've developed a design expertise which has helped our clients improve the image of their brands, increase market share and gain a significant competitive advantage in their respective categories.
30 Lake Center Executive Park • Suite 170 • 401 Route 73 North • Marlton NJ 08053

Campbell's
CHUNKY
Soup That Eats Like A Meal.
TACKLING
HUNGER
TOUR 2004
NFL
PUSH
POP
CANDY
New!
Energizing Nutrition
Essential Vitamins, Calcium, and Soy Protein
V8
Splash
Smoothies
Peach
Mango
Citrus
Blend
K'NEX
50
MODEL
BUILDING SET
8+
BEGINNER TO K'NEXPERT!
BONUS
MOTOR!
UN MOTEUR EN PRIME!
20
MODEL
BUILDING SET
6-12
BEGINNER TO INTERMEDIATE!
WINGS 'N WHEELS
PER BOWL
XXXVI
HAMPIONS
Patriots
SUPER BOWL XXXVI
FICIAL VIDEO
Through our ForceSight™ process, we develop design solutions that capture the essence and attitude of a brand. We understand the consumer's ability to be motivated by enjoyable experiences. Connecting with consumers through "enjoyment" builds a more lasting, trusted association with a brand. We share this philosophy with our clients – market leaders who own the world's most highly recognizable brands.
D/F
DESIGN FORCE
Building Global Brand Leaders by Design™

Call us at **856.810.2277** x10 • Visit us online at **www.designforceinc.com**

MARIA  STROSTER

OLD NAVY
NETWORK
Tune In...

DiGIORNO
RISING CRUST PIZZA
SUPREME

Fabulous
RANCHVIEW
Rangers

PEPSI

Hi-Yo Silver!

N
W
E
S

PHILIP MORRIS

MUST BE
KRAFT
MAYO!

Grand
Cafe

NESTLE

SweetTweets

TARGET

TRICK R TREAT
TOYS R US

HONEY, I SHRUNK THE PAYMENTS!

Tan Bodies
FAST
BREAK
20 oz.

PEPSI

James
Taylor

4 ME

18
Springbrook

Life is a Sport
Gatorade
Thirst Quencher
Drink it up.

the sauce

A.1. Steak & Cheese.
It's Back. It's Bold.

QUARTER BACK
SACK

MC DONALDS

pocketcard

Genuine
McDonald's
Fries

signals

MARDI
GRAS
WATER
BOTTLE

PumpinStyle

MEDELA

THE GREAT AUSTRALIAN
BARBECUE COOKOFF

MGM
Studios

O.N.N.
OLD NAVY NETWORK

GB

GORDON BUILDERS

Castrol
OPENING PLAY
NFL

HINSDALE
HORNETS

LOGO DESIGN+LETTERING T 773.525.2081 C 312.531.2700 E mstroster@earthlink.net

M A R I A  S T R O S T E R

Get Back
WITH
BIG
Mac

Express
yourself.
PHILIP MORRIS

JOIN
OLD NAVY
NETWORK
A CLUB JUST FOR KIDS 6-11

KRAFT
Whip-ups

TOONENSTEIN
WARNER BROS.

DALANDAN
Citrunpop

Wild
CHERRY
PEPSI

MUST
BE
MAYO!
KRAFT

ENTERPRISE CAFE

Disney
That Darn Cat!

TOASTMASTER

SEASON'S
GREETINGS

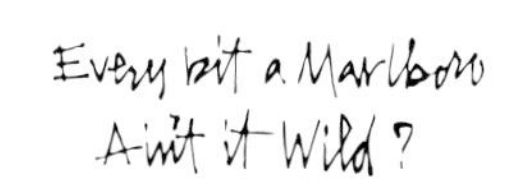
Every bit a Marlboro
Ain't it Wild?

CYCLE
SMITHY

Valentine Mix
BRACHS

Marlboro
Music

CREMESAVERS

La Lupita

Peace

IDM

WINTER
CARNIVALE
20/30 CLUB

WOK
EASTMAN OUTDOORS

YOUR SHERPA
.COM

fingers
&toes
nail spa

100 days
of summer
game
FOOD NETWORK

smoothest
VOX VODKA

Liquid fast. Advil strong.

WEST LOOP
CANINE CLUB

TAKE THE CHALLENGE
Advil
LIQUI-GELS

PEPSI
PEPSI

Hip & Hoppin'
TARGET

LOGO DESIGN+LETTERING T 773.525.2081 C 312.531.2700 E mstroster@earthlink.net

JONCLUND ·COM 330-655-0784

Lund

TWO
A
Day
SNOKIST
PRODUCT OF THE U.S.A. PRODUCT OF THE U.S.A.

Parker Brothers
Nostalgia
GAME COLLECTION
Relive the Fun!

Chick-fil-A
PEACH BOWL
ACC VS SEC

It's all BIG in...
TEXAS

LOWES ISLAND

The Hollywood
BUNGALOW
Co.

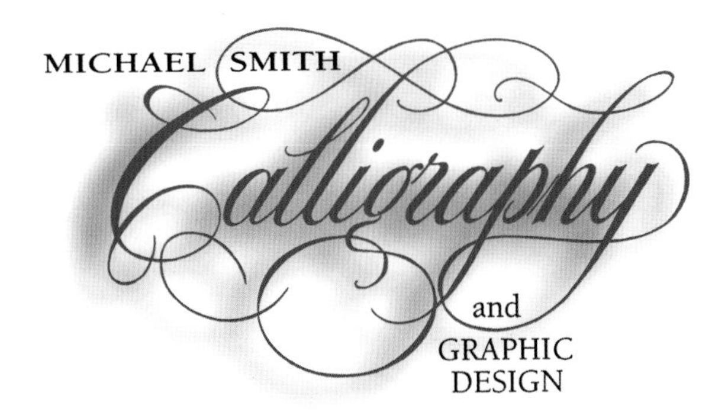
MICHAEL SMITH
Calligraphy
and
GRAPHIC
DESIGN

Kiss my grits!

THE TWENTY-SIX PILLARS OF STRENGTH
ON WHICH OUR CULTURE RESTS

Elephant
Peachtree Golf Center

Ashly
and
Greg

caribbean
jazz

MICHAEL SMITH CALLIGRAPHY • www.myquillworks.com
4105 Hillcrest View Ct. • Suwanee • GA 30024
Ph/770-271-9399 • Fax/770-271-9935 • myquill@bellsouth.net

Design &
Illustration

PARK * CITY
DINER

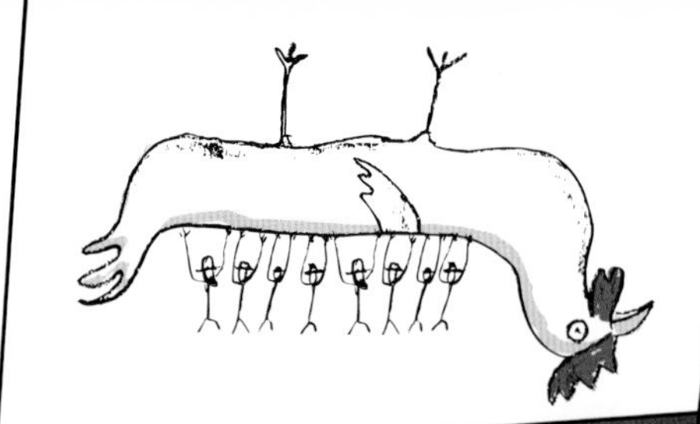

{entreprenerd}

POP
arts + music
festival
JULY 3-4, 2004

COOLBON

ROCKY RIVER
BREWING Co.

FIN'S
ISLAND BAR
AT ROCKY RIVER BREWING CO.

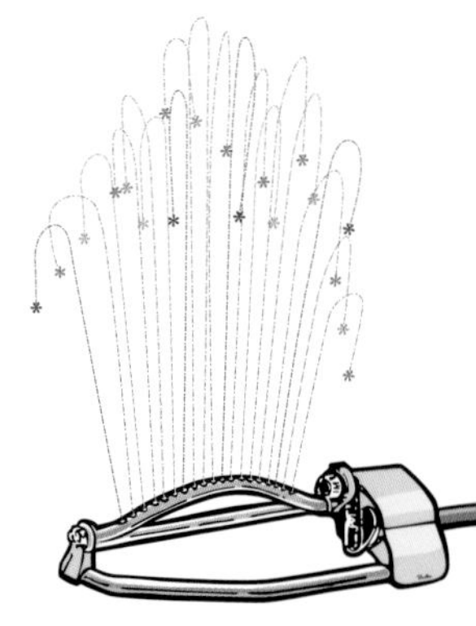

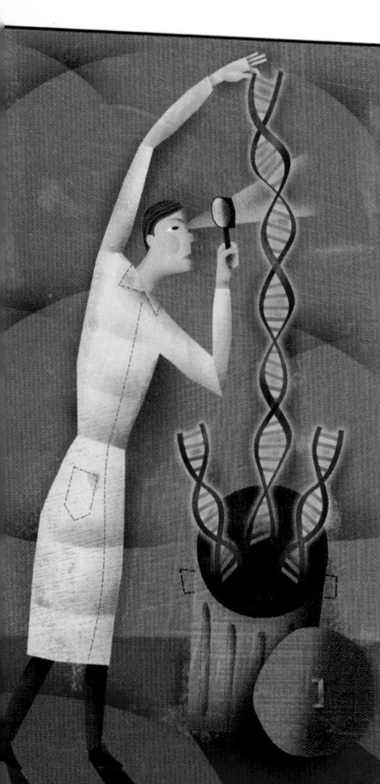

Newbomb
ART/WORK

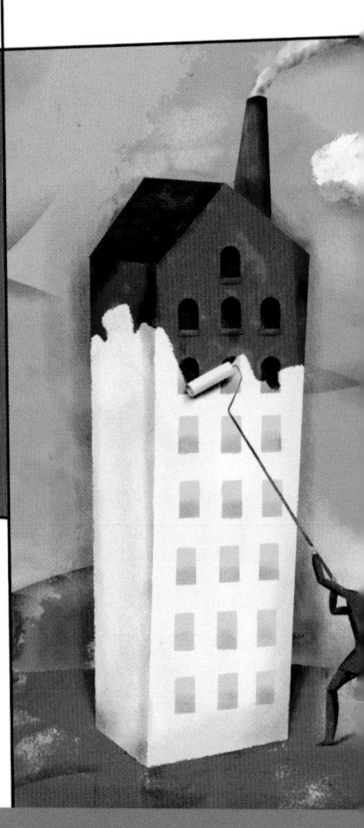

On the Rise
ARTISAN BREADS & PASTRIES
EST. 2001

Absolutely
80s

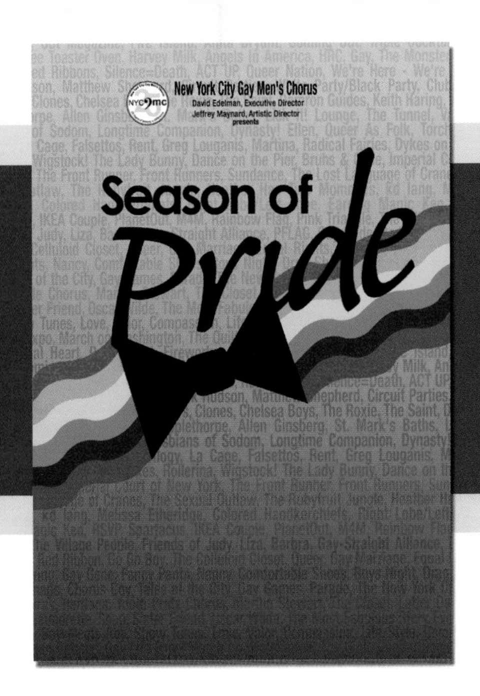
New York City Gay Men's Chorus
David Edelman, Executive Director
Jeffrey Maynard, Artistic Director
presents
Season of Pride

Acting Out Design

Scott J. Fowler
(212) 757-6493
www.ActingOutDesign.com

PACIFIC
OCEAN
GROUP
INC.
Our
Primary Care
is Your
Well-Being

1909
SANTA MONICA PIER
90th
ANNIVERSARY
Celebrate
Pier Days!
October 2&3
1999

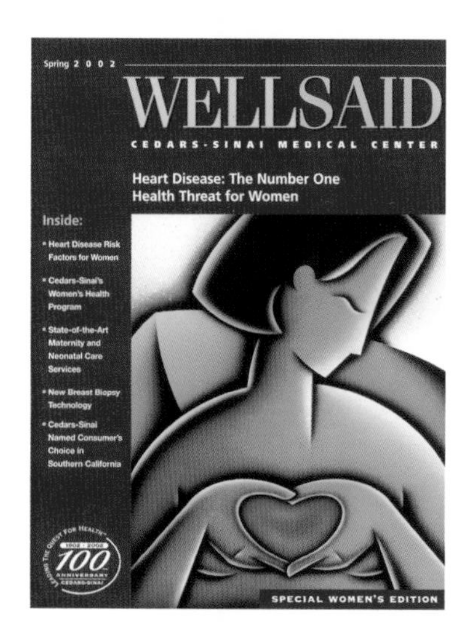
Spring 2002
WELLSAID
CEDARS-SINAI MEDICAL CENTER
Heart Disease: The Number One
Health Threat for Women
Inside:
• Heart Disease Risk Factors for Women
• Cedars-Sinai's Women's Health Program
• State-of-the-Art Maternity and Neonatal Care Services
• New Breast Biopsy Technology
• Cedars-Sinai Named Consumer's Choice in Southern California
100
SPECIAL WOMEN'S EDITION

THE ASSOCIATES OF CEDARS-SINAI
Private Tour of
The Cathedral of Our Lady of the Angels

SANTA MONICA
PUBLIC
LIBRARY

Hidden Valley Ranch

C·R·E·S·T

Dado

DIANE
KUNTZ
DESIGN

Diane Kuntz Design is an award-winning studio that has been creating positive images for companies for over twenty years. We specialize in logo design and corporate identity packages, brochures and annual reports for many corporate, entertainment and healthcare clients. We are known for our high-end design capabilities as well as for developing lasting client relationships. For more information call 310.451.3601 or visit **www.dianekuntzdesign.com**

SANTA MONICA PIER
90th
ANNIVERSARY

tel 310.451.3601 | fax 310.899.3785 | d.kuntz@verizon.net

A Animals

B Bottle cap
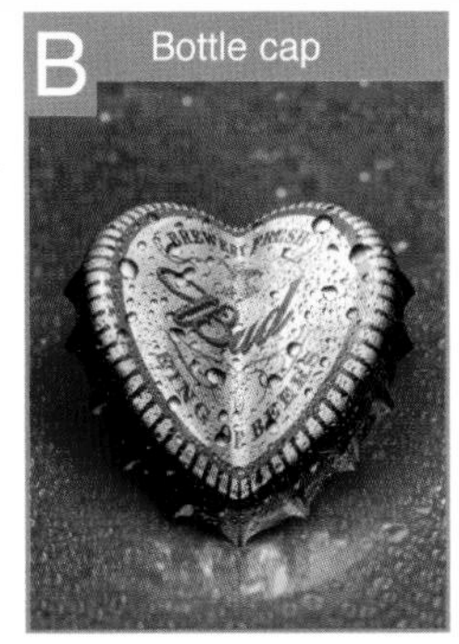

C Comic Strips

Did you steal Mrs. Jones's car?

D Drawing

E Elegant

F FX - Special FX

G Girls

H How To
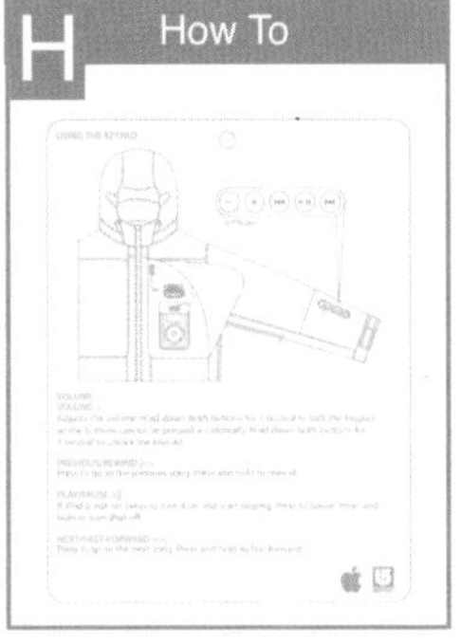

I Ice Cream

J Jam

K Kids

L Lion

M Maps
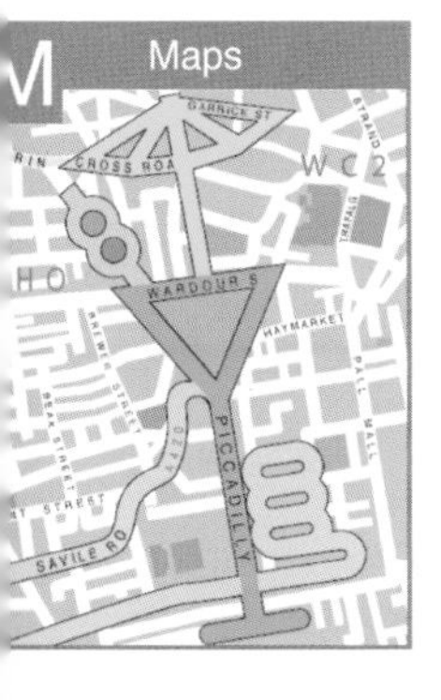
WC2
PICCADILLY

Find Your Solution
www.aareps.com

N Nicholson

O Orange

P Penquin

Q Queen Mary

R Retro Pin-up

S Splash

T Twist
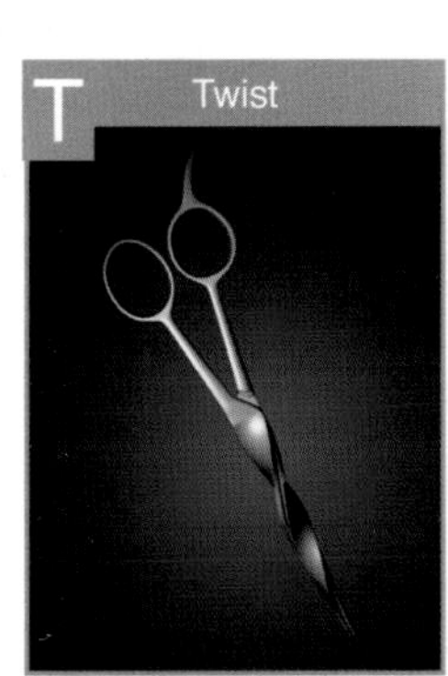

U US Open

LIGHTNING RODDICK
HIS ARM IS DANGEROUS
OFFICIAL CARD OF
HOT SHOTS
OFFICIAL CARD OF THE US OPEN

V VEGF
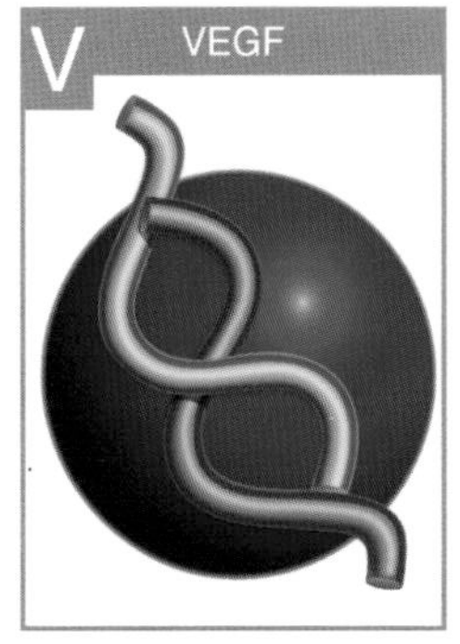

W Water
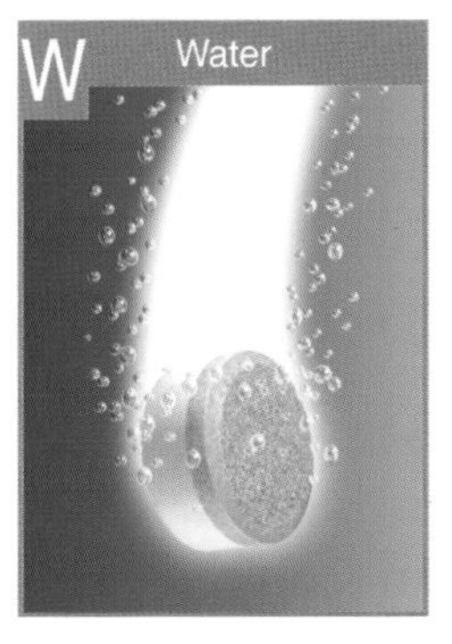

X X-Rayed

Y Youth Culture

Z Zima

ZIMA
3-DAY WEEKEND

AA REPS

AA Reps, Inc.
353 West 53rd Street - Suite 1W
New York, NY 10019

Phone: 212.682.2462
Fax: 212.582.0090
Web: www.aareps.com

John Alvin Studio

LAWSU

Gary Ciccarelli

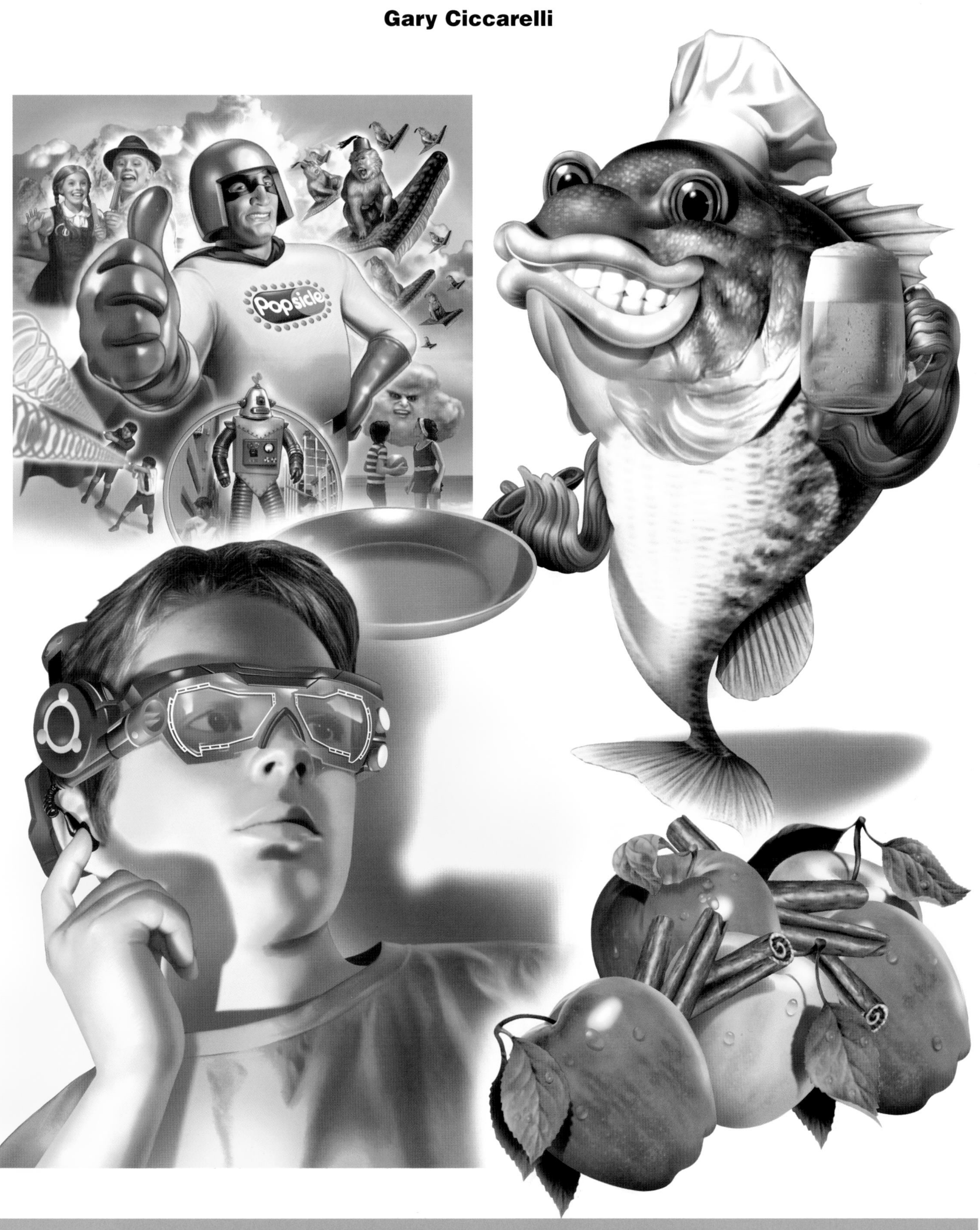
Popsicle

2
2
KENT GAMBLE

American Artists Reps, Inc.
353 West 53rd Street - Suite 1W
New York, NY 10019
Phone: 212.682.2462
Fax: 212.582.0090
Email: info@aareps.com

The Greatest Moments In Banking!
324 B.C.
The First Check
A financial tool from a simpler time, when fur was trendy, steaks were served al dente, and the phrase "going out clubbing" had an entirely different meaning.
1827
The Mattress Safe
What could possibly penetrate the solemn fortress of a 14 thread-count pima cotton sheet and pigeon feathers?
1945
The Free Toaster
Originally created as a space heater/self-tanner, bankers repackaged this mechanism as a bread-toasting device.
2005
"Thank You"
Rewards for Banking
For most banks, an occasional free lollipop may seem like a great way to say, "thank you."
We, however, think you deserve more. We're talking real rewards. Like electronics, clothes and travel.
All for the regular banking you do anyway.
Like using online bill pay or having a savings account.
It's all part of ThankYou from Citi.
Rewards for your Citi credit card and now for banking.
Banking hasn't been this fun since, well...never.
Just call us at 1-888-511-CITI or visit citi.com.
citibank
Live richly.

Bill Garland

P.O.V
points of view
Full
Service
Design
P.O.V
points of view
Garland

t-nine
K2
VSH
k2women kick ass!

Studio Liddell

801

Rowland

John Blackford

John Blackford

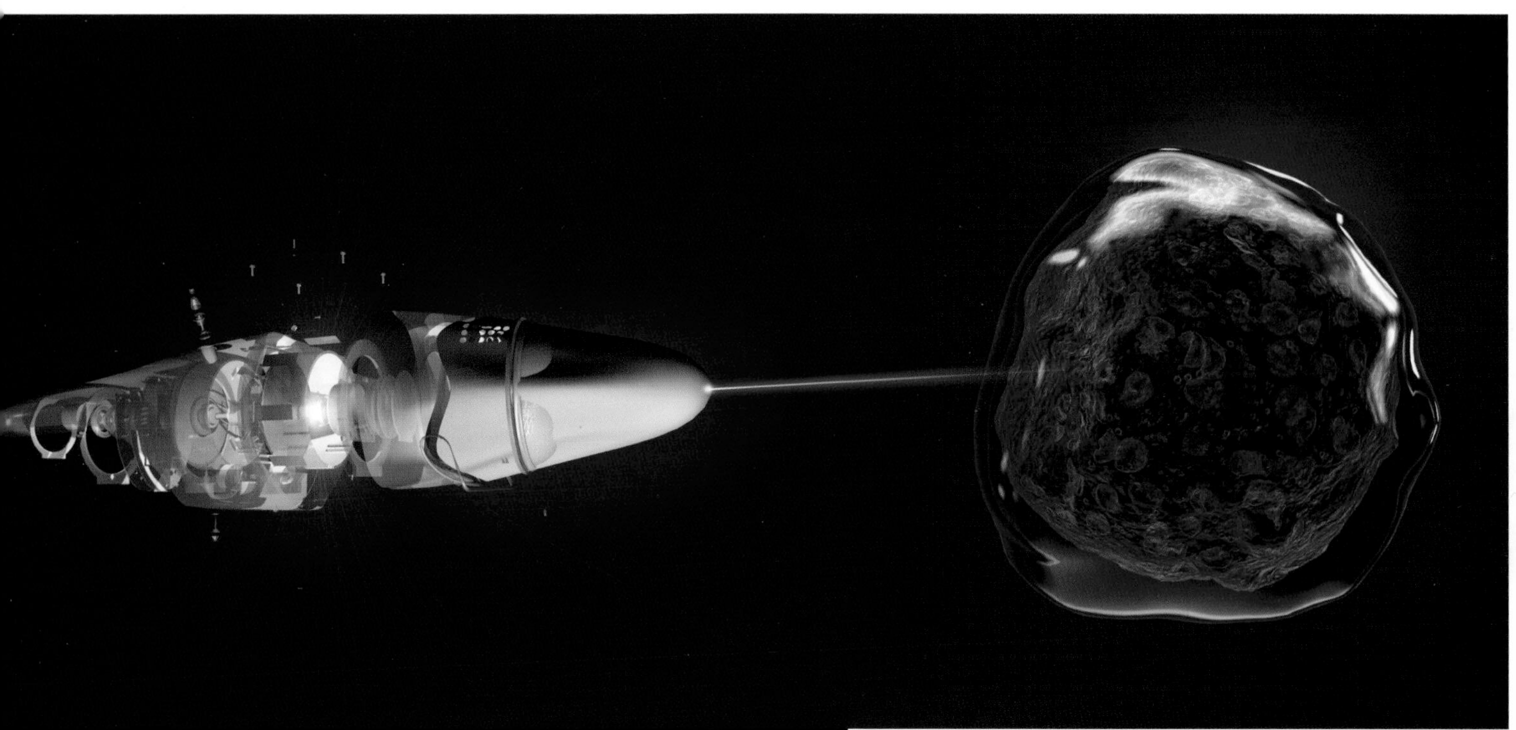

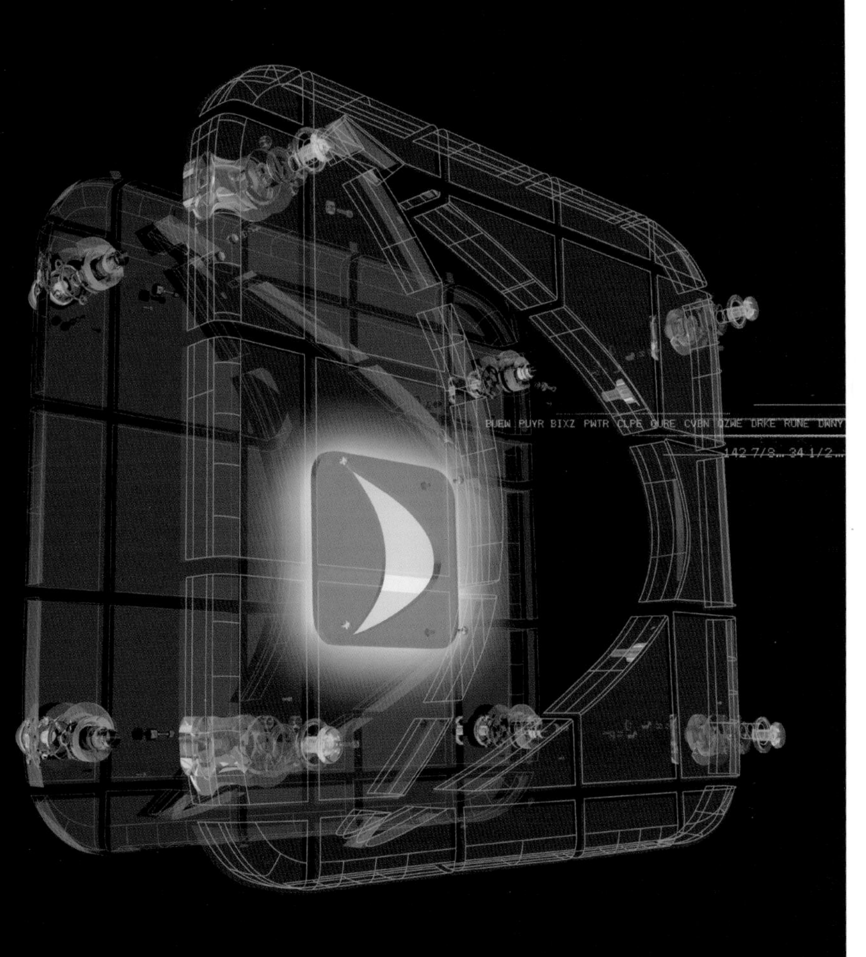

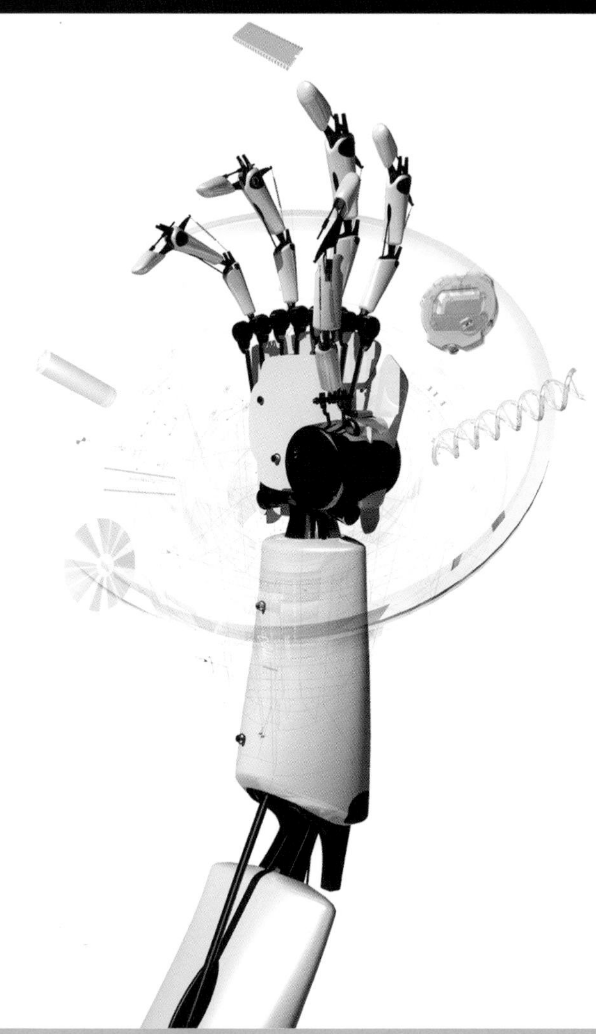

Jacques Fabre

J. FABRE
J. FABRE
J. FABRE
J. FABRE

American Artists Reps, Inc.
353 West 53rd Street - Suite 1W
New York, NY 10019
Phone: 212.682.2462
Fax: 212.582.0090
Email: info@aareps.com

Garth Glazier

CLEVELAND
Crunch
Nestlé
CRUNCH
ZIMA
3-DAY WEEKEND
ZIMA
ZIMA
NABISCO
Newtons
RITZ
SnackWells
OREO
Chips Ahoy!
AIR CRISPS

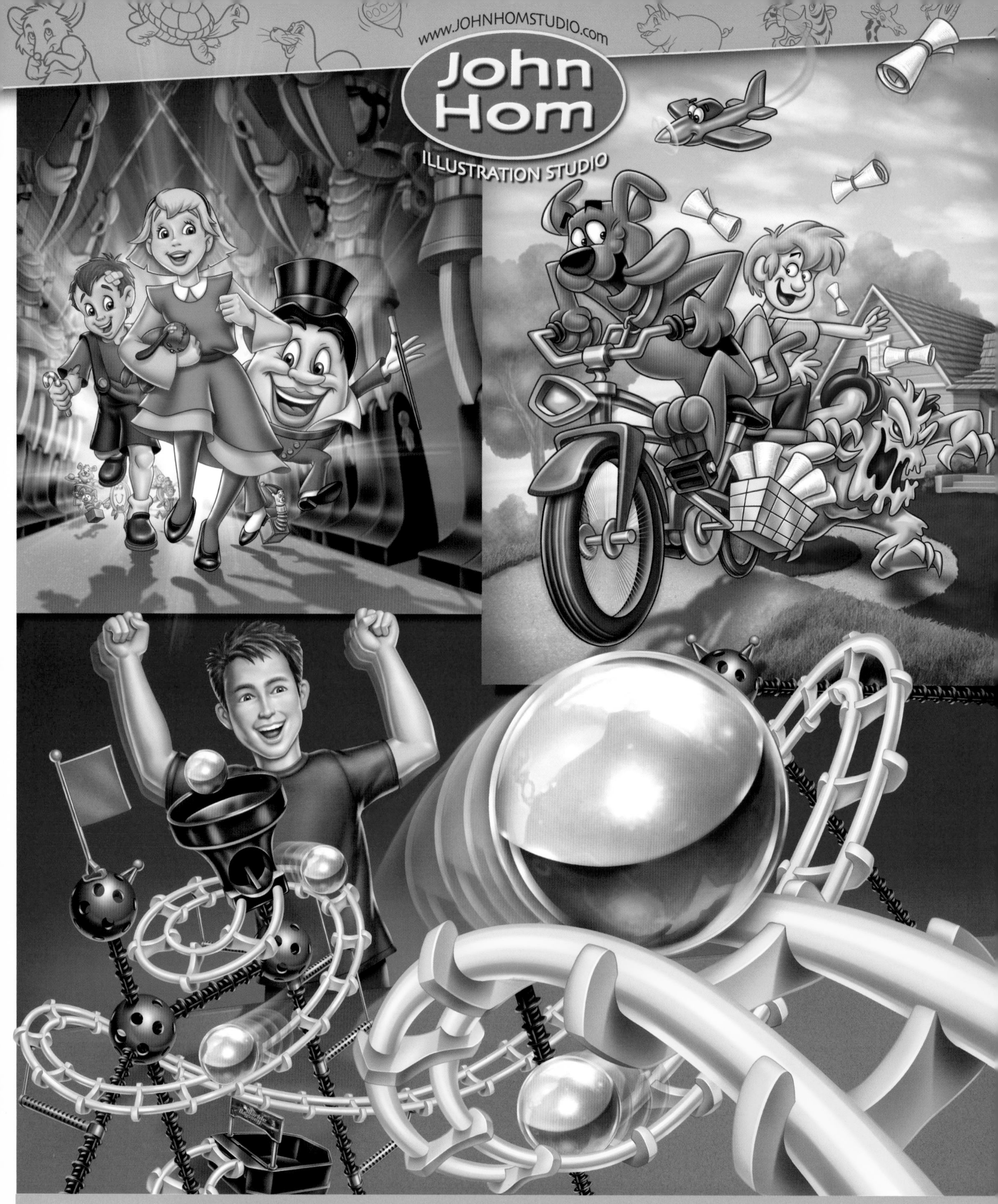

WWW.JOHNHOMSTUDIO.com
John Hom
ILLUSTRATION STUDIO

AA REPS

www.JOHNHOMSTUDIO.com
John Hom
ILLUSTRATION STUDIO
DIG 'EM

AA REPS

Marcel Laverdet

AA REPS

Find Your Solution
www.aareps.com

American Artists Reps, Inc.
353 West 53rd Street - Suite 1W
New York, NY 10019
Phone: 212.682.2462
Fax: 212.582.0090
Email: info@aareps.com

Chris Hopkins

Matt Zang

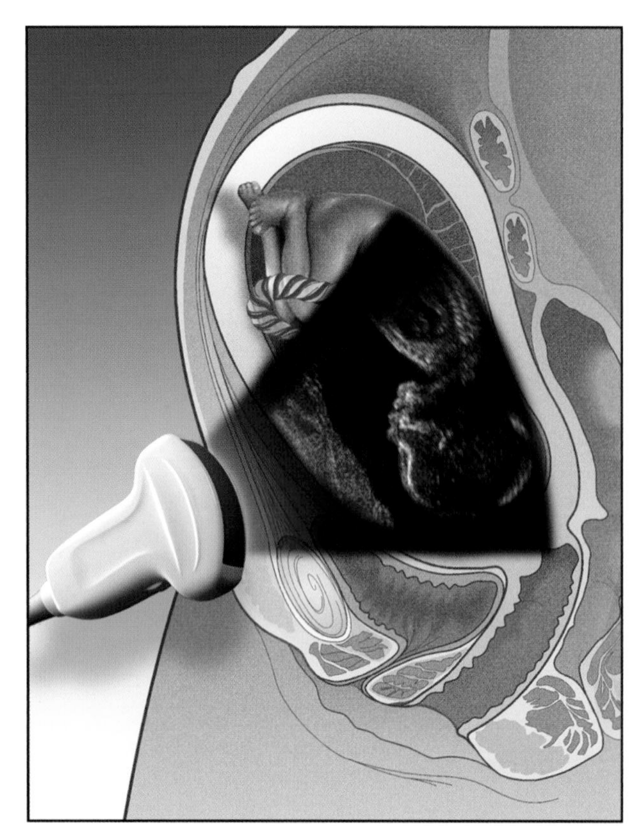

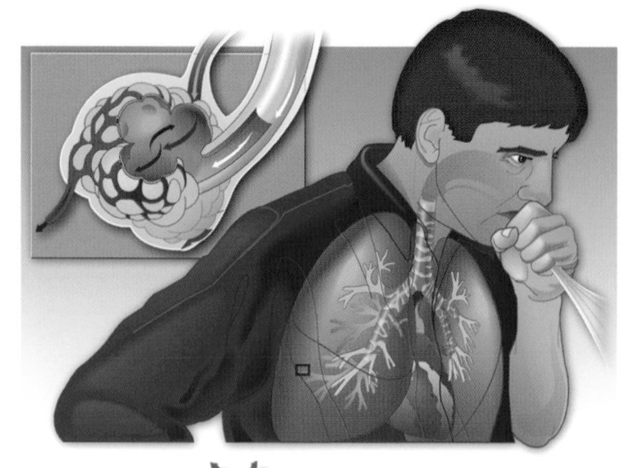

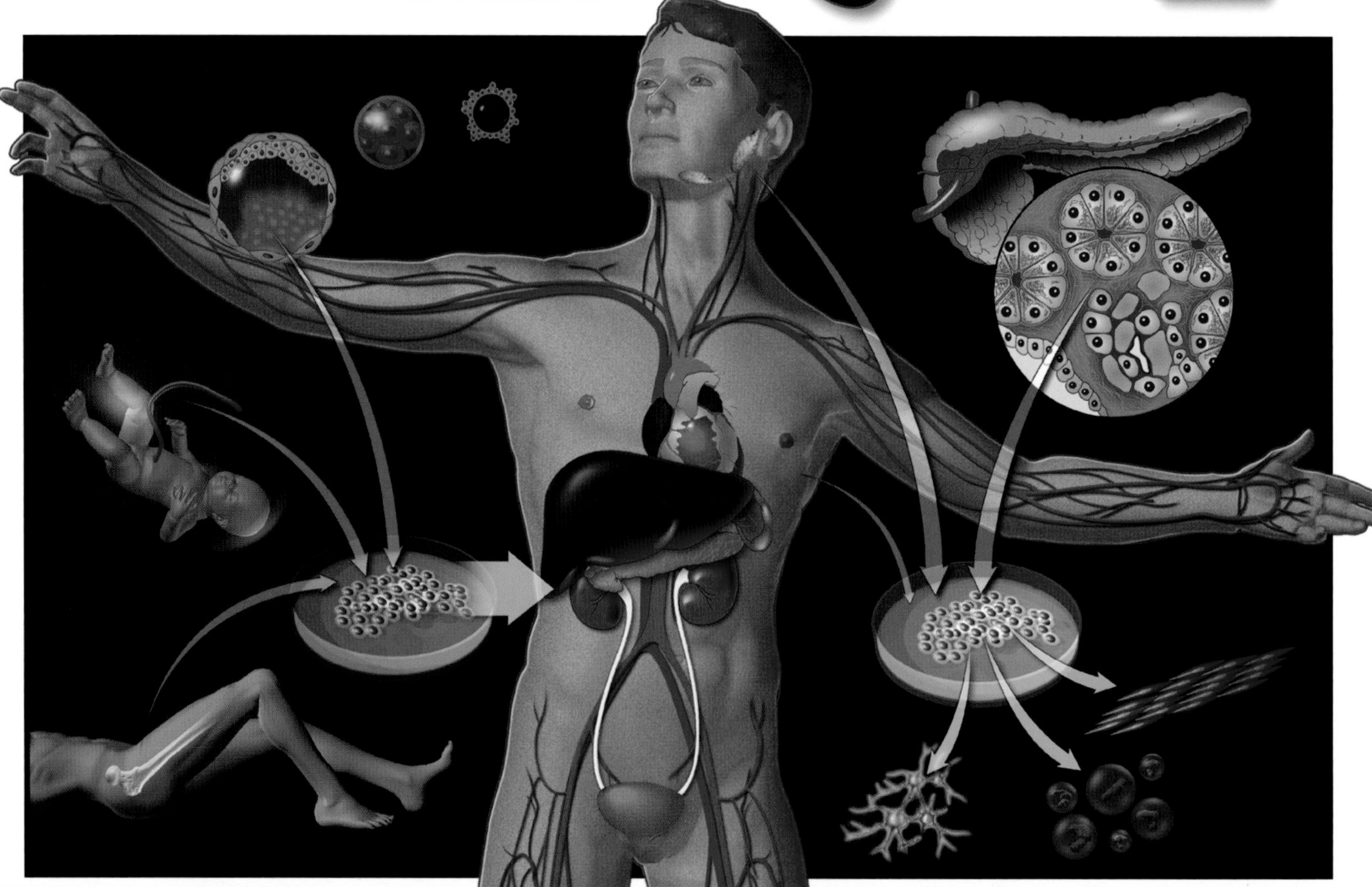

Xoop Productions

SAFETY TESTED

Keith Batcheler

Riddell

Satoshi Kambayashi / Paquebot

0 1 2 3 4 5 6 7 8 9
%

THE BOSS

TAXI

PURGATORY PIZZA
BEELZEBUB BEER
Catechism Cookies
PEARLY GATE PORK RINDS
HELLFIRE HOOPS
Stygian Salsa Dip
Hail Bloody Mary
Vatican Candy
OLD NICK

AA REPS

David Semple

$120

Mike Jaroszko

Russell Farrell

R·FARRELL

05
R·FARRELL

Jean-pascal Donnot

CLIQUEZ ICI !

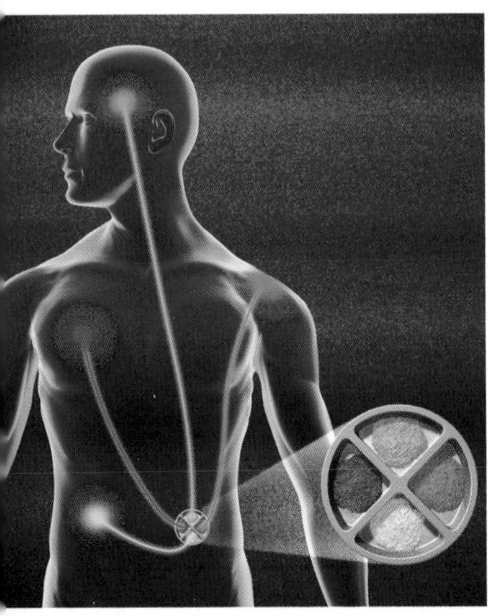

SWIFT

DALIA

Prater

Bonnie Hofkin

Latitude
51:32
N
W
E
S

Tony Randazzo

Xtreme
27

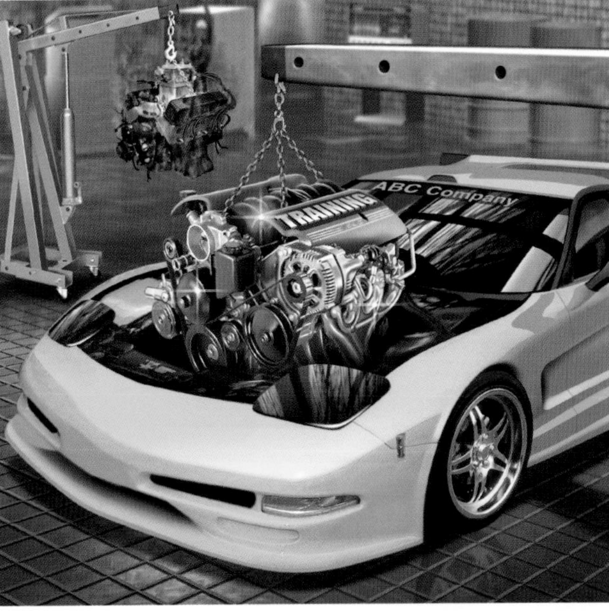

ABC Company
TRAINING

5
16

Hot Wheels
3
2
1

Jim Hummel

The
Adventures of
SillyBilly

HUMMEL

"WE MIGHT AS WELL LEAVE NOW. IF THEY'RE GOING TO BUILD ALL THOSE HOUSES HERE, THEY MUST NOT WANT US AROUND ANYMORE."

American Artists Reps, Inc.
353 West 53rd Street - Suite 1W
New York, NY 10019
Phone: 212.682.2462
Fax: 212.582.0090
Email: info@aareps.com

Jake Rickwood

LIGHTNING RODDICK
HIS ARM IS DANGEROUS
OFFICIAL CARD OF
HOT SHOTS
OFFICIAL CARD OF THE US OPEN
AMERICAN EXPRESS
REWARDS
ANDREW S. RODDICK

Jim Steck

CRUSTY
O's
7

AA REPS

American Artists Reps, Inc.
353 West 53rd Street - Suite 1W
New York, NY 10019
Phone: 212.682.2462
Fax: 212.582.0090
Email: info@aareps.com

Stan Watts

Candy Lab

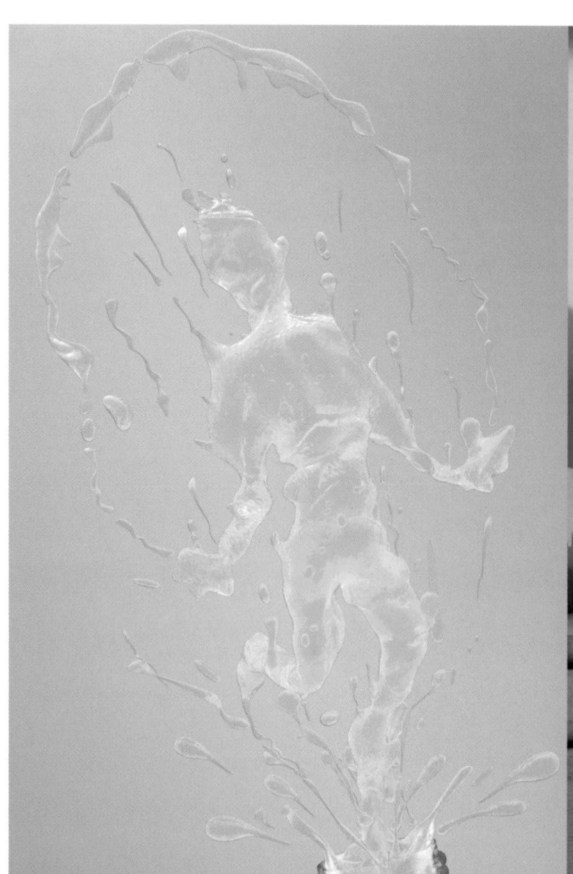

3
4
5

NIKE
HIGHLY EVOLVED SHOES
NIKE SHOX

ILLUSTRATION • GRAPHICS • CREATIVE & BRAND CONSULTANCY • INTERACTIVE • GAME DEVELOPMENT
WEB DESIGN • CHARACTERS • ANIMATED ENCOUNTERS • 3D RENDERING • STORYBOARDS
EXHIBITIONS • PAINTINGS • LIVE ART • MAGAZINES • TOYS • ROBOTS • MERCHANDISE

virgin atlantic

virgin atlantic

virgin atlantic

BERNSTEIN & ANDRIULLI WWW.BA-REPS.COM
e ARTINFO@BA-REPS.COM **p 212-682-1490** f 212-286-1890

© 2005 R.J. REYNOLDS TOBACCO CO.
CAMEL
PLEASURE
TO
BURN
CAMEL LIGHTS
11 mg. "tar", 0.9 mg. nicotine av. per cigarette by FTC method.
Actual amount may vary depending on how you smoke.
For T&N info, visit www.rjrttarnic.com.
SURGEON GENERAL'S WARNING: Smoking Causes Lung Cancer, Heart Disease, Emphysema, And May Complicate Pregnancy.
SINCE 1913

BEAUTY

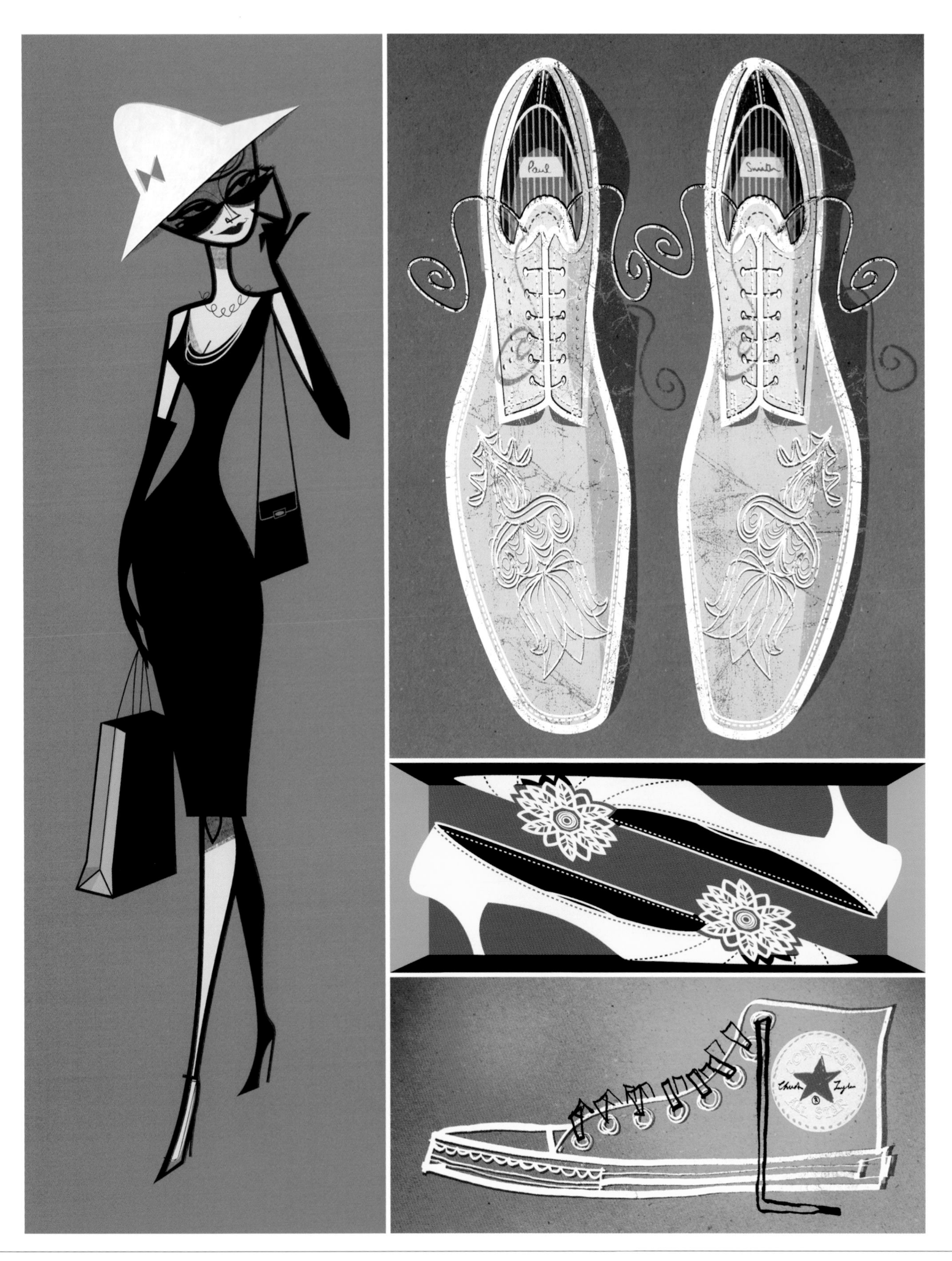
Paul
Smith

The True
and Outstanding
Adventures of the
Hunt Sisters
Elisabeth
Robinson
'A story to treasure...
I loved it'
ADRIANA TRIGIANI

新年快乐
Felices Fiestas
Buone Feste
Frohe Festtage
Meilleurs Voeux
Boas Festas
Season's Greetings
God Jul
Kellemes
Joulua

BERNSTEIN & ANDRIULLI WWW.BA-REPS.COM
e ARTINFO@BA-REPS.COM **p 212-682-1490** f 212-286-1890

NIKE SB
NIKE SB

FIND YOUR FLAVOR
ABSOLUT
Country of Sweden
RASPBERRI
Feel the intense burst of natural Raspberry, blended with vodka distilled from grain grown in the rich fields of southern Sweden. The distilling and flavoring of vodka is an age-old Swedish tradition dating back more than 400 years.
Absolut since 1879.
(80 PROOF) 750
RASPBERRI
ONE WAY
BAR 20
WASHINGTON
HAIR CUT $

BERNSTEIN & ANDRIULLI WWW.BA-REPS.COM
e ARTINFO@BA-REPS.COM **p 212-682-1490** f 212-286-1890

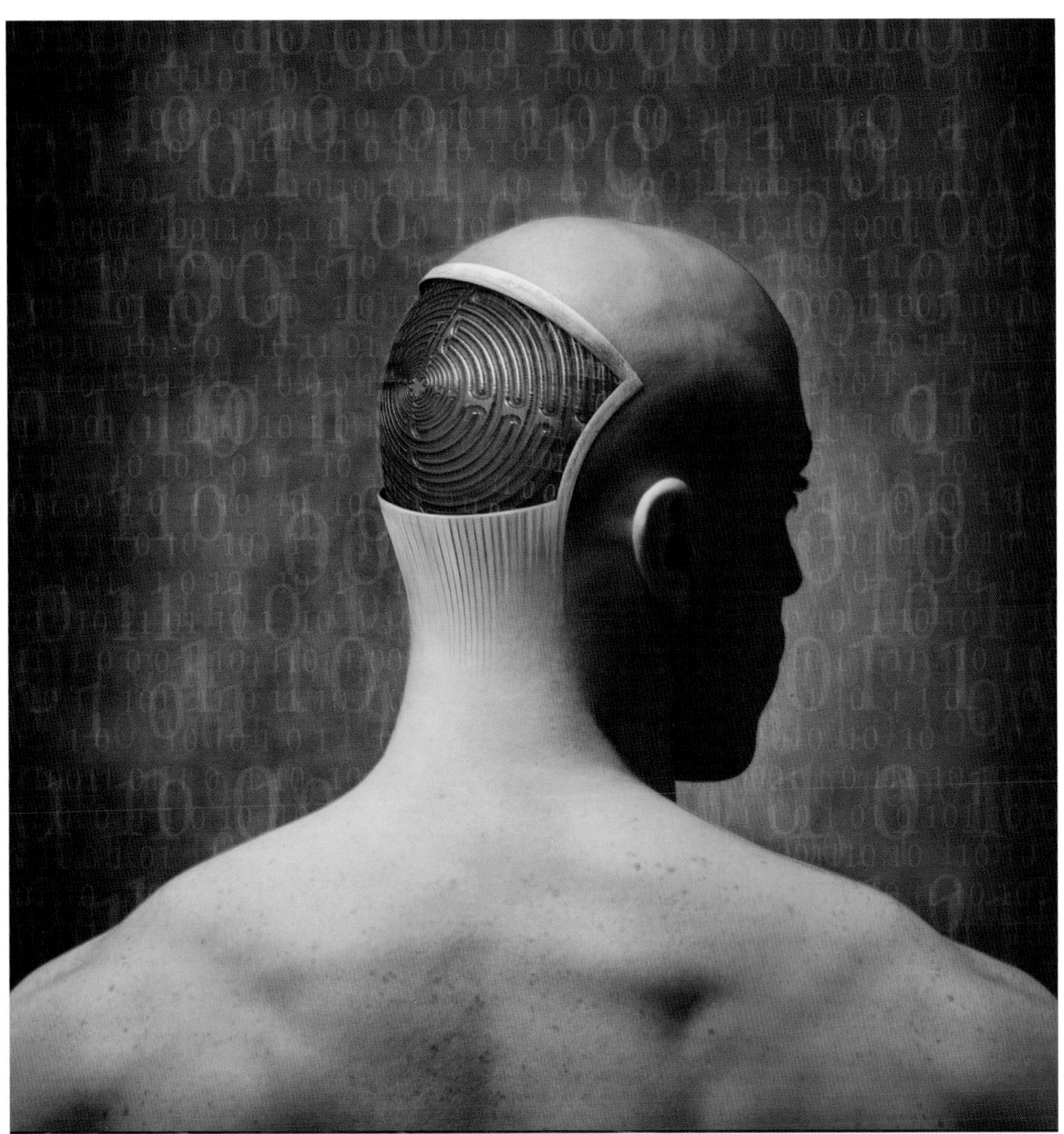

BERNSTEIN & ANDRIULLI WWW.BA-REPS.COM
e ARTINFO@BA-REPS.COM **p 212-682-1490** f 212-286-1890

SKAGGS
NEWMAN

BERNSTEIN & ANDRIULLI WWW.BA-REPS.COM
e ARTINFO@BA-REPS.COM **p 212-682-1490** f 212-286-1890

HANS CHRISTIAN ANDERSON'S

THE TINDERBOX

by Charles Way

For TICKETS call
01273 685861

Gardner Arts Centre

NOVEMBER 22 to DECEMBER 31

GARDNER ARTS CENTRE
University of Sussex
Brighton, BN1 9RA

BERNSTEIN & ANDRIULLI WWW.BA-REPS.COM
e ARTINFO@BA-REPS.COM **p 212-682-1490** f 212-286-1890

Sax

BRITISH TECHNOLOGY GROUP
Genius is one per cent inspiration and ninety nine per cent perspiration
Thomas Edison
1847~1931

AUSTRALIAN
SUPERFINE
MERINO

Busch
GARDENS
FLORIDA

FOR ALL FILMS
FILMS FOR ALL

FIONA CAIRNS

At home in the evening, my favourite armchair and a warming glass of Three Barrels brandy
There's no better place to be.

BERNSTEIN & ANDRIULLI WWW.BA-REPS.COM
e ARTINFO@BA-REPS.COM p 212-682-1490 f 212-286-1890

Paradise Lost

RI.

ROYAL
INSTITUTE
OF
PAINTERS
IN
WATERCOLOURS

PETER KRAMER

3D DIGITAL IMAGES

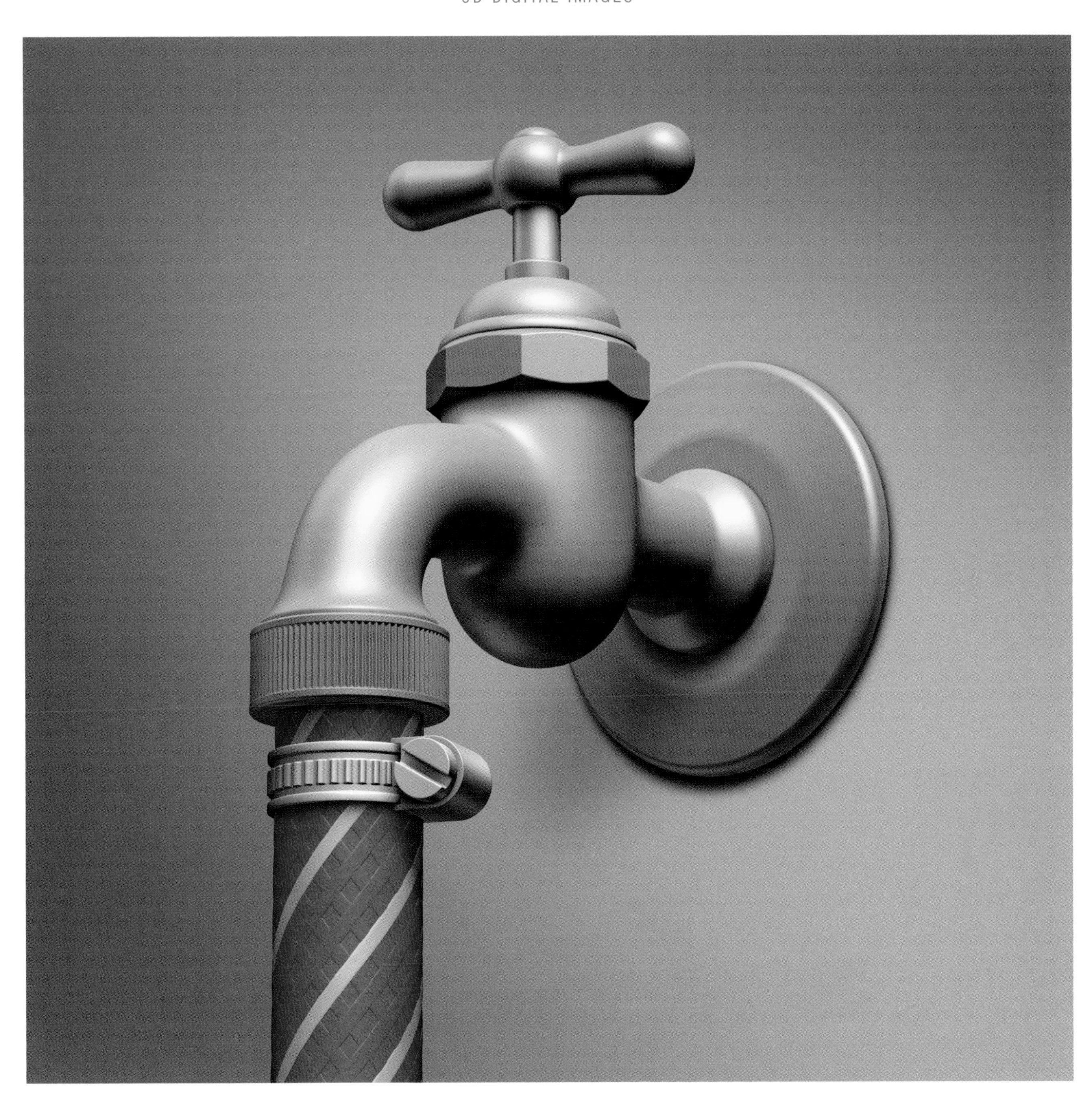

EZ DUZ IT
JAN OREGON
OREGON
020154
05

BERNSTEIN & ANDRIULLI WWW.BA-REPS.COM
e ARTINFO@BA-REPS.COM **p 212-682-1490** f 212-286-1890

MOZ

BERNSTEIN & ANDRIULLI WWW.BA-REPS.COM
e ARTINFO@BA-REPS.COM p 212-682-1490 f 212-286-1890

CAMEL
LIGHTS
TURKIS
END

BERNSTEIN & ANDRIULLI WWW.BA-REPS.COM
e ARTINFO@BA-REPS.COM p 212-682-1490 f 212-286-1890

THEY CANNOT
1% FREE
WE WON'T GO!

WE GOT IT
THEY DON'T.
Timberland

BERNSTEIN & ANDRIULLI WWW.BA-REPS.COM
e ARTINFO@BA-REPS.COM p 212-682-1490 f 212-286-1890

STEAKS
GIRLS
GIRLS
GIRLS
Live show
FASTER
DONUTS
DINER
RENO
BIGGEST LITTLE CITY IN THE WORLD
LUCKY STAR CAFE

MELO
Carmelo

BERNSTEIN & ANDRIULLI WWW.BA-REPS.COM
e ARTINFO@BA-REPS.COM p 212-682-1490 f 212-286-1890

Coca-Cola
CLASSIC
C.N.S.
CHUCH!
2
08
BROADWAY
RYLON

ebY

BERNSTEIN & ANDRIULLI WWW.BA-REPS.COM
e ARTINFO@BA-REPS.COM **p 212-682-1490** f 212-286-1890

GOOD
VIBRATIONS
THE BEACH BOYS MUSICAL

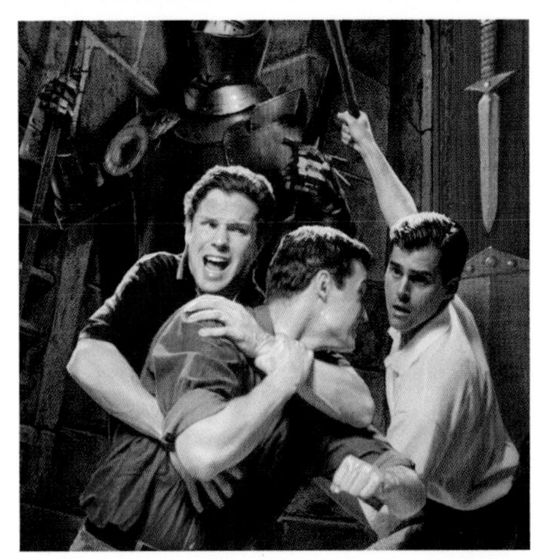

ebay
TIVOLI CITY

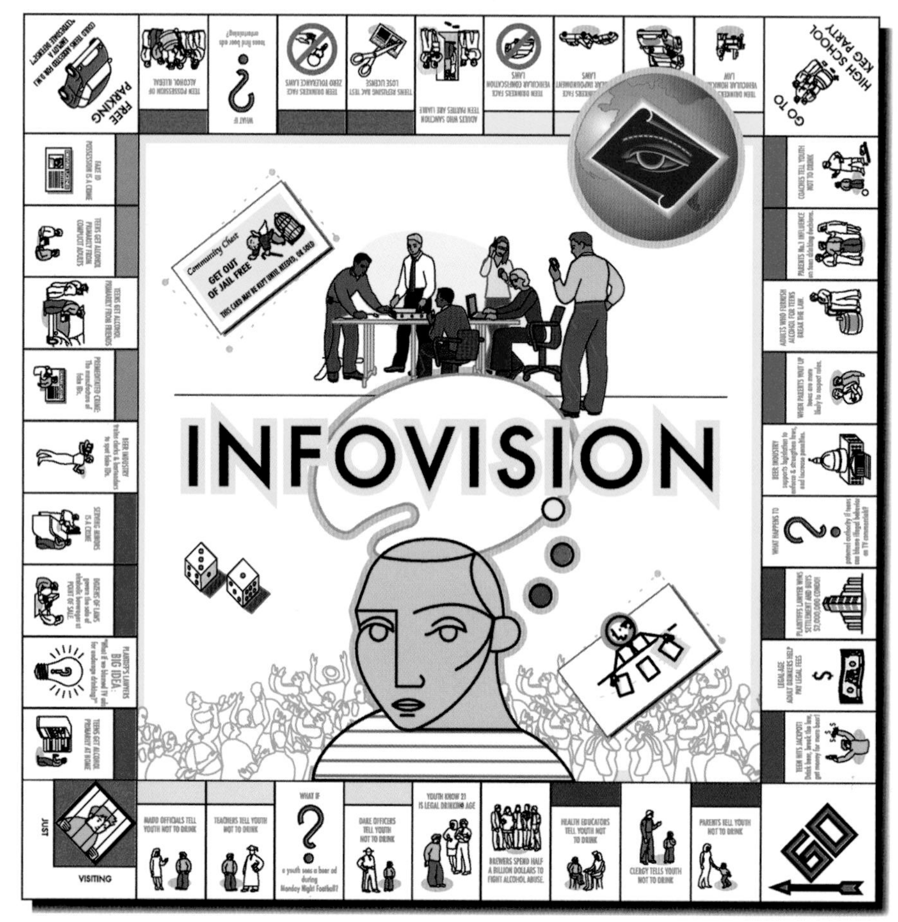
INFOVISION
FREE PARKING
GO TO HIGH SCHOOL KEG PARTY
Community Chest
GET OUT OF JAIL FREE
THIS CARD MAY BE KEPT UNTIL NEEDED, OR SOLD
JUST VISITING
GO
MADD OFFICIALS TELL YOUTH NOT TO DRINK
TEACHERS TELL YOUTH NOT TO DRINK
WHAT IF
DARE OFFICERS TELL YOUTH NOT TO DRINK
HEALTH EDUCATORS TELL YOUTH NOT TO DRINK
BREWERS SPEND HALF A BILLION DOLLARS TO FIGHT ALCOHOL ABUSE
CLERGY TELLS YOUTH NOT TO DRINK
PARENTS TELL YOUTH NOT TO DRINK

BERNSTEIN & ANDRIULLI WWW.BA-REPS.COM
e ARTINFO@BA-REPS.COM **p 212-682-1490** f 212-286-1890

JOHN HARWOOD
3D DIGITAL IMAGES

MAXIM
HOT
100
mocha
vanilla
NESCAFÉ
Ice
NESCAFÉ
Ice
-29
mm Hg

BERNSTEIN & ANDRIULLI WWW.BA-REPS.COM
e ARTINFO@BA-REPS.COM **p 212-682-1490** f 212-286-1890

december

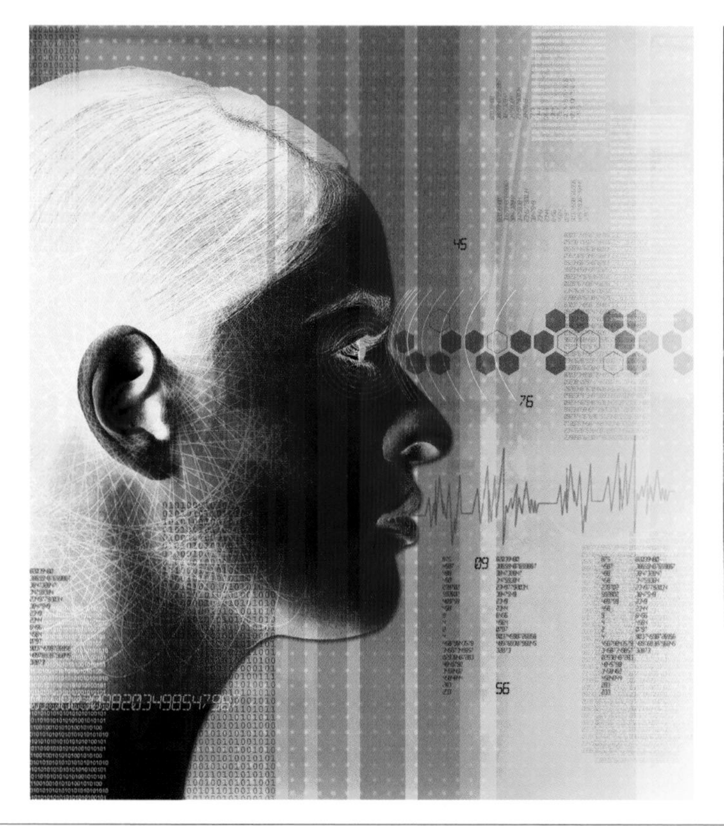

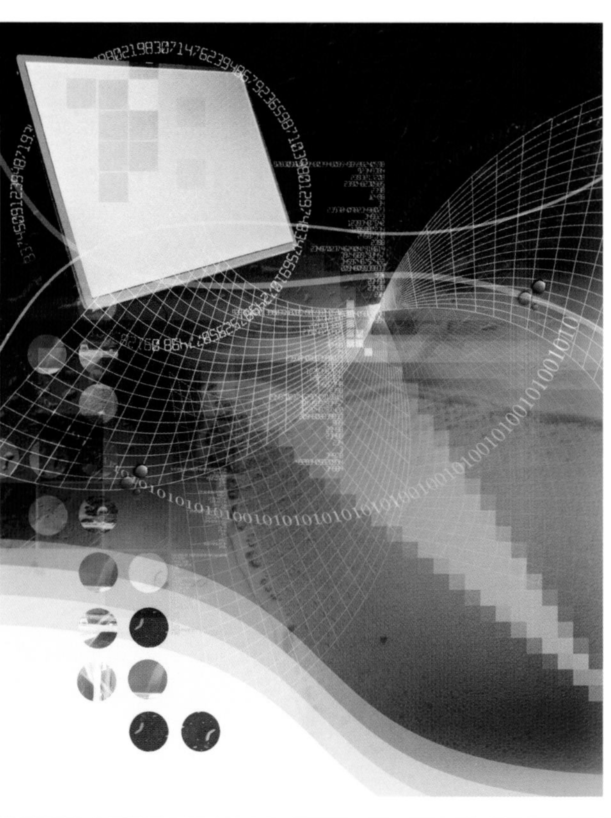

MOET
Moet & Ch

BERNSTEIN & ANDRIULLI WWW.BA-REPS.COM
e ARTINFO@BA-REPS.COM **p 212-682-1490** f 212-286-1890

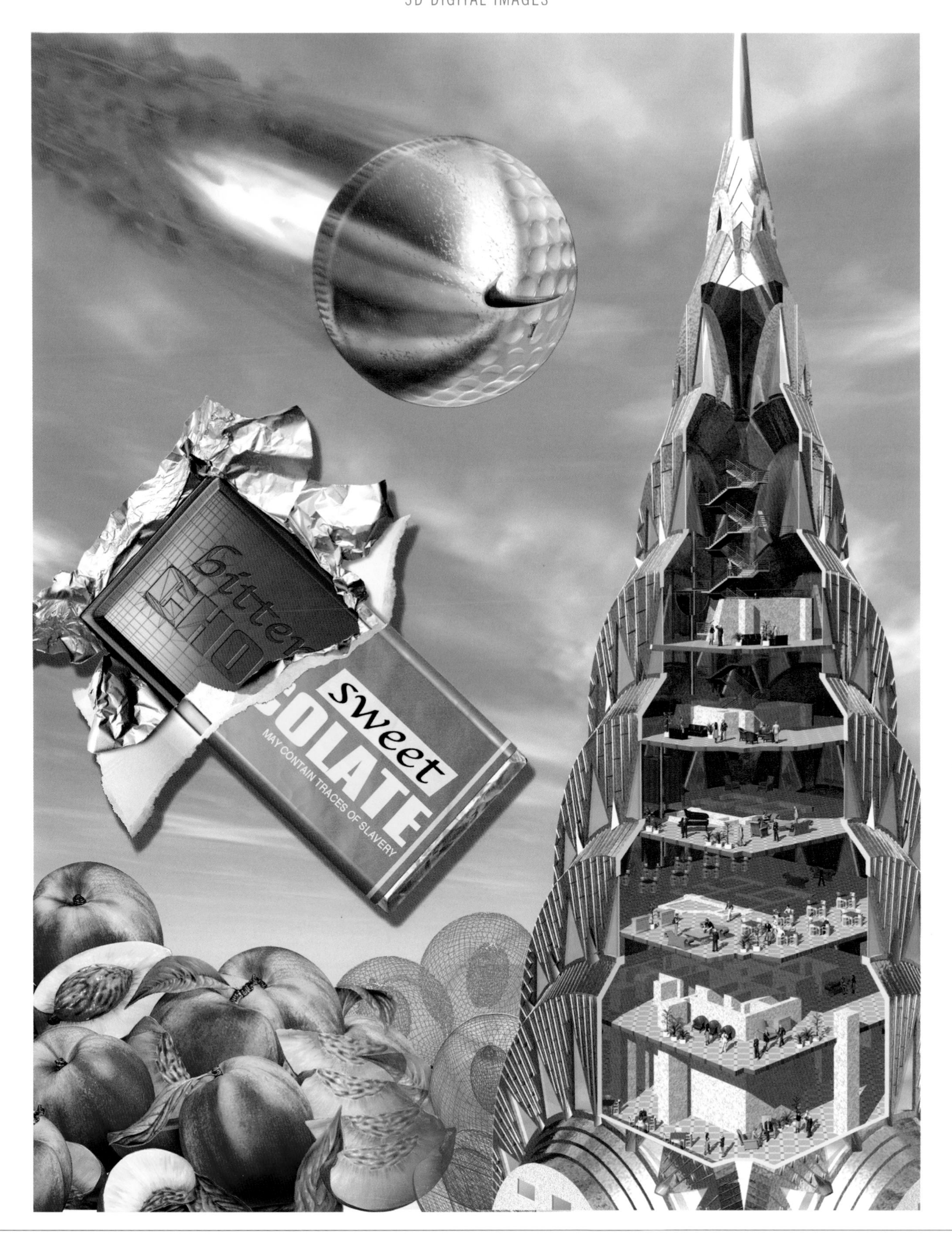

bitter
sweet
COLATE
MAY CONTAIN TRACES OF SLAVERY

RRAKECH
Rio
SOUK
Buenos air
Leather Goods
mumbai
BAZaar
BALI

BERNSTEIN & ANDRIULLI WWW.BA-REPS.COM
e ARTINFO@BA-REPS.COM **p 212-682-1490** f 212-286-1890

HOWZAT!

nice weather for ducks.

DIA DE LOS MUERTOS

BERNSTEIN & ANDRIULLI WWW.BA-REPS.COM
e ARTINFO@BA-REPS.COM **p 212-682-1490** f 212-286-1890

Raingirl
SUPER LUNGS
BAD FEELINGS
Air Sickness Bag - Limited Edition
ROYAL ELASTICS
jon burgerman
The Heroes of burgertown
3D RENDERS BY JS3D
JULES@JS3D.CO.UK

BERNSTEIN & ANDRIULLI WWW.BA-REPS.COM
e ARTINFO@BA-REPS.COM p 212-682-1490 f 212-286-1890

Dr. Doodle
circa 1931

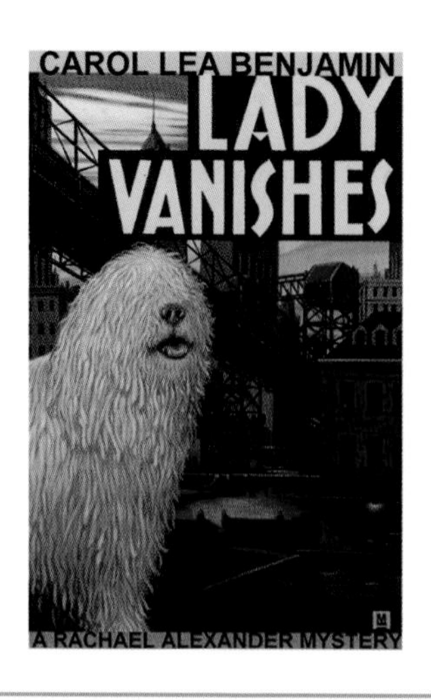
CAROL LEA BENJAMIN
LADY
VANISHES
A RACHAEL ALEXANDER MYSTERY

Sprint

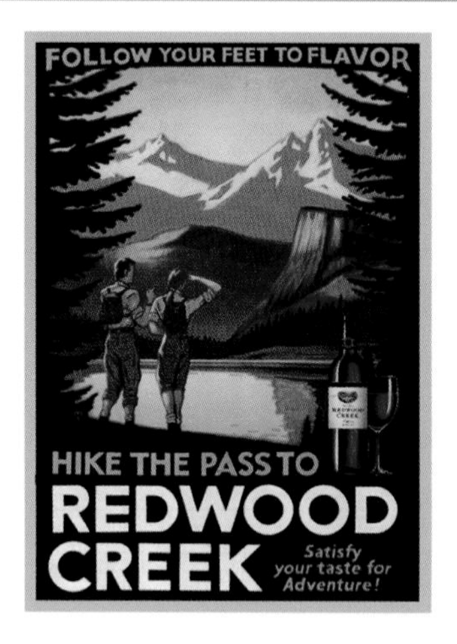
FOLLOW YOUR FEET TO FLAVOR
HIKE THE PASS TO
REDWOOD
CREEK
Satisfy
your taste for
Adventure!

PEERLESS
COFFEE & TEA
FAMILY ROASTED SINCE 1924
THE PEERLESS COFFEE COMPANY WAS FOUNDED IN 1924 TO BRING THE FINEST COFFEE IN THE WORLD TO THE SAN FRANCISCO BAY AREA, A PLACE WITH A PASSION FOR GOOD LIVING, CUISINE AND COFFEE. FOR OVER THREE GENERATIONS THE FAMILY-OWNED BUSINESS HAS ROASTED ONLY THE MOST PRIZED COFFEE BEANS. WE INVITE YOU TO ENJOY PEERLESS COFFEE IN YOUR HOME AND SHARE IN THIS BAY AREA TRADITION.

PRESENTS
ATTACK OF THE KILLER
CHIHUAHUA
STARRING
RAY-BEAL

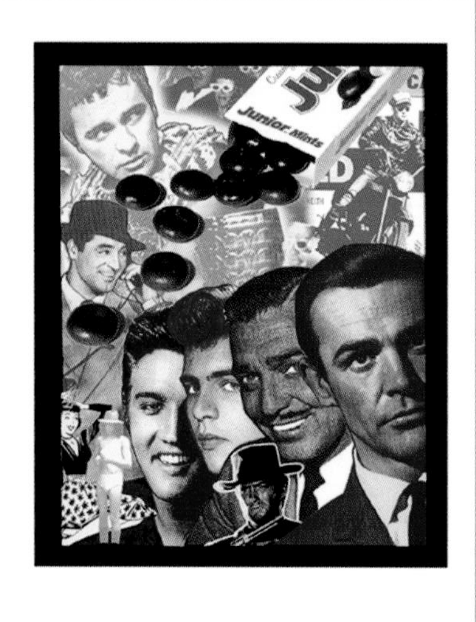
Junior Mints

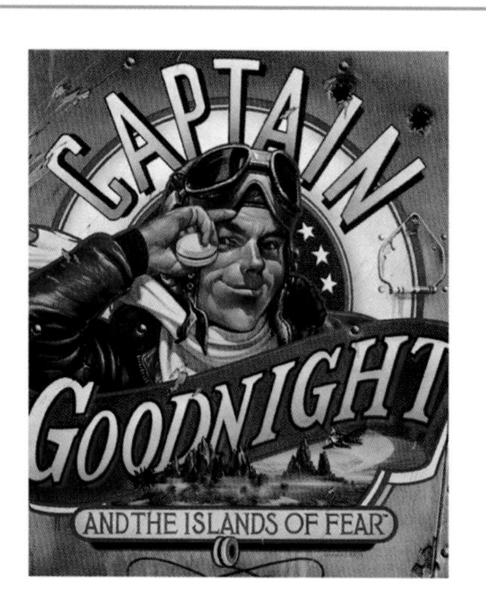
CAPTAIN
GOODNIGHT
AND THE ISLANDS OF FEAR

NORTH AMERICA'S GRAND MOUNTAIN RESORT
ALT. 11,440 FT.
WORLD CHAMPIONSHIP BIRDS OF PREY DOWNHILL
BEAVER CREEK
COLORADO

MCMACKENGRAPHICS

PHONE & FAX (860) 489-3460

EMAIL:MCMACKENGRAPHIX@OPTONLINE.NET   WWW.MCMACKENGRAPHICS.COM

BERNSTEIN & ANDRIULLI WWW.BA-REPS.COM
e ARTINFO@BA-REPS.COM **p 212-682-1490** f 212-286-1890

anton PETROV

215.232.6666 fax 215.232.6585 www.illustrationOnLine.com **DEBORAH WOLFE LTD**

215.232.6666 fax 215.232.6585 www.illustrationOnLine.com **DEBORAH WOLFE LTD**

bob OSTROM

EARTHDAY
1.
2.

MUSEUM

215.232.6666 fax 215.232.6585 www.illustrationOnLine.com **DEBORAH WOLFE LTD**

215.232.6666 fax 215.232.6585 www.illustrationOnLine.com **DEBORAH WOLFE LTD**

jesse REISCH

215.232.6666 fax 215.232.6585 www.illustrationOnLine.com **DEBORAH WOLFE LTD**

ross JONES

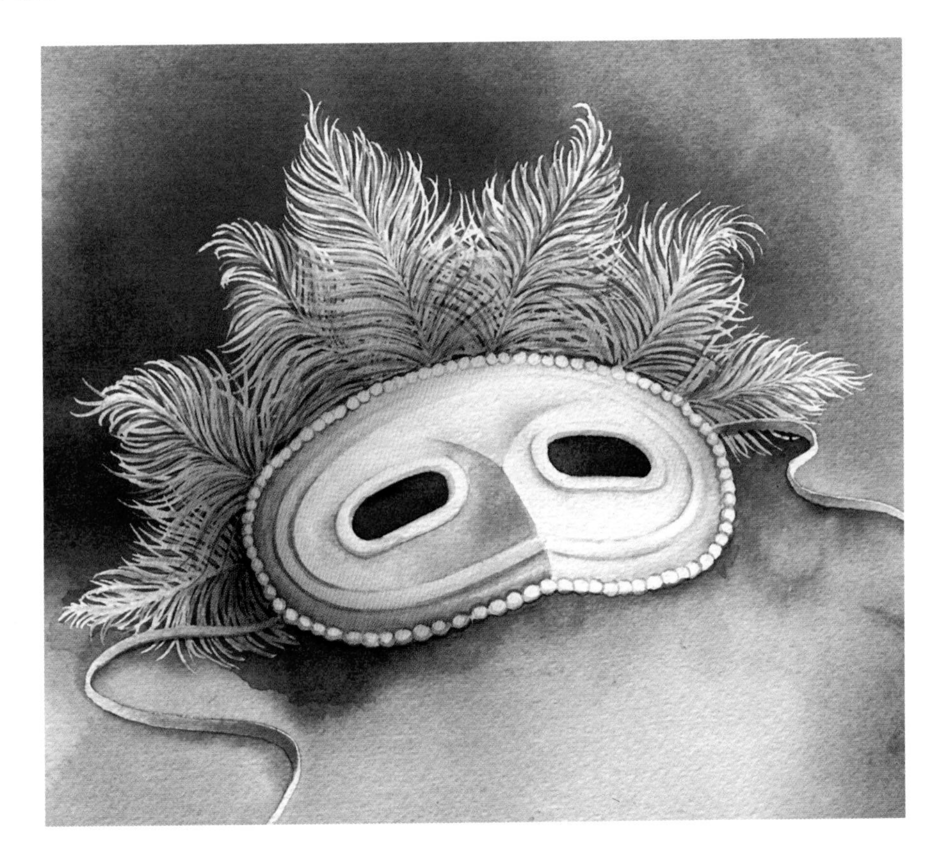

See you
love, Amanda

215.232.6666 fax 215.232.6585 www.illustrationOnLine.com **DEBORAH WOLFE LTD**

philip HOWE

P. HOWE

dan **WETZEL**

215.232.6666 fax 215.232.6585 www.illustrationOnLine.com **DEBORAH WOLFE LTD**

paula McARDLE

FRANCE
N
W
E
S

215.232.6666 fax 215.232.6585 www.illustrationOnLine.com **DEBORAH WOLFE LTD**

bob KAYGANICH

215.232.6666 fax 215.232.6585 www.illustrationOnLine.com **DEBORAH WOLFE LTD**

215.232.6666 fax 215.232.6585 www.illustrationOnLine.com DEBORAH WOLFE LTD

nancy HARRISON

215.232.6666 fax 215.232.6585 www.illustrationOnLine.com **DEBORAH WOLFE LTD**

sharon & joel HARRIS

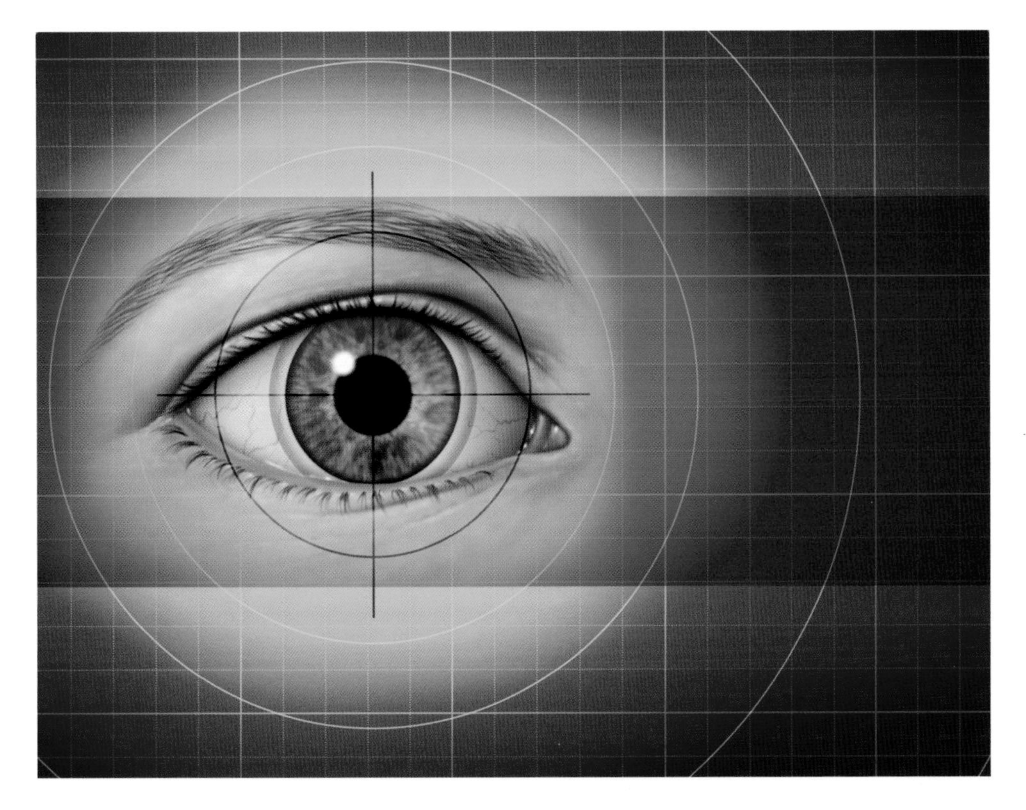

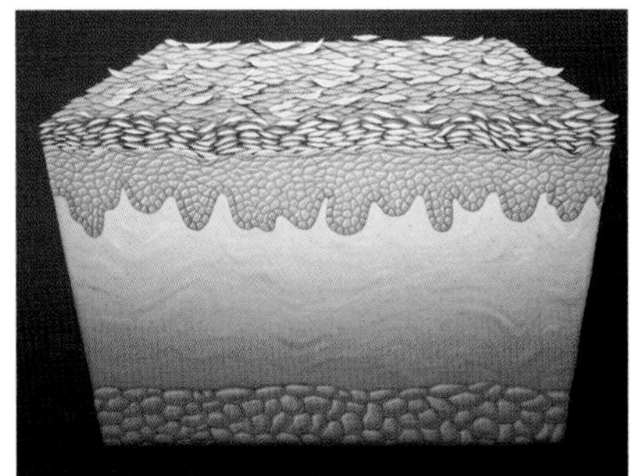

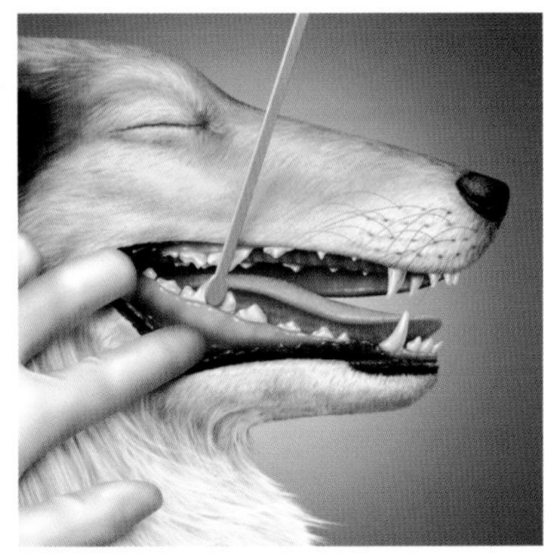

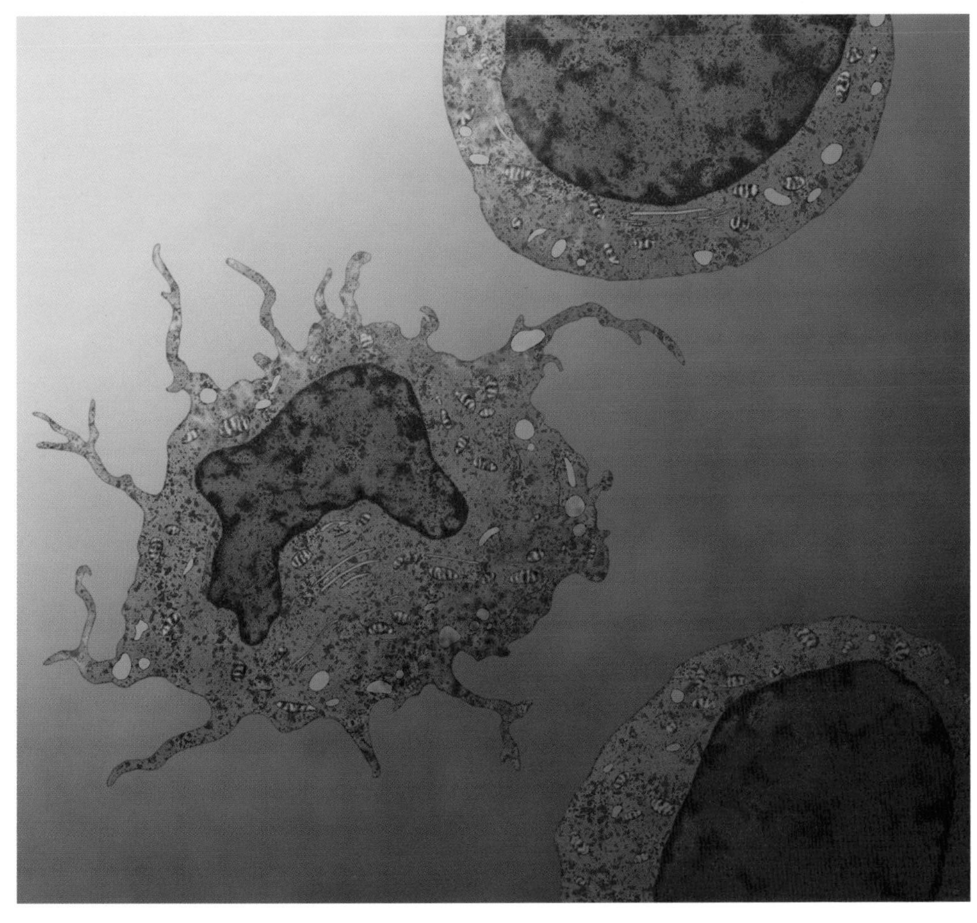

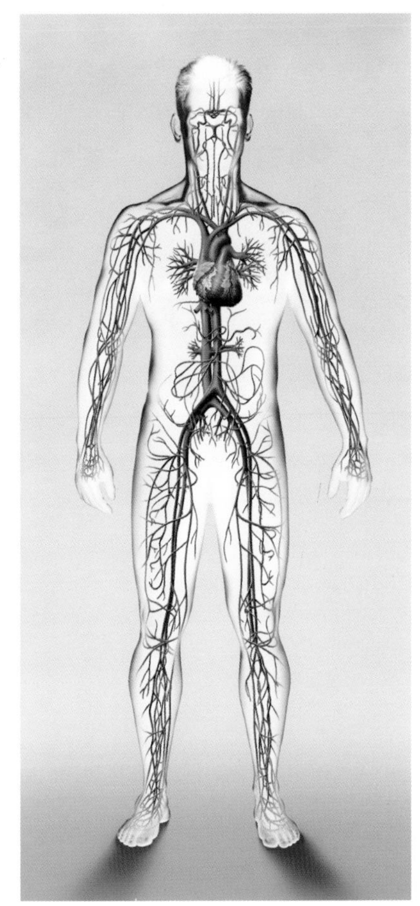

215.232.6666 fax 215.232.6585 www.illustrationOnLine.com **DEBORAH WOLFE LTD**

j.t. MORROW

the art of imitation

morrow

215.232.6666 fax 215.232.6585 www.illustrationOnLine.com **DEBORAH WOLFE LTD**

graham **PARSLOW**

215.232.6666 fax 215.232.6585 www.illustrationOnLine.com **DEBORAH WOLFE LTD**

paine **PROFFITT**

STOCKS
BUSINESS

A
follow
trans-
atlantic

culture
sports
entertain

215.232.6666 fax 215.232.6585 www.illustrationOnLine.com **DEBORAH WOLFE LTD**

On life's journey,
faith
nourishment
On life's
journey,
faith is
nourishment
faith
On life's journey,
faith
nourishment

215.232.6666 fax 215.232.6585 www.illustrationOnLine.com **DEBORAH WOLFE LTD**

amy WUMMER

todd DAMAN

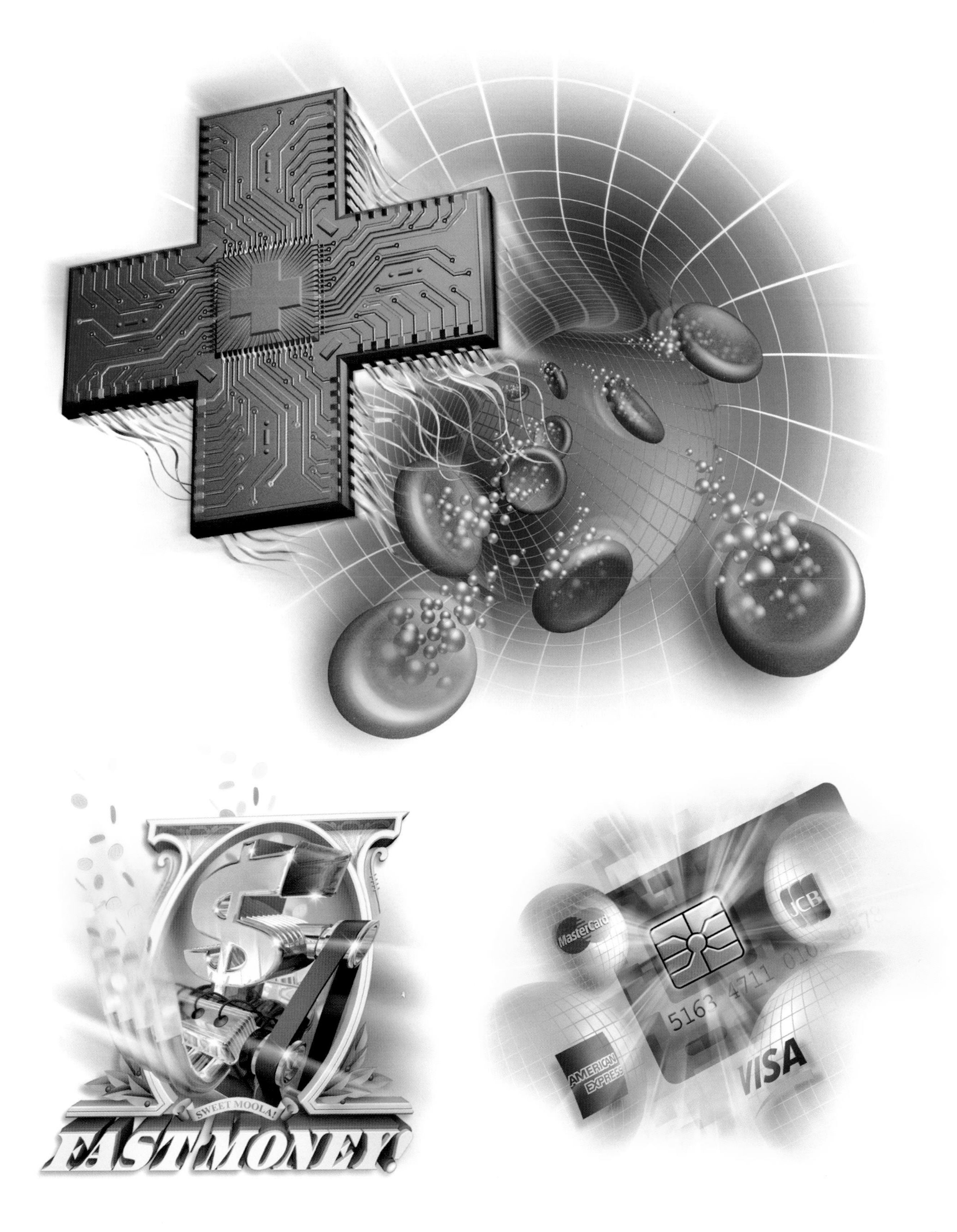
SWEET MOOLA!
FAST MONEY!
MasterCard
JCB
5163 4711
AMERICAN EXPRESS
VISA

215.232.6666 fax 215.232.6585 www.illustrationOnLine.com **DEBORAH WOLFE LTD**

dan McGEEHAN

215.232.6666 fax 215.232.6585 www.illustrationOnLine.com **DEBORAH WOLFE LTD**

stephen mercer **PERINGER**

"AN ABSOLUTE MASTERPIECE!"—JONATHAN KELLERMAN
JAMES ELLROY
A NOVEL BASED ON HOLLYWOOD'S MOST NOTORIOUS MURDER CASE
The BLACK DAHLIA

215.232.6666 fax 215.232.6585 www.illustrationOnLine.com **DEBORAH WOLFE LTD**

25
5¢

215.232.6666 fax 215.232.6585 www.illustrationOnLine.com **DEBORAH WOLFE LTD**

richard **WALDREP**

GODDARD

215.232.6666 fax 215.232.6585 www.illustrationOnLine.com **DEBORAH WOLFE LTD**

215.232.6666 fax 215.232.6585 www.illustrationOnLine.com **DEBORAH WOLFE LTD**

john SCHREINER

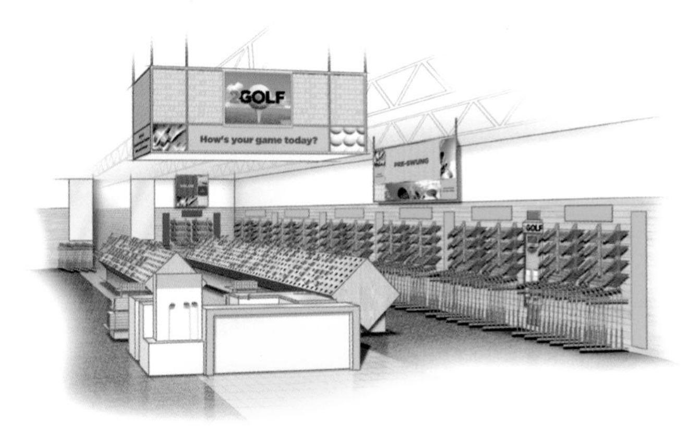
GOLF
How's your game today?

Chocolate Peanut Butter Cup
TURKEY HILL
Chocolate
Peanut Butter Cup
TURKEY HILL
ICED TEA

215.232.6666 fax 215.232.6585 www.illustrationOnLine.com **DEBORAH WOLFE LTD**

simon SHAW

215.232.6666 fax 215.232.6585 www.illustrationOnLine.com **DEBORAH WOLFE LTD**

philip WILLIAMS

ANNUAL INVENTORS' FAIR
DREAM MAKER
HAPPY
SAD
FUNNY
WEIRD
BORING
EXCITING
SWEET
COLORFUL
VANILLA ICE CREAM
Ping Pong Paddle Tester
Auto Page Turner
Bowling Ball Nutcracker
CAKE-O-RATER
WASH RINSE DRY
warm air

215.232.6666 fax 215.232.6585 www.illustrationOnLine.com **DEBORAH WOLFE LTD**

robert KEMP

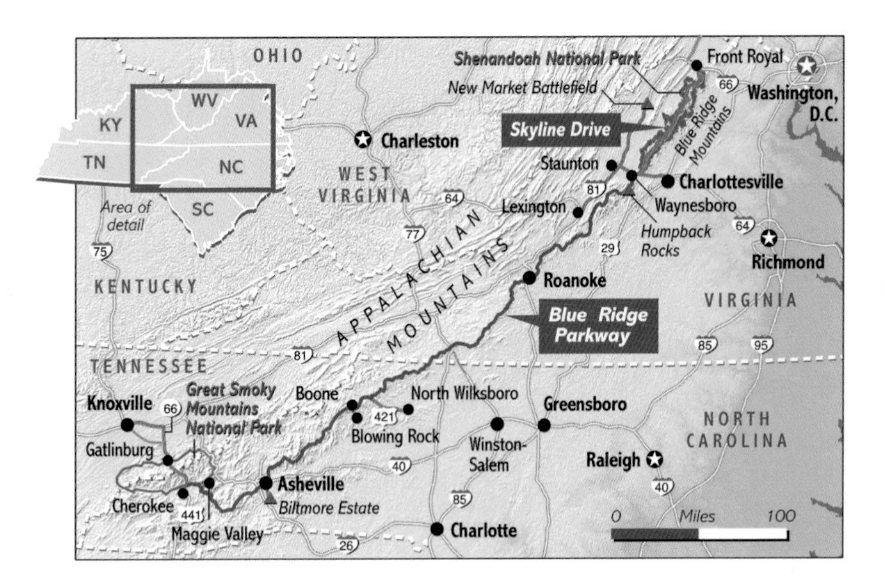

OHIO
Shenandoah National Park
New Market Battlefield
Front Royal
Washington, D.C.
66
WV
KY
VA
TN
NC
SC
Area of detail
Charleston
Skyline Drive
Blue Ridge Mountains
Staunton
Charlottesville
WEST VIRGINIA
64
81
Lexington
Waynesboro
Humpback Rocks
77
75
29
Richmond
KENTUCKY
APPALACHIAN MOUNTAINS
Roanoke
VIRGINIA
Blue Ridge Parkway
TENNESSEE
81
85
95
Knoxville
Great Smoky Mountains National Park
Boone
North Wilksboro
Greensboro
NORTH CAROLINA
66
421
Gatlinburg
Blowing Rock
Winston-Salem
Raleigh
40
Asheville
40
Cherokee
441
Biltmore Estate
85
Maggie Valley
26
Charlotte
0
Miles
100

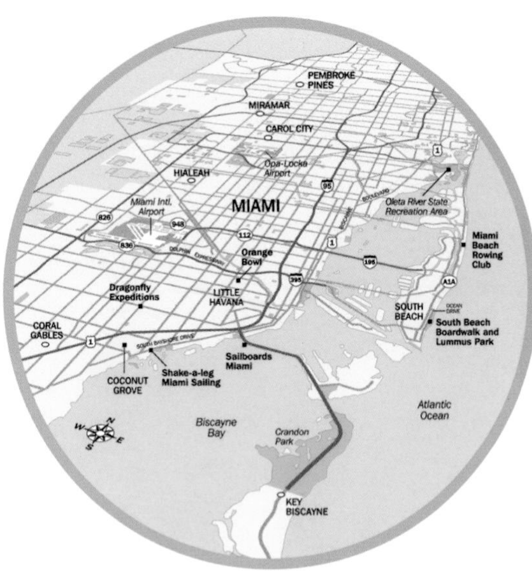

PEMBROKE PINES
MIRAMAR
CAROL CITY
HIALEAH
Opa-Locka Airport
Miami Intl. Airport
MIAMI
Oleta River State Recreation Area
Miami Beach Rowing Club
Orange Bowl
Dragonfly Expeditions
LITTLE HAVANA
SOUTH BEACH
South Beach Boardwalk and Lummus Park
CORAL GABLES
Sailboards Miami
Shake-a-leg Miami Sailing
COCONUT GROVE
Biscayne Bay
Crandon Park
Atlantic Ocean
KEY BISCAYNE

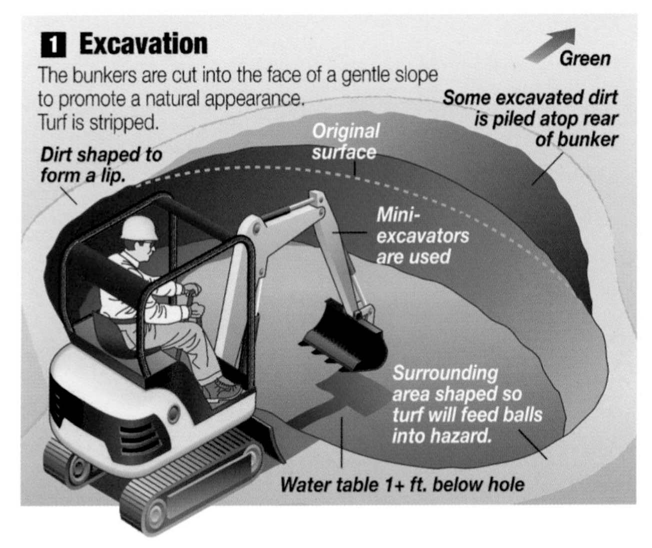

1 Excavation
The bunkers are cut into the face of a gentle slope to promote a natural appearance. Turf is stripped.
Green
Some excavated dirt is piled atop rear of bunker
Original surface
Dirt shaped to form a lip.
Mini-excavators are used
Surrounding area shaped so turf will feed balls into hazard.
Water table 1+ ft. below hole

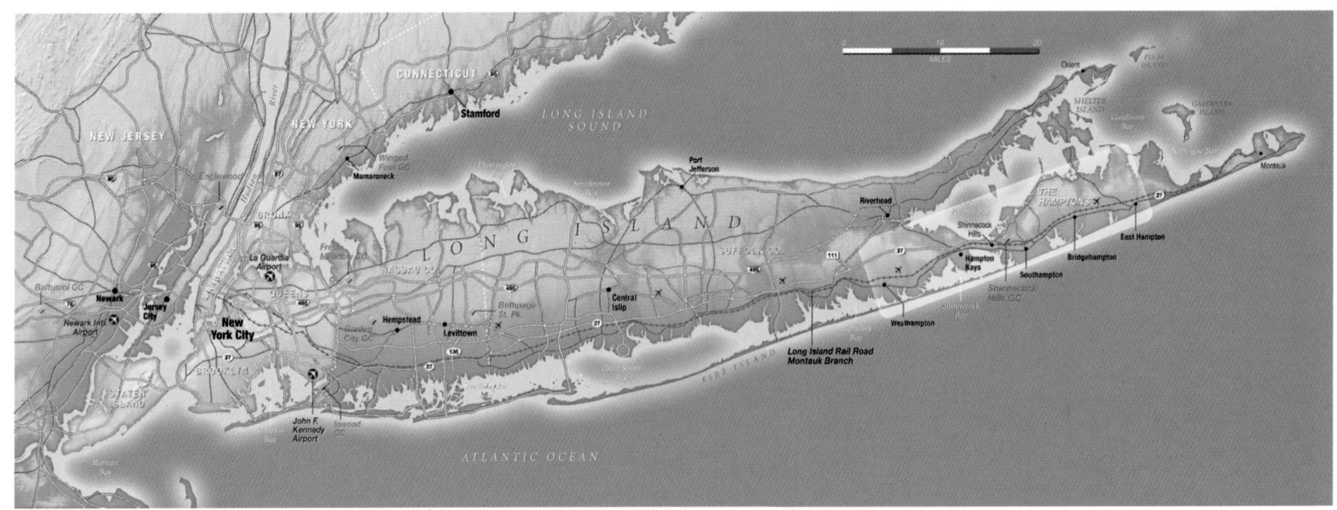

CONNECTICUT
Stamford
LONG ISLAND SOUND
NEW JERSEY
NEW YORK
Mamaroneck
Port Jefferson
Riverhead
THE HAMPTONS
Montauk
East Hampton
Bridgehampton
Southampton
Hampton Bays
LONG ISLAND
SUFFOLK CO.
NASSAU CO.
La Guardia Airport
QUEENS
Newark
Jersey City
New York City
Newark Intl. Airport
Hempstead
Levittown
Central Islip
Westhampton
Long Island Rail Road Montauk Branch
BROOKLYN
STATEN ISLAND
John F. Kennedy Airport
ATLANTIC OCEAN

215.232.6666 fax 215.232.6585 www.illustrationOnLine.com **DEBORAH WOLFE LTD**

mark COLLINS

BIOLAB
KEEP OUT

215.232.6666 fax 215.232.6585 www.illustrationOnLine.com **DEBORAH WOLFE LTD**

Garry Colby
Illustration

Noah's Ark

Stock images available

CLIFF KNECHT
ARTIST REPRESENTATIVE

309 Walnut Road • Pittsburgh, PA 15202
PHONE 412.761.5666 • FAX 412.761.4072
www.artrep1.com

Artist
GARRY COLBY

J. Walker

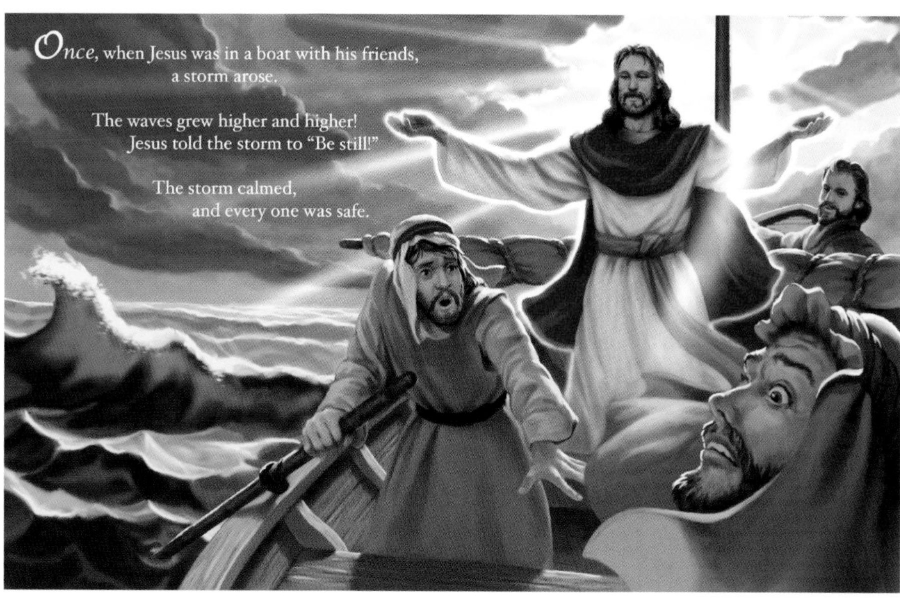
Once, when Jesus was in a boat with his friends,
a storm arose.
The waves grew higher and higher!
Jesus told the storm to "Be still!"
The storm calmed,
and every one was safe.

Stock images available

CLIFF KNECHT
ARTIST REPRESENTATIVE

309 Walnut Road • Pittsburgh, PA 15202
PHONE 412.761.5666 • FAX 412.761.4072
www.artrep1.com

Artist
JOHN WALKER

Stock images available

309 Walnut Road • Pittsburgh, PA 15202
PHONE 412.761.5666 • FAX 412.761.4072
www.artrep1.com

Artist
PHIL WILSON

©LORIOSIECKI
©LORIOSIECKI
©LORIOSIECKI

Stock images available

CLIFF KNECHT
ARTIST REPRESENTATIVE

309 Walnut Road • Pittsburgh, PA 15202
PHONE 412.761.5666 • FAX 412.761.4072
www.artrep1.com

Artist
JOHN WARD

SHARRON EVANS

www.sharronevans.com sharron@sharronevans.com 415 239•7024

diane teske harris • kevin bapp • carlene howard williams • roger roth • geoffrey moss • phillip dvorak
BAPP
JIM BEAM
?
?
?
?
?
• diane teske harris • kevin bapp • carlene howard williams • roger roth • geoffrey moss • phillip dvorak •

MARION MOSKOWITZ REPRESENTS INC

212 517 4919 www.moskyreps.com 315 east 68th st new york city 10021

diane teske harris • kevin bapp • carlene howard williams • roger roth • geoffrey moss • phillip dvorak

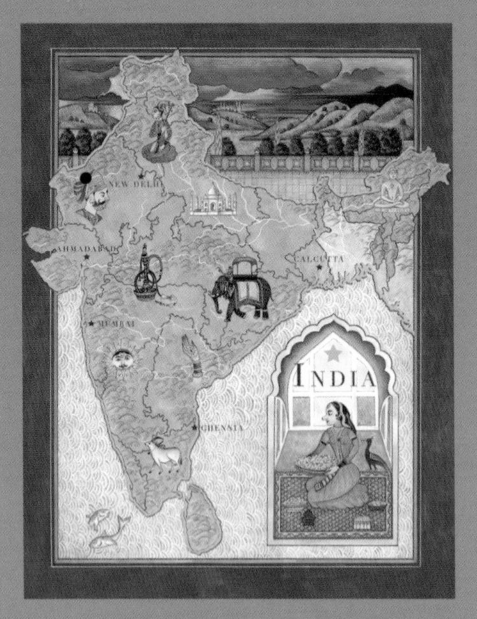
INDIA

DAVE STEVENSON

RAFAEL LOPEZ

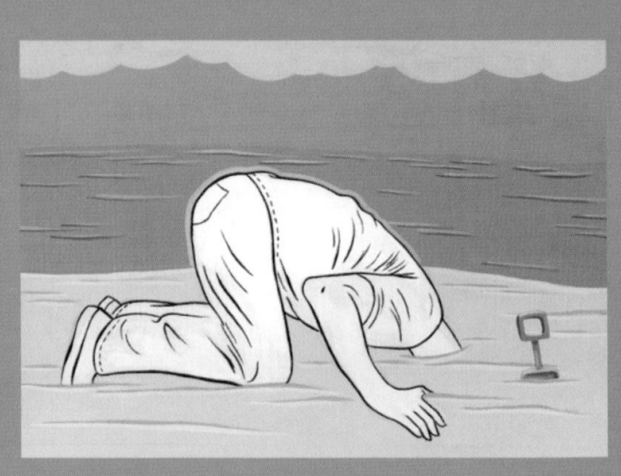

OMAR LEE

CHRIS BUZELLI

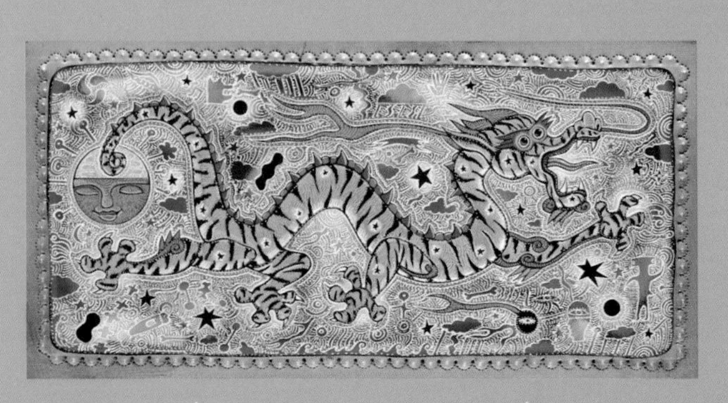

JOEL NAKAMURA

JOEL NAKAMURA

| MARTHA RICH |

m. rich

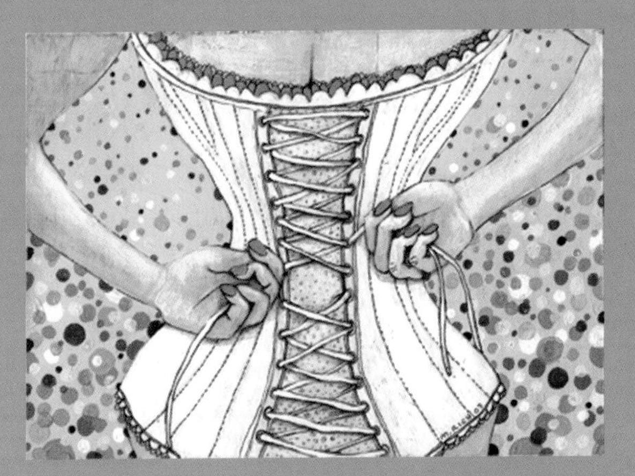

JENNIFER VAUGHN ARTIST AGENT

JENVAUGHNART.COM

415 | 666 | 3447

'Alauahio
Moloka'i
Kalawao
Pailolo Channel
SCALE MILES
0 2 4 6 8
MIGRATIONS A.D. 300-1300
COOK 1777-79
PACIFIC OCEAN
'Akialoa
Hokukano Heiau
Halekii - Pihana Heiau
WAILUKU
Maui
Lana'i
Keomuku
LAHAINA
Kalo
Piilanihale Heiau
CAPTAIN JAMES COOK
KING KAMEHAMEHA I
MAALAEA BAY
HALEAKALA CRATER
HANA
Maui Discovered
MOLOKINI
KAUPO
Kaho'olawe
H.M. BARK ENDEAVOUR
'Akohekohe
WA'A KAULUA
'Ahinahina
'Ohi'a Lehua
Kokia Keokeo
I'iwi

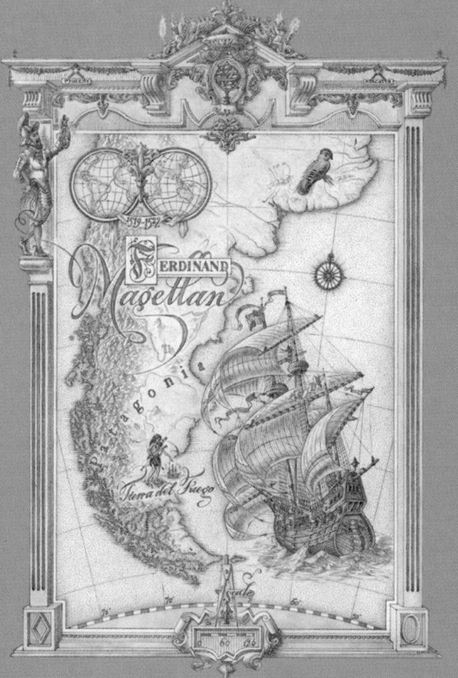

FERDINAND Magellan
Tierra del Fuego

the Black Death
EUROPE
BLACK SEA
MEDITERRANEAN SEA
1346
1347
1348
1349
1350
1352

JENNIFER VAUGHN ARTIST AGENT

JENVAUGHNART.COM

415 | 666 | 3447

1 כוס פריקה (חיטה
200 גרם בשר כבש טחון
שליש כוס שמן זית
1 בצל גדול קצוץ דק
1 כף עלי נענע מיובשים
מלח, פלפל שחור גרוס
למרינדת העוף:
רבע כוס שמן זית
1 כף עלי זעתר טרי
חצי כפית סומק
מלח, פלפל שחור
להגשה:
4 חצאי

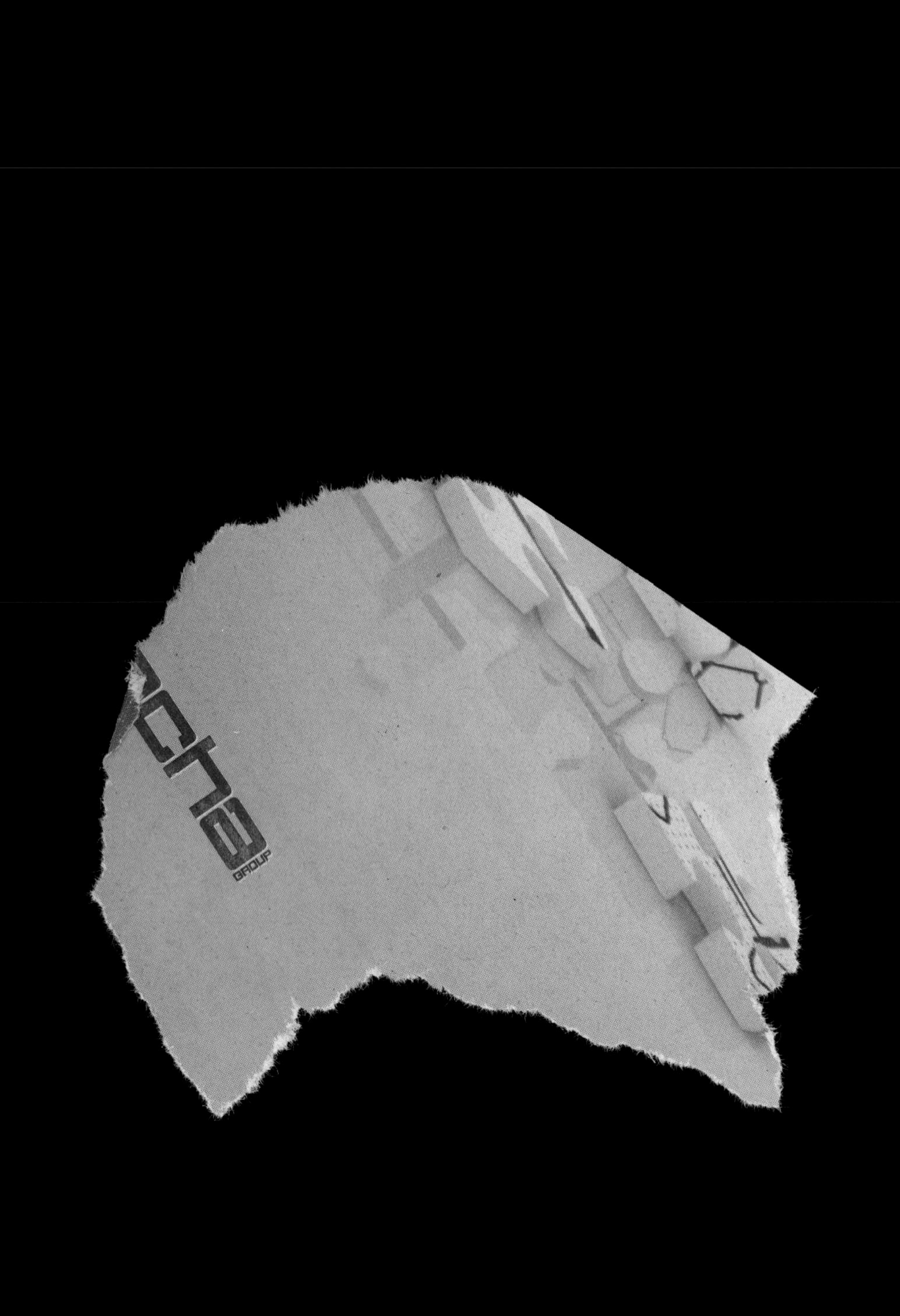

RAFAEL LOPEZ

GlENdaLE
JazZ
BLUES
2005
RAFAEL

JENNIFER VAUGHN ARTIST AGENT
JENVAUGHNART.COM
415|666|3447

| DAVID GROFF |

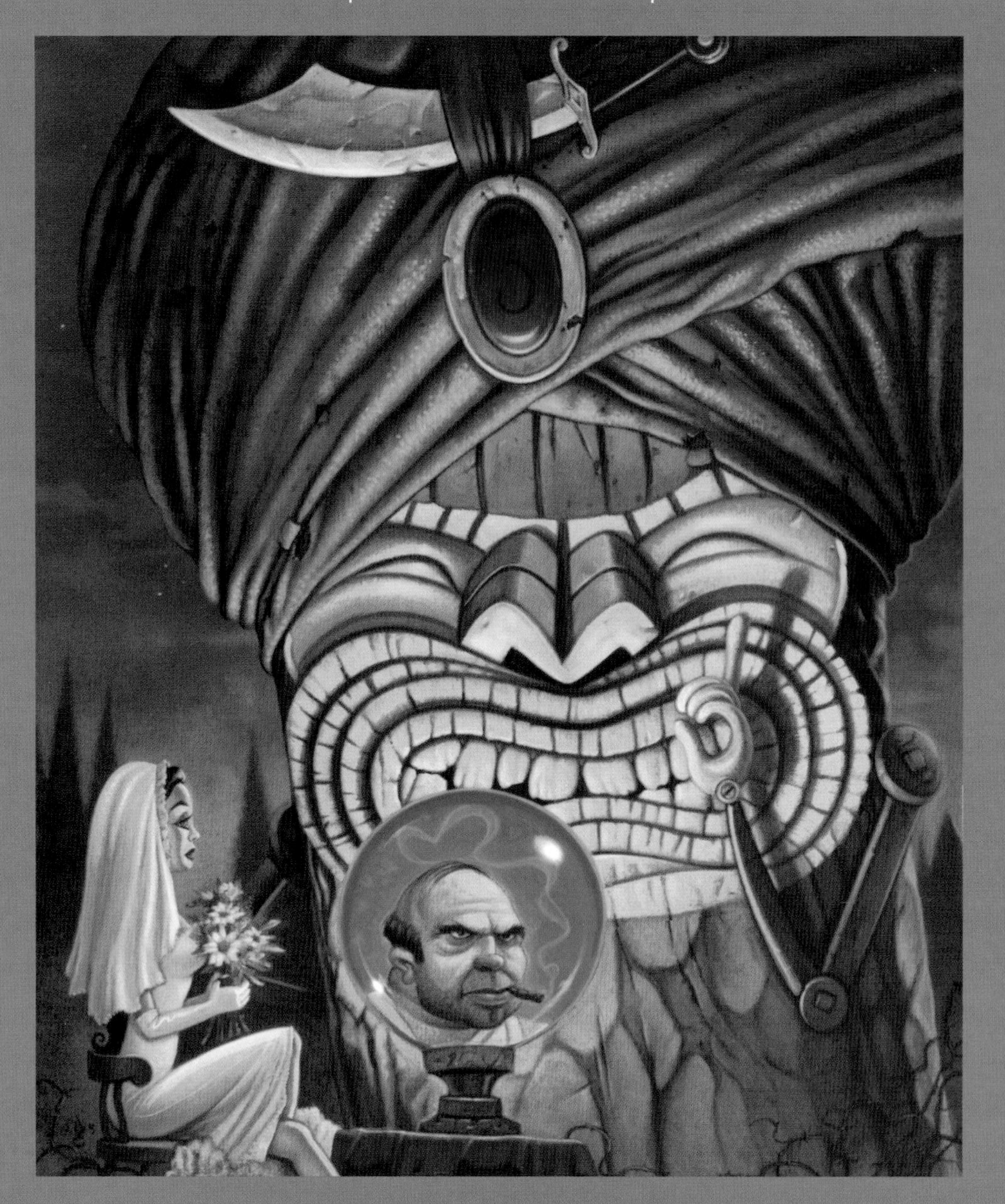

JENNIFER VAUGHN ARTIST AGENT

JENVAUGHNART.COM

415|666|3447

| CHRIS BUZELLI |

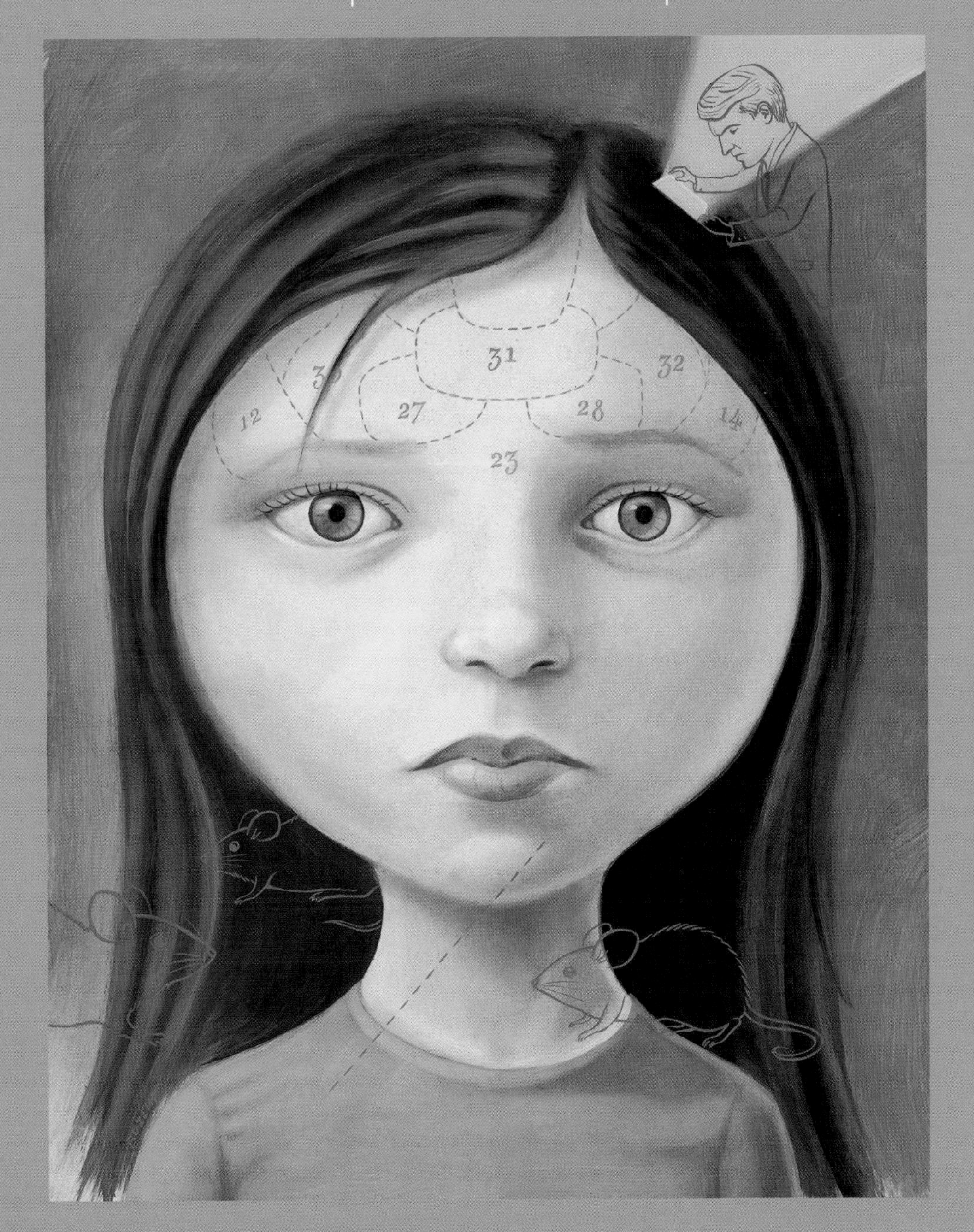
31
32
12
27
28
14
23

JENNIFER VAUGHN ARTIST AGENT

JENVAUGHNART.COM

415|666|3447

BOOKMAKERS LTD.

Celebrating 30 Years of Creating Success Stories

For 30 years, BOOKMAKERS has represented a group of the best illustrators in the business and provided the industry with award-winning design, as well as production.

We're looking forward to helping create a success story out of *your* next project.

SUSAN BANTA

AMY BISHOP

DAVID BROOKS

LINDY BURNETT

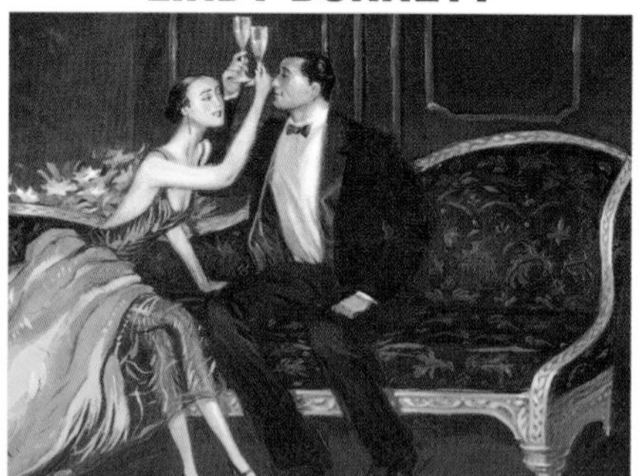

LISA CARLSON

BARB COUSINS

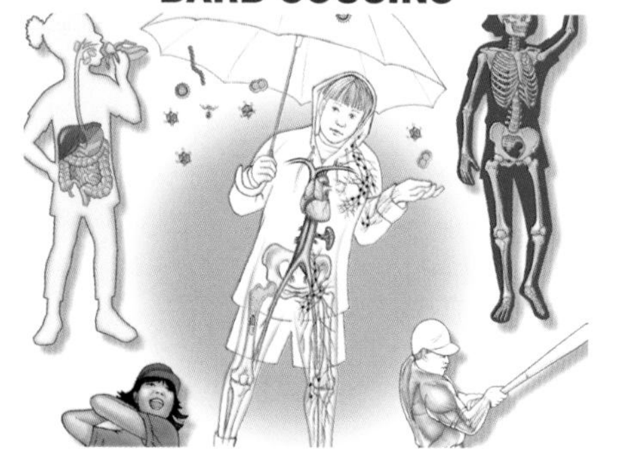

MOLLY DELANEY

TEDDY EDINJIKLIAN

JIM GORDON

LYDIA HALVERSON

TM & © Warner Bros. Entertainment Inc.

JODIE McCALLUM

P.O. Box 1086, 40 Mouse House Road, Taos, NM 87571 • 505.776.5435 • Fax 505.776.2762
email: bookmakers@newmex.com • website: bookmakersltd.com

BOOKMAKERS LTD.

Celebrating 30 Years of Creating Success Stories

KATHI McCORD

TED McNEIL

GOODBEAR

JUDITH MITCHELL

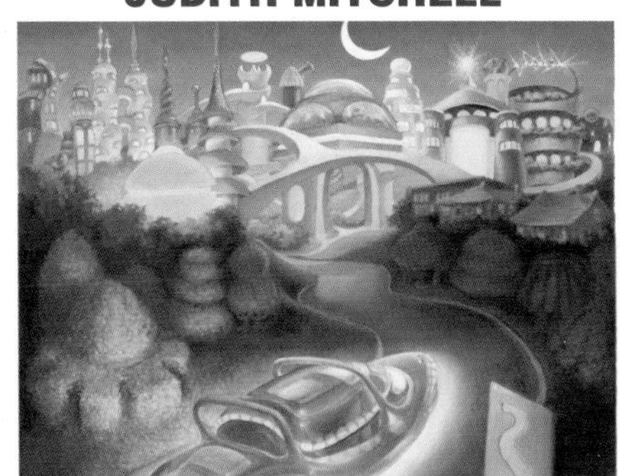

CAROL NEWSOM

BOB NOREIKA

PHILOMENA O'NEILL

KAREN PELLATON

Today's Special:
Hot Chili

KAREN C. RHINE

MARSHA SERAFIN

HOT
PEPPERS

DICK SMOLINSKI

JIM SPENCE

EVERLAST

BETH FOSTER WIGGINS

P.O. Box 1086, 40 Mouse House Road, Taos, NM 87571 • 505.776.5435 • Fax 505.776.2762
email: bookmakers@newmex.com • website: bookmakersltd.com

BOOKMAKERS LTD.

Representing
DAVID BROOKS

P.O. Box 1086, 40 Mouse House Road, Taos, NM 87571 • 505.776.5435 • Fax 505.776.2762
email: bookmakers@newmex.com • website: bookmakersltd.com

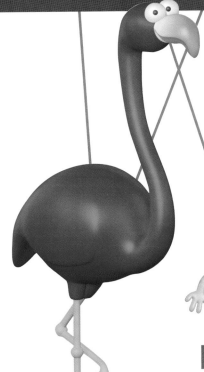

Louise Alexandra Ellis

www.irmeliholmberg.com Phone 516.887.5348

eFax 212.202.4356

REPRESENTED BY

IRMELI HOLMBERG

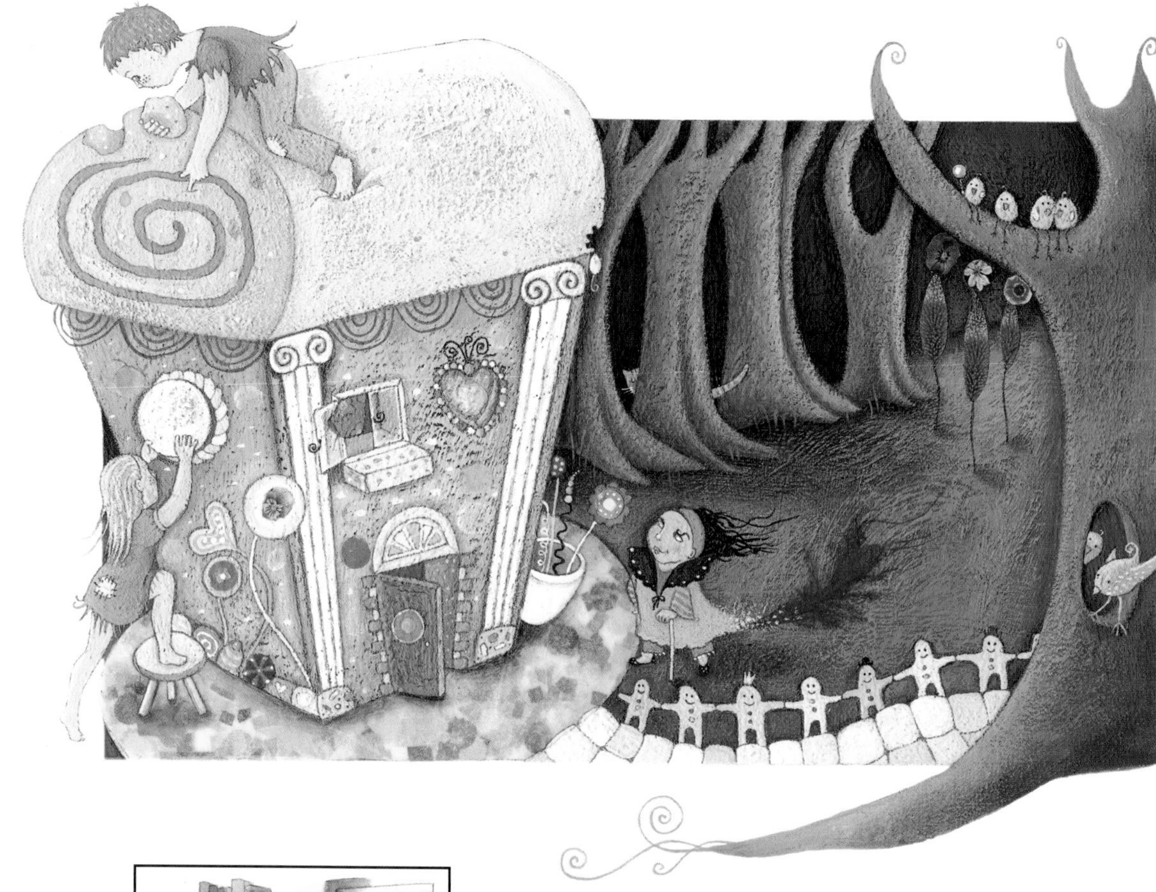

CITIZEN

Suzanne Mogensen

ШТА ЈЕ УЧИТЕЉИЦА САЊАЛА
МА
МА
БА
ТА
ТА

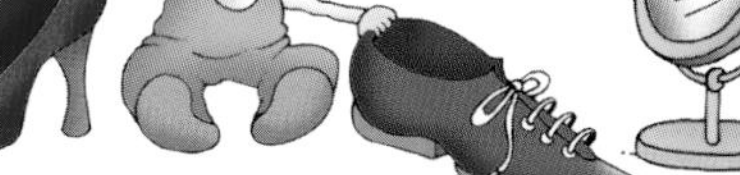

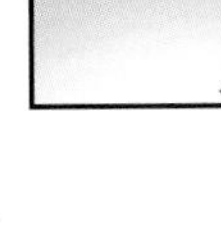

www.irmeliholmberg.com Phone 516.887.5348 eFax 212.202.4356

I'M
A
KID

MAME

REPRESENTED BY IRMELI HOLMBERG

www.irmeliholmberg.com Phone 516.887.5348 eFax 212.202.3456

REPRESENTED BY IRMELI HOLMBERG

Rosemary Hill

B
i
g
D I C K
LITTLE

Tina Bela Limer

REPRESENTED BY

IRMELI HOLMBERG

www.irmeliholmberg.com Phone 516.887.5348

eFax 212.202.4356

Ruth Rivers

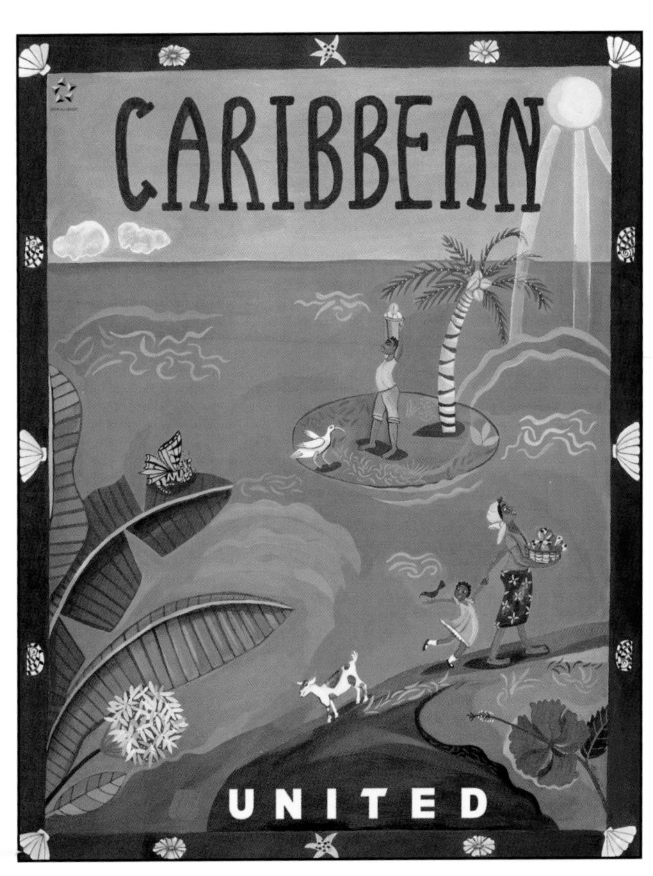
CARIBBEAN
UNITED

Melisande Potter

Jenny Law

REPRESENTED BY IRMELI HOLMBERG
www.irmeliholmberg.com Phone 516.887.5348 eFax 212.202.4356

Kristin Barr

Barry Ablett

Suzanna Hubbard

REPRESENTED BY

IRMELI HOLMBERG

www.irmeliholmberg.com

Phone 516.887.5348 eFax 212.202.4356

Laurie Keller

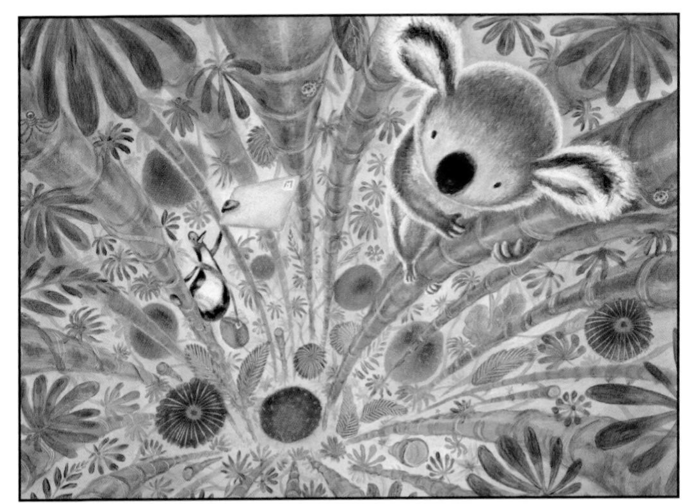

Jeff Spackman

www.irmeliholmberg.com Phone 516.887.5348 eFax 212.202.3456

REPRESENTED BY IRMELI HOLMBERG

WILLIAM ERSLAND

Mark Preston

REPRESENTED BY

IRMELI HOLMBERG

收骨丈之子

www.irmeliholmberg.com Phone 516.887.5348 eFax 212.202.3456

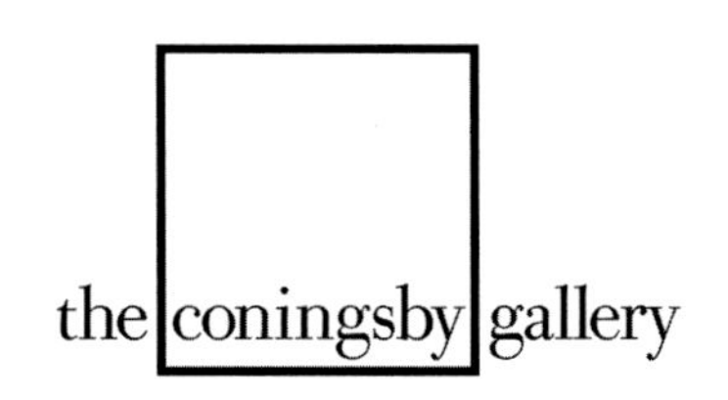

the coningsby gallery

début **art** • Illustrators, Photographers and Fine Artists Agents
30 Tottenham Street, London, W1T 4RJ. United Kingdom.
Tel: 01144 20 7636 1064 Fax: 01144 20 7580 7017
The Coningsby Gallery • Tel: 01144 20 7636 7478
email: **info@debutart.com** • **www.debutart.com**

début **art**

a little wild
Coca-Cola

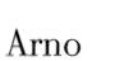

Arno

violence

Vault49

Vault49

Levi's

Pat Morgan

Clio RENAULT sport

Container

MINISTRY OF SOUND

Matthew Dartford

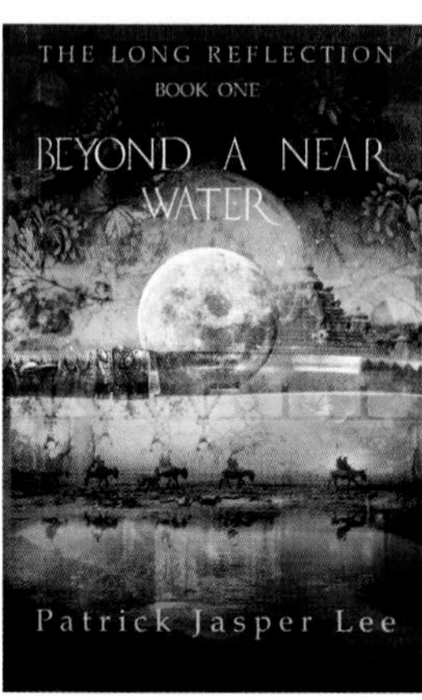

THE LONG REFLECTION
BOOK ONE
BEYOND A NEAR WATER
Patrick Jasper Lee

Steve Rawlings

David Newton

Since 1985, *début* **art** (based in London, England and now with offices in New York, Amsterdam and Sydney) has proactively sought out genuinely leading contemporary image-makers & clients who create original, progressive and commercially successful media material. Today, *début* **art** and the highly artistic illustrators it promotes, are widely regarded, both in the UK and around the world, as representing one of the finest and most contemporary talent groupings in the field of illustration.

Full portfolios for every artist can be reviewed and requested via our web site at www.debutart.com

The Coningsby Gallery stages some 30 exhibitions per year by selected leading illustrators, photographers and fine artists. A review of previous exhibitions, a look at upcoming shows and a photo tour of the gallery itself can be accessed at www.coningsbygallery.com

Contact: Andrew Coningsby, Samuel Summerskill or Kelly Fysh.

'Beauty is truth, truth beauty'
John Keats

www.debutart.com

Ric Machin

Sarah Howell

Nick Reddyhoff

MINI CONVERTIBLE
UK PRESS LAU
14 - 19 JUNE 2006
SEVILLE, SPAIN

Barry Downard

H
2

Matthew Cooper

Warren Holder

David Newton Photo-Illustration

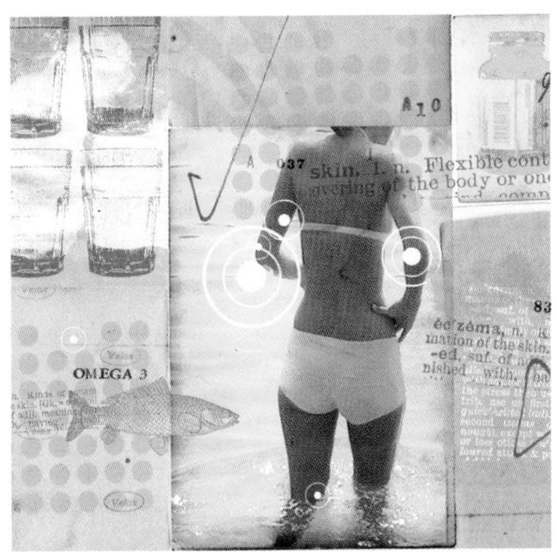
OMEGA 3

Bridget Strachan

Benedict Campbell

Kid Spaniard

EASY
PEASY!
COMPUTING

Harry Malt

David Newton Photo-Illustration

www.debutart.com

Alex Williamson

Tim Ashton

AC/DC
OLYMPUS

James Carey

VH1 IMMORTALS

Flatliner V2

698 EKU

Darren Hopes

Andy Baker

MONTANA
NORTH DAKOTA
OREGON
IDAHO
NEVADA
UTAH
COLORADO
KANSAS
NEW MEXICO
OKLAHOMA

Serge Seidlitz

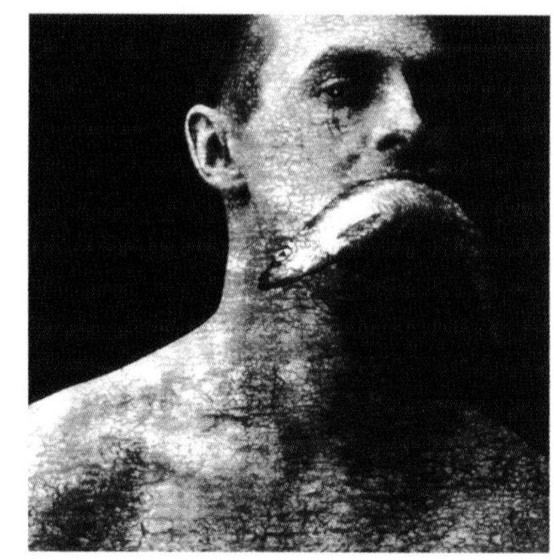

Ewan Fraser

Spiral

VoIP
Service

Peter Crowther Associates

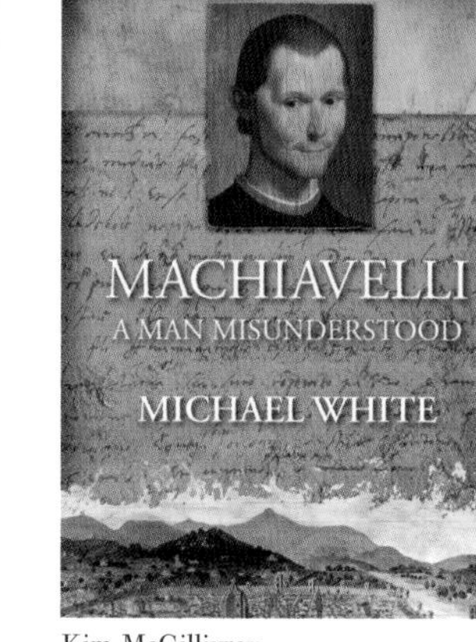
MACHIAVELLI
A MAN MISUNDERSTOOD
MICHAEL WHITE

Kim McGillivray

www.debutart.com

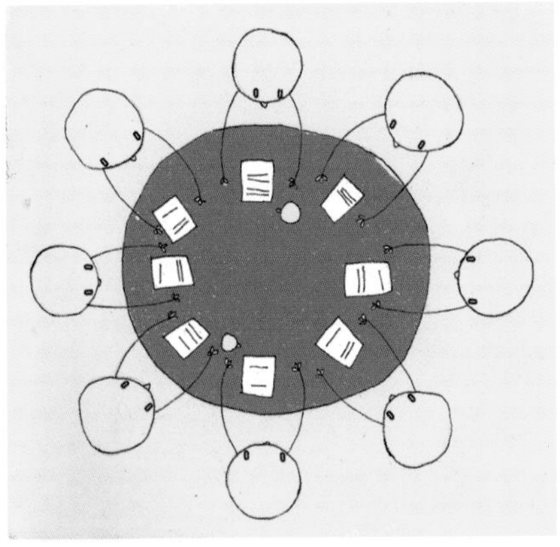

Craig Shuttlewood

Carol Del Angel

Marina Caruso

Oliver Burston

Matt Herring

DIGIT
GRAPHICS
InDesign rules
MADE IN THE U.K.
DESIGN NATION
British design 2005

Peter Quinnell

James Taylor

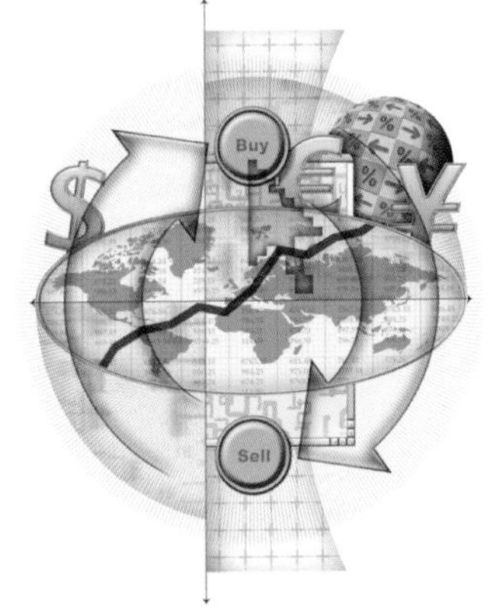
Buy
Sell

Neil Leslie

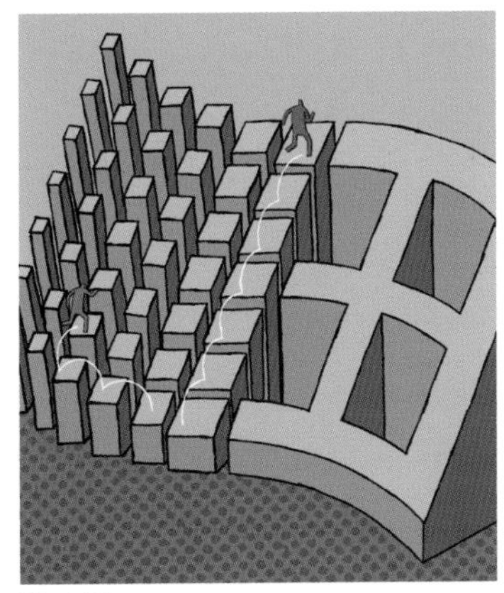

Tim Ellis

Neil Webb

David Angel

Redseal

www.debutart.com

CONRAD REPRESENTS

951 COLLEGE AVE. MENLO PARK, CA 94025 / T 650.322.0904 F 650.322.0905 E james@conradreps.com W conradreps.com

Steve Stankiewicz

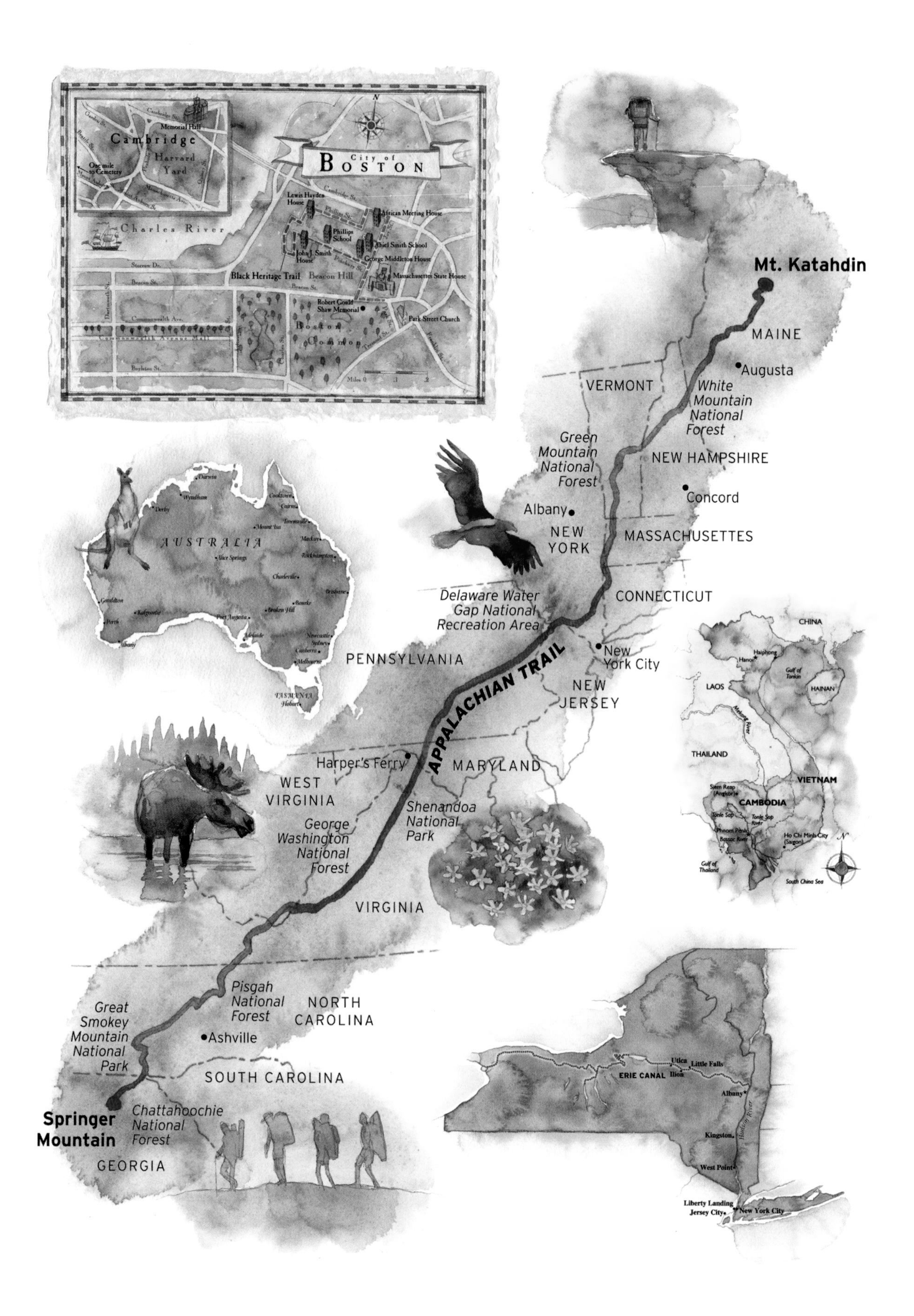
City of
BOSTON
Cambridge
Harvard Yard
Memorial Hall
Charles River
Lewis Hayden House
African Meeting House
Phillips School
Abiel Smith School
John J. Smith House
George Middleton House
Black Heritage Trail
Beacon Hill
Massachusettes State House
Robert Gould Shaw Memorial
Park Street Church
Boston Common
AUSTRALIA
Darwin
Cairns
Townsville
Mackay
Rockhampton
Alice Springs
Brisbane
Port Augusta
Broken Hill
Adelaide
Sydney
Canberra
Melbourne
TASMANIA
Hobart
Mt. Katahdin
MAINE
Augusta
VERMONT
White Mountain National Forest
Green Mountain National Forest
NEW HAMPSHIRE
Concord
Albany
NEW YORK
MASSACHUSETTES
Delaware Water Gap National Recreation Area
CONNECTICUT
PENNSYLVANIA
APPALACHIAN TRAIL
New York City
NEW JERSEY
Harper's Ferry
MARYLAND
WEST VIRGINIA
Shenandoa National Park
George Washington National Forest
VIRGINIA
Pisgah National Forest
NORTH CAROLINA
Great Smokey Mountain National Park
Ashville
SOUTH CAROLINA
Springer Mountain
Chattahoochie National Forest
GEORGIA
CHINA
Hanoi
Haiphong
Gulf of Tonkin
LAOS
HAINAN
THAILAND
VIETNAM
CAMBODIA
Ho Chi Minh City (Saigon)
Gulf of Thailand
South China Sea
ERIE CANAL
Utica
Little Falls
Ilion
Albany
Kingston
West Point
Liberty Landing
Jersey City
New York City

Eve Steccati

SHANGHAI
N
W
E
S
Beijing
XINJIANG
GANSU
SHANDONG
Yellow Sea
CHINA
JIANGSU
Nanjing
Shanghai
Hangzhou
ANHUI
QINGHAI
ZHEJIANG
Nanchang
XIZANG (TIBET)
JIANGXI
FUJIAN
SICHUAN
HUNAN
Guilin
GUANGDONG
Guangzhou
YUNNAN
Hong Kong
South China Sea
Zhongshan Road N.
Huangpu River
The Bund
Oriental Pearl TV Tower
PUDONG
Hua Hai Road
Yuyuan Garden
Fuxing Garden
Zhongshan Road W.
Zhongshan Road S.
Pudong Road

CONRAD REPRESENTS

951 COLLEGE AVE. MENLO PARK, CA 94025 / T 650.322.0904 F 650.322.0905 E james@conradreps.com W conradreps.com

Leland Klanderman

BIG HOUSE
BRAND
Ca'del Solo
Big House Red

CONRAD REPRESENTS
951 COLLEGE AVE. MENLO PARK, CA 94025 / T 650.322.0904 F 650.322.0905 E james@conradreps.com W conradreps.com

Robin Moline

CONRAD REPRESENTS

951 COLLEGE AVE. MENLO PARK, CA 94025 / T 650.322.0904 F 650.322.0905 E james@conradreps.com W conradreps.com

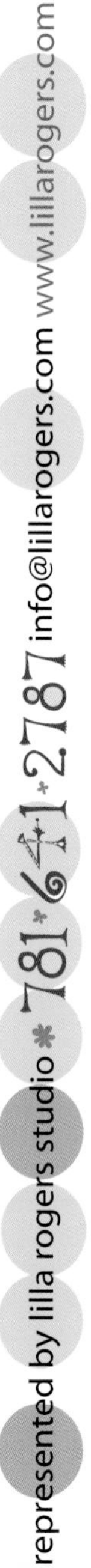
represented by lilla rogers studio * 781·641·2787 info@lillarogers.com www.lillarogers.com

READING
IS
COOL

SARAJO FRIEDEN

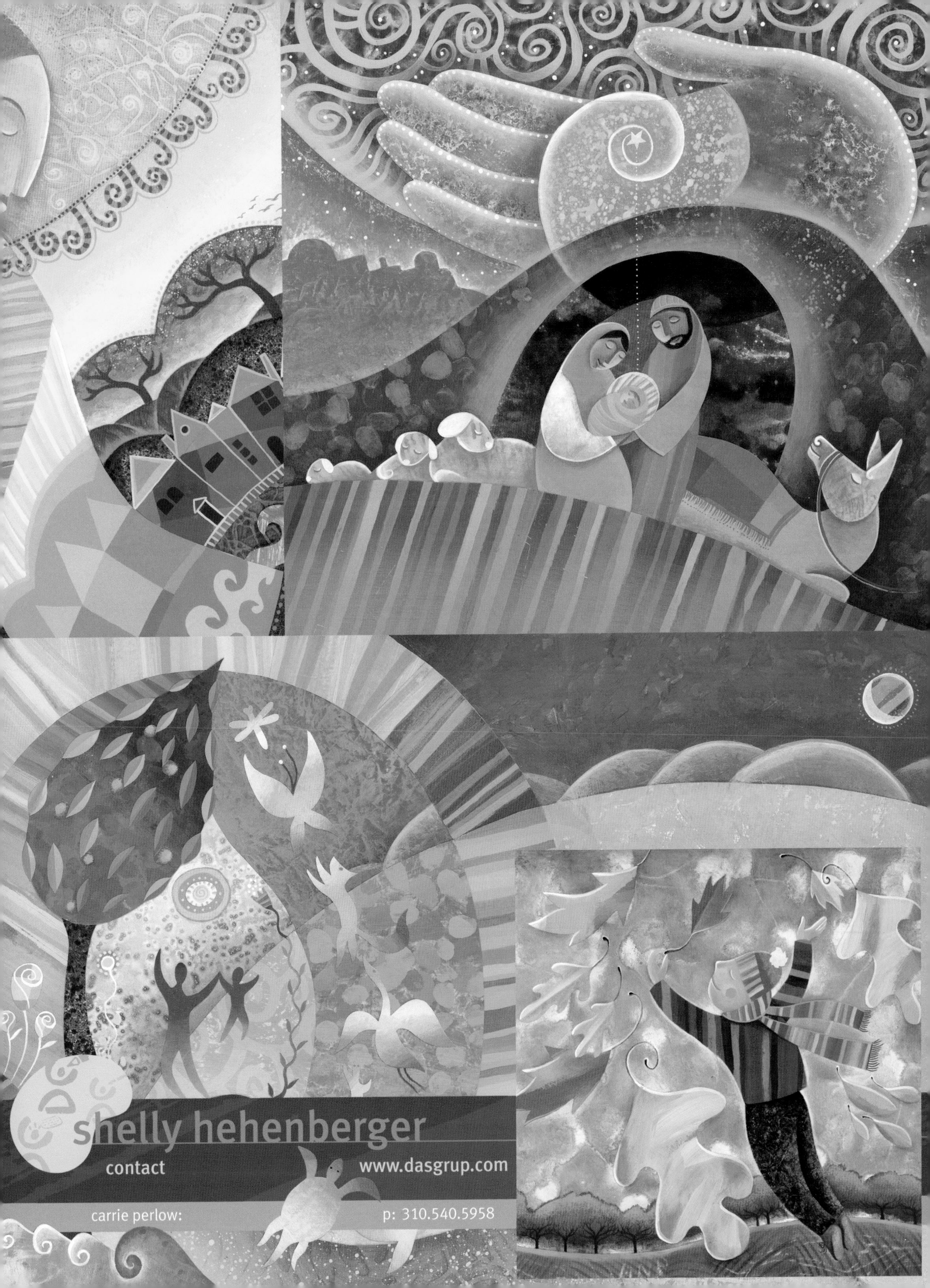
shelly hehenberger
contact
www.dasgrup.com
carrie perlow:
p: 310.540.5958

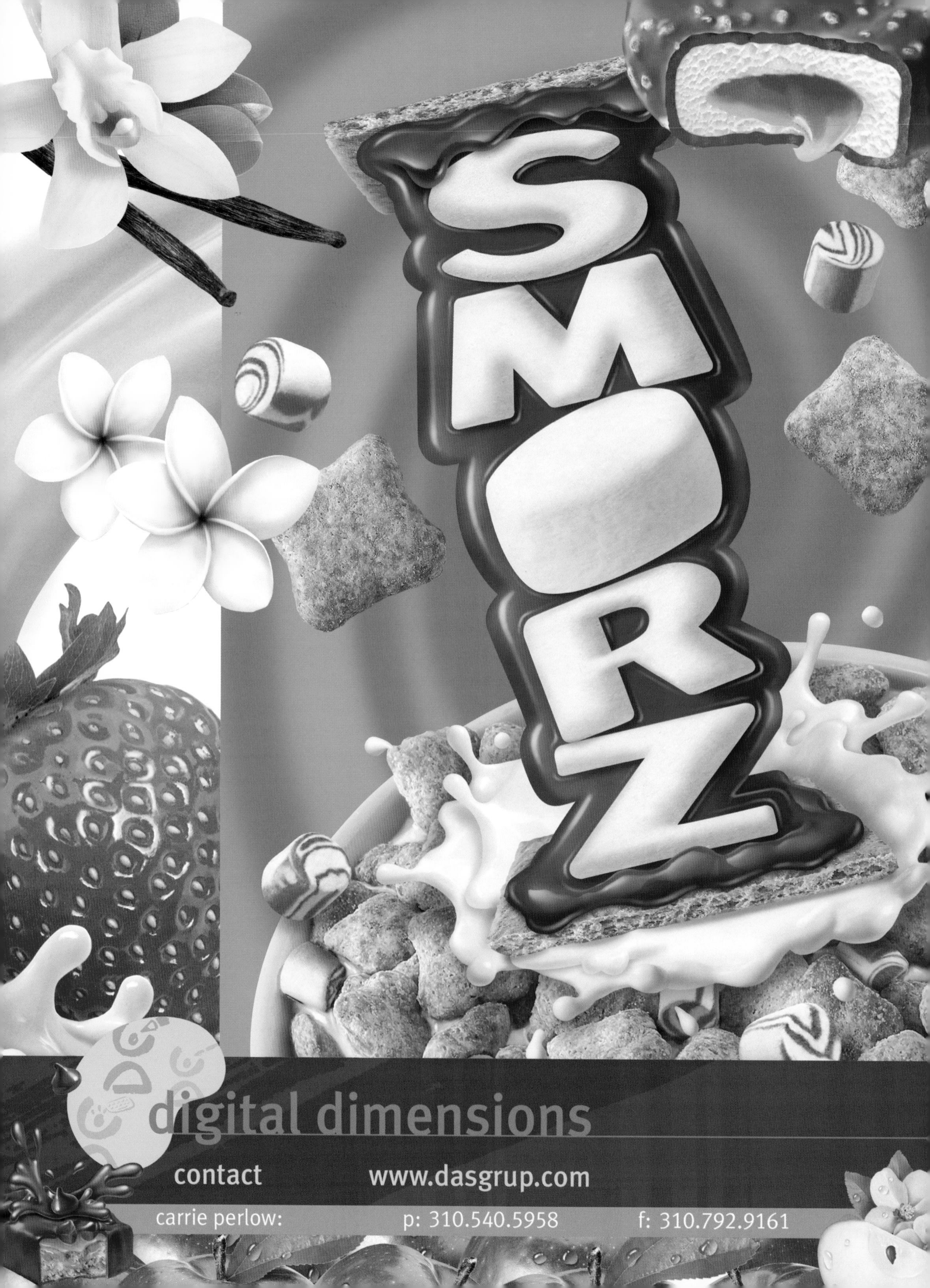

SMORZ
digital dimensions
contact
www.dasgrup.com
carrie perlow:
p: 310.540.5958
f: 310.792.9161

BEN & JERRY'S
ELWOOD
www.dasgrup.com

WHITE
SPORK
HENDERLING
ATTACK
PG-13
KELLY
NIELSEN
KOELSCH
PHILLIPS
BOULINGER
BEAUTY
MARTINEZ
PICKERING
HQ: 212.333.2551
SHANNON ASSOCIATES
A GLORIOUS LOVE STORY WITH MUNCHKINS! in Fanaticolor
GABOR
ROE
HANSEN

CHARLESWORTH
FRANCIS
HENDERLING
SWEARINGEN
SIMON
BERNARDIN
KELTIE
AMIT
COMPOR
BATTLE OF THE TITANS
RICHARDSON
ONG
MAC
GILPIN
BRODNER
ANDREASEN
PANG
BAEZ
KOELSCH
REBENSCHIED
GORDON
PAPP
JASINSKI
OBERDIECK
CALL
ROBINSON
WWW.SHANNONASSOCIATES.COM
MAYA
HANSEN
MOURNING
JAY JAY
COHEN
BRENNAN
ROE
HARRINGTON
FARICY
GABOR
PHILLIPS
YUCEL
PICKERING
SHROADES
ELWELL
NEUBECKER
BRUNELLO
DIBLEY
BATES
MITCHELL
RAVEN
PROCTOR
HELQUIST
WILL TERRY
LI'L SOPHIE
SMITH

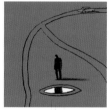

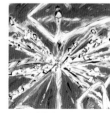

194 THIRD AVE NYC 10003
(212)475-0440
MORGAN
GAYNIN
INC.
MORGANGAYNIN.COM

SARAH HOLLANDER

JANUARY **Michael Crampton**

FEBRUARY **Mona Daly**

MARCH **Hugh Syme**

APRIL **Kenny Kiernan**

MAY **Dave Henderson**

LEMONADE

JUNE **Mike Wimmer**

JULY **Charlie Hill**

Boordy Vineyards
Summer Concerts

AUGUST **Rowan Barnes Murphy**

SEPTEMBER **Dahl Taylor**

HALLOWEEN PARTY

OCTOBER **Kevin Rechin**

NOVEMBER **Bill Ledger**

DECEMBER **Tom Newsom**

susan gal

www.galgirlstudio.com

Ice
Cream

ART
REP

Represented by Lisa Freeman, Inc 317.920.0068 www.lisafreeman.com lisa@lisafreeman.com

Great illustrators represent **Gerald & Cullen Rapp**

Brian Ajhar

Philip Anderson

Daniel Baxter

Brian Biggs

Stuart Briers

David M. Brinley

Lonnie Busch

Harry Campbell

Gerald
Cullen
Jonathan Carlson

R. Gregory Christie

Jack Davis

Robert de Michiell

Dynamic Duo Studio

Leo Espinosa

Phil Foster

Mark Fredrickson

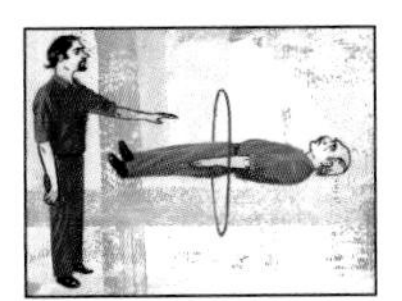
Arthur E. Giron

Asaf Hanuka

Tomer Hanuka

Peter Horjus

Celia Johnson

R A P P INC
Douglas Jones

James Kaczman

J.D. King

Laszlo Kubinyi

PJ Loughran

Bernard Maisner

Coco Masuda

Hal Mayforth

Grady McFerrin

Bruce Morser

James O'Brien

AND
Dan Page

John Pirman

R
Fred Rix

Marc Rosenthal

Alison Seiffer

Seth

Whitney Sherman

James Steinberg

Elizabeth Traynor

Anders Wenngren

Michael Witte

Noah Woods

R
Brad Yeo

And **Gerald & Cullen Rapp** has represented great illustrators since 1944

420 Lexington Ave., PH, NY, NY 10170 | Phone 212 889 3337 | Fax 212 889 3341 | www.rappart.com

WWW.THEISPOT.COM/REP/RAPP

T : 212.889.3337 F : 212.889.3341

WHITNEY SHERMAN ILLUSTRATION

REPRESENTED BY GERALD & CULLEN RAPP, NYC

CLIENTS : BUSINESS WEEK, STANFORD MAGAZINE, THE ...ZINE GROUP, SOUTHERN POVERTY LAW CENTER, NEW YORK TIMES, UITGEVERIJ LANNOO NV, AMERIC... ...EDERATION OF TEACHERS, NATIONAL PUBLIC RADIO, HARVARD BUSINESS REVIEW, WARNER BROTH...

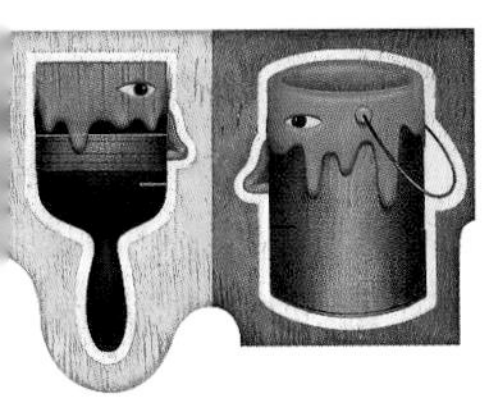

Riccardo Stampatori

Gerald & Cullen Rapp
212 889 3337
www.rappart.com
www.riccardostampatori.com

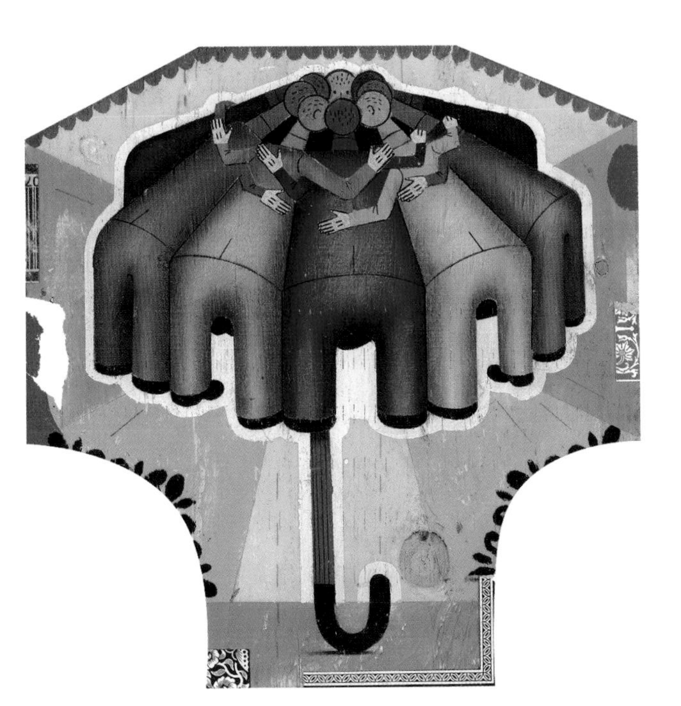

220A

m
M
110000000000011000000011010000

Jessell

Aspland

Locke

Dawson

(918) 749-9424 Suzanne Craig Represents

Suzanne Craig Represents

www.suzannecraig.com
T: (918) 749-9424
F: (918) 749-5165

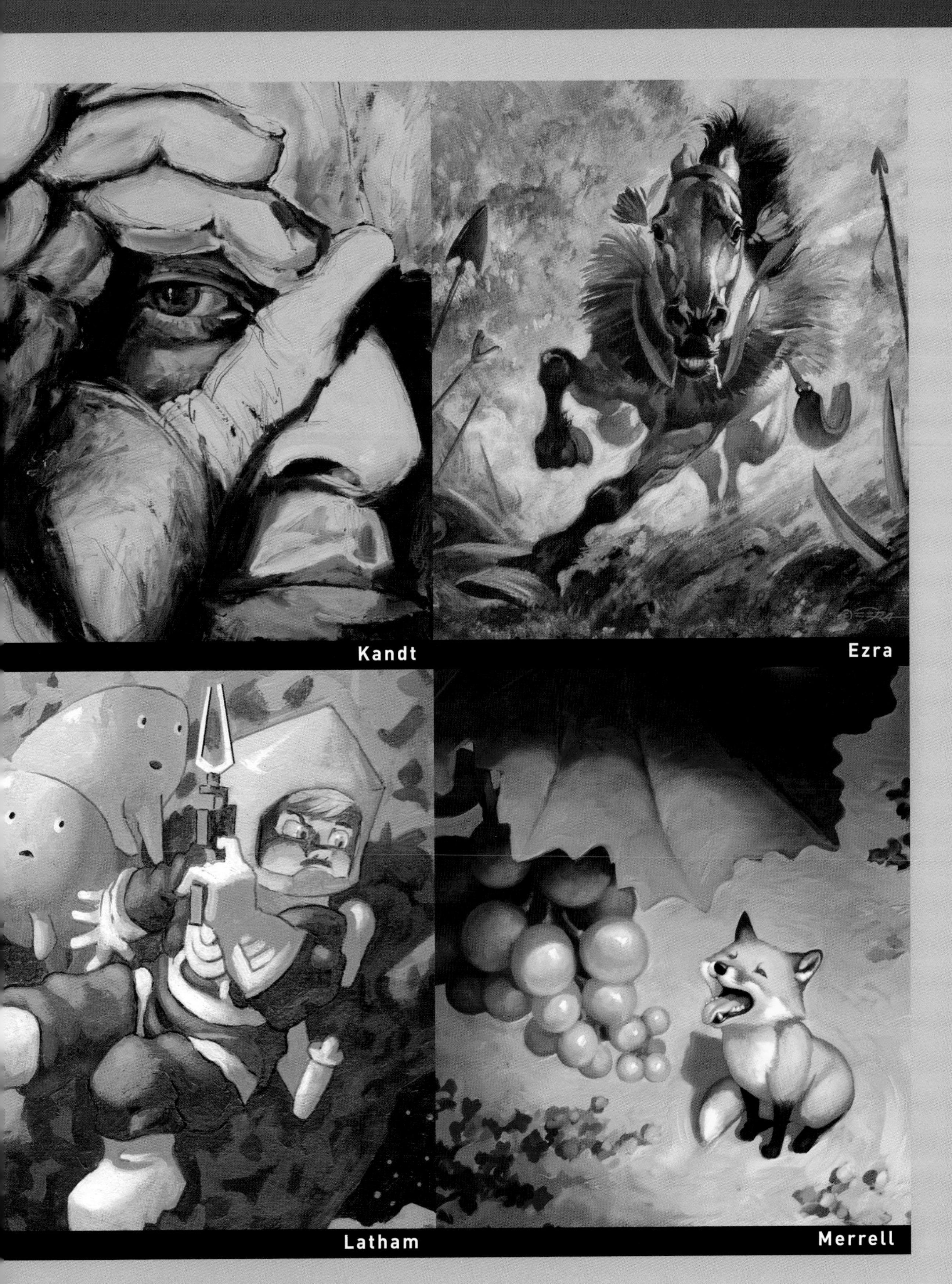
Kandt
Ezra
Latham
Merrell

www.ArtAgent.com

SHAKERS
VOTE
VOTE
WHEAT

Michael Fisher

Wayne Watford

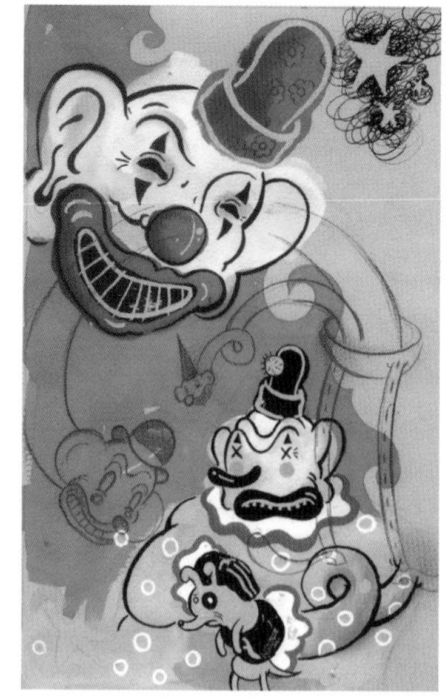

Jason Lynch

Joey Feldman

Maral Sassouni

Kelly Pierce

Capstone Digital Imaging

OUT

Greg Hargreaves

Jim Chow

ArtAgent.com

A Subsidiary of Carol Guenzi Agents: Art Management: Photography / Illustration / Film / New Media / Stock

Phone: 303-820-2599 Fax: 303-820-2598 Toll: 800-417-5120

WWW.ARTAGENT.COM

Coca-Cola

CHRISTER ERIKSSON

TOM WARD

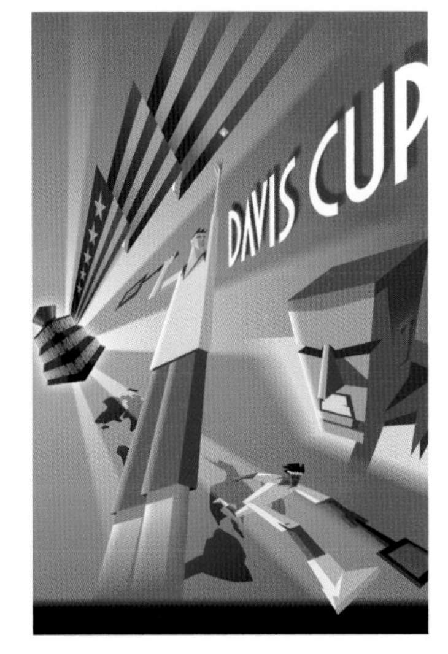
DAVIS CUP

TRUE

TOD KAPKE

KYM FOSTER

Dope State
Classics

JUAN ALVAREZ

TATJANA KRIZMANIC

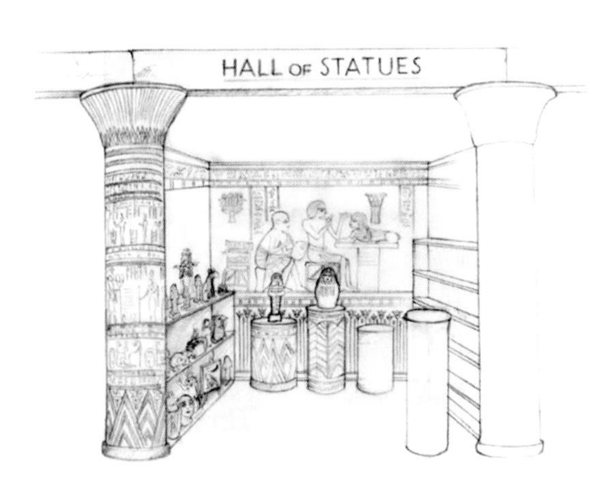
HALL OF STATUES

HALLER/BUCHANAN

BRUCE HUTCHISON

ArtAgent.com

A SUBSIDIARY OF CAROL GUENZI AGENTS: ART MANAGEMENT: PHOTOGRAPHY / ILLUSTRATION / FILM / NEW MEDIA / STOCK

PHONE: 303-820-2599 FAX: 303-820-2598 TOLL: 800-417-5120

Christopher Shaner

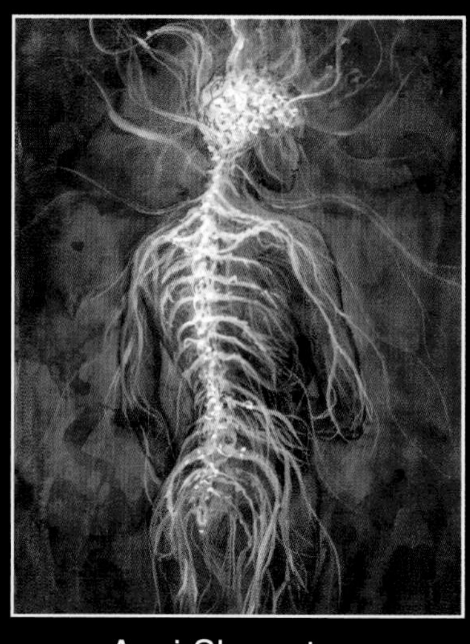

Angi Shearstone

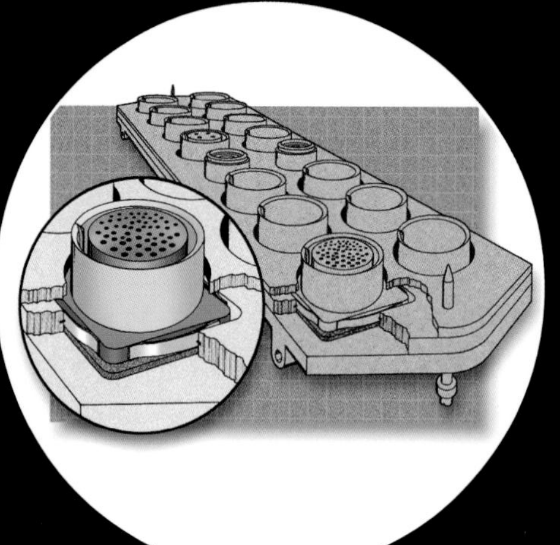

Doug Andersen

Heidi Graf

Jeannie Morgan

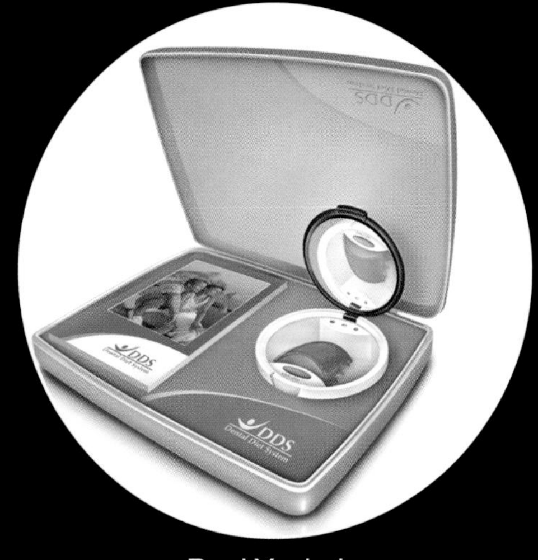
DDS
DDS
DDS
Dental Diet System

Paul Yuskales

LOCOMOBILE

Warren Markey

Wiseman says:
see more at
cmurph.com

Christopher Murphy

Robert VanKeirsbilck

Herman Agency

www.HermanAgencyInc.com

JOHN NEZ

DOREEN GAY-KASSEL

DEBORAH ZEMKE

Art for all your needs

BARRY GOTT

Bakery

BOB MCMAHON

JAN SPIVEY GILCHRIST

ELIZABETH BUTTLER

MIKE LESTER

Snuffy's Specials
all you can eat
fluffy waffles
cream puffs
I'm stuffed!
TAMARA PETROSINO

JILL NEWTON

THIERRY COURTIN

PETE WHITEHEAD

www.HermanAgencyInc.com
Ronnie@HermanAgencyInc.com

MARK WEBER

Photo
ALBUM
ANNE CATHARINE BLAKE

GIDEON KENDALL

KEVIN SERWACKI

Keiko Motoyama

28017 Seashell Way, Rancho Palos Verdes, CA 90275
Tel/Fax: 310.544.1751
e-mail: mokkun@aol.com

Artist's agent: Christina A. Tugeau
Tel: 203.438.7307
For additional work see:
American Showcase
21, 22, 23, 24, 25
Directory of Illustration
18, 19, 20

HOT DOGS

Judy Love
Illustration
68 Agassiz Ave
Belmont
MA 02478
pterosauria
Pterodactyl
"wing finger"

© Judy Love from *Can I Bring My Pterodactyl to School, Ms. Johnson?* by Lois Grambling, Charlesbridge Publishing, 2006

Robert
Snyder
219.465-3246

what2wnt@jorsm.com

www.robertsnyderillustrates.com

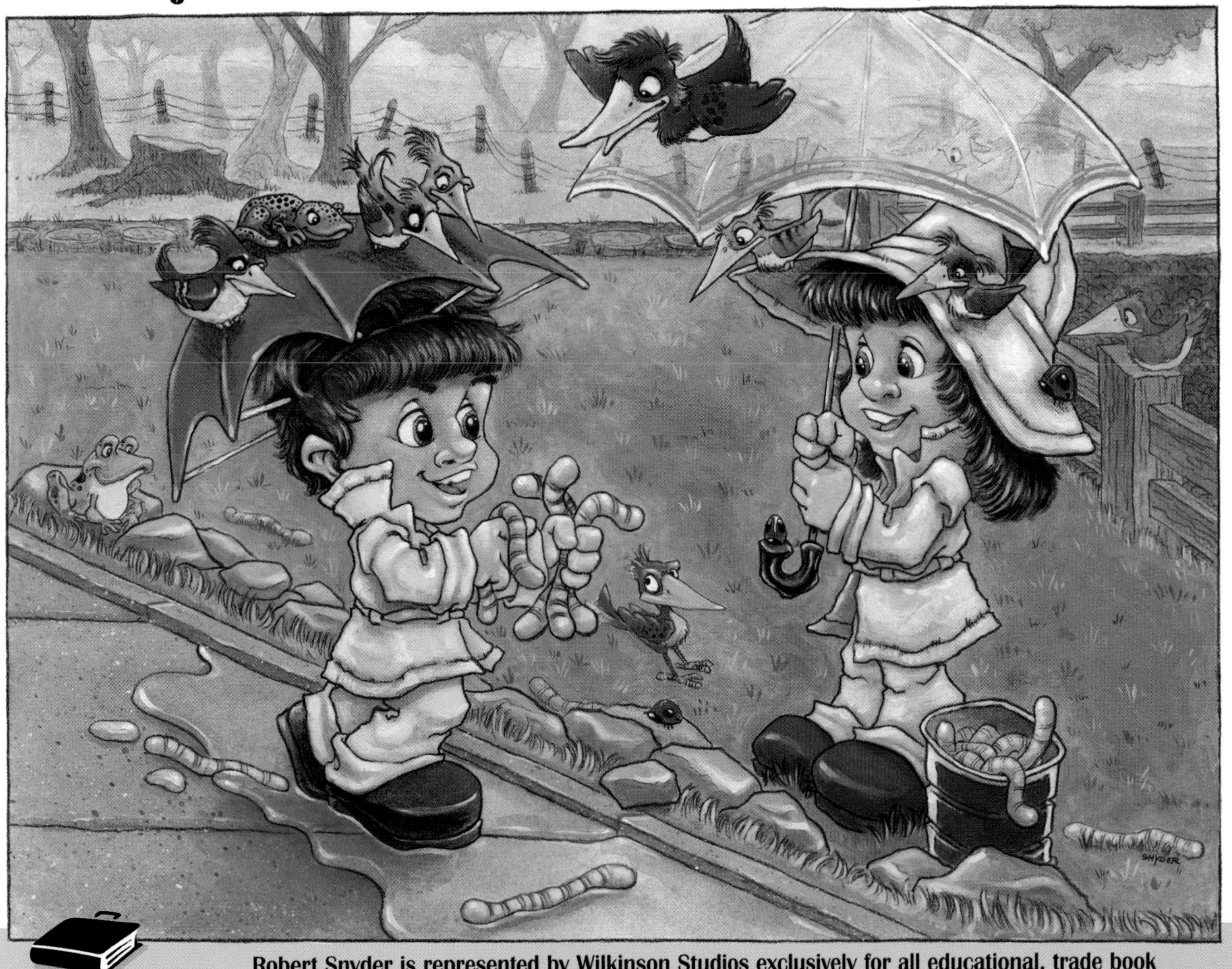
SNYDER

Wilkinson
STUDIOS, INC

Robert Snyder is represented by Wilkinson Studios exclusively for all educational, trade book and children's market publishing work. Please contact the artist directly for all other markets.

Phone: 312.226.0007 Fax: 312.226.0404

www.wilkinsonstudios.com

J H O E A D N G N E E
ARTIST REPRESENTATIVE

JIM SALVATI

JIM SALVATI

BLACK LAVA
Lolani Kopes'
JAVA
Hawaiian
Estate Coffee

Italy

CHART OF NURSES
Yak Yak Yak
Nurse COLD HANDS
NURSE GABBY
NURSE SMILEY
NURSE TWEETY
NURSE GRUMPY
Nurse Lotsa HANDS

helenravenhillrepresents
tel 816 333 0744 fax 816 333 0745 web ravenhill.net
lynn rowe reed

helenravenhillrepresents
tel 816 333 0744 fax 816 333 0745 web ravenhill.net

doug bowles

TUGEAU
2
Jeremy & Nicole Tugeau
Artist Representatives
216.707.0854
2225 Bellfield Avenue
Cleveland Heights, OH 44106
www.tugeau2.com

Paula Pertile
Illustrations for Kids
http://www.paulapertile.com
paula@paulapertile.com
(415) 668-7156

Member SCBWI, GraphicArtistsGuild,
PictureBookArtistsAssociation, ChildrensBookCouncil

Karol Kaminski

Jeremy & Nicole Tugeau

TUGEAU 2

Artist Representatives

216.707.0854

www.tugeau2.com

Gina Capaldi

TUGEAU
2
Jeremy & Nicole Tugeau
Artist Representatives

216.707.0854
www.tugeau2.com

hk
portfolio

rémy simard

viviana garofoli

david austin clar

nan brooks

www.hkportfolio.com MELA BOLINAO
telephone 212 689.7830 facsimile 212 689.7829

MELA BOLINAO www.hkportfolio.com
telephone 212 689.7830 facsimile 212 689.7829

kristin kest

eldon doty

MELA BOLINAO of hk portfolio represents 42 meticulously hand-selected illustrators from around the world. Draw on this amazing collection of highly-regarded artists.

tiphanie beeke
hector borlasca
linda bronson
nan brooks
lindy burnett
abby carter
randy chewning
david austin clar
ande cook
steve cox
carolyn croll
bandelin-dacey studios
renée daily
jack e. davis
eldon doty
kathi ember
viviana garofoli
claudine gévry
amanda harvey
rob hefferan
jannie ho
laura huliska-beith
susan keeter
anne kennedy
kristin kest
anthony lewis
stephen lewis
margeaux lucas
john manders
hiroe nakata
macky pamintuan
valeria petrone
mike reed
mick reid
rémy simard
jamie smith
judy stead
peggy tagel
george ulrich
john wallace
sue williams
sachiko yoshikawa

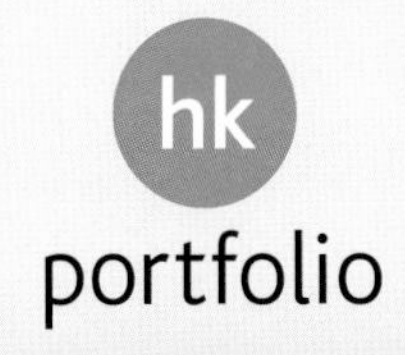
hk

portfolio

Kim Malek

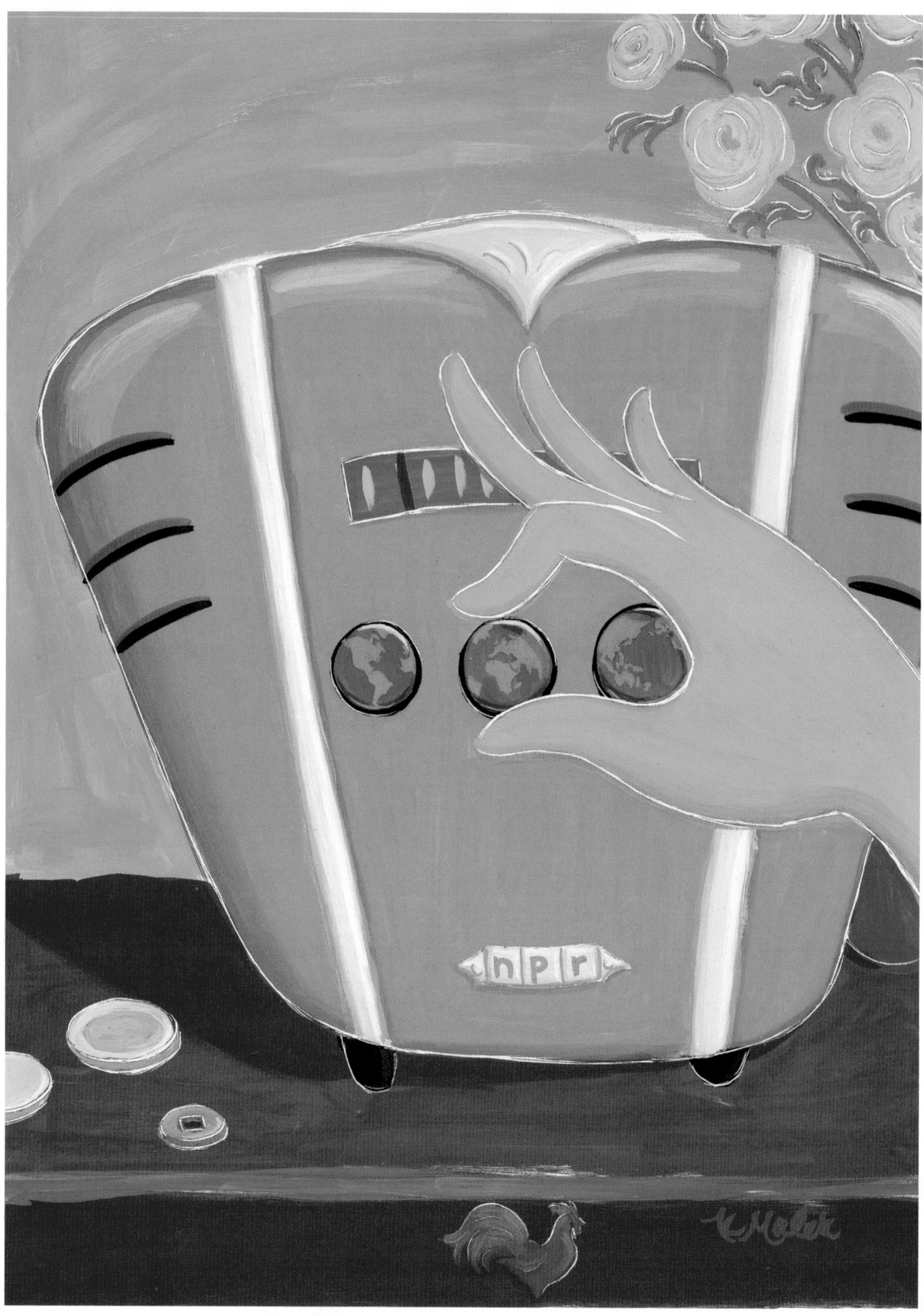
npr
K. Malek

Connecting You With Your Worlds | NPR Calendar 2005

Product | Packaging | People | Places
www.malekstudio.com

christine prapas
Artist Representative

p 503.245.9511 **f** 503.245.9512 **w** www.christineprapas.com

Jim
Edmon

ILLUSTRATION

Represented by Melissa Mackey
PLANET REP 800-847-5101

edmon.net / jim@edmondesign.com
STUDIO 800-530-5678

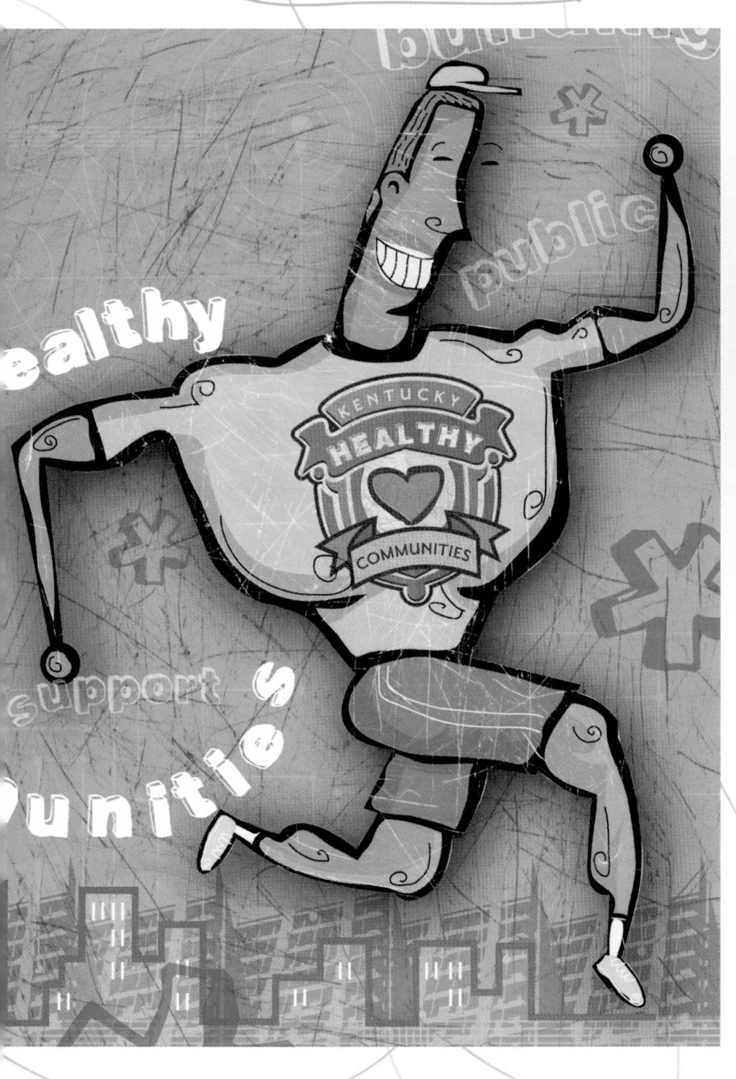
public
ealthy
KENTUCKY
HEALTHY
COMMUNITIES
support
unities

Tom Barrett

Susan Spellman

Abuelita

Janice Skivington

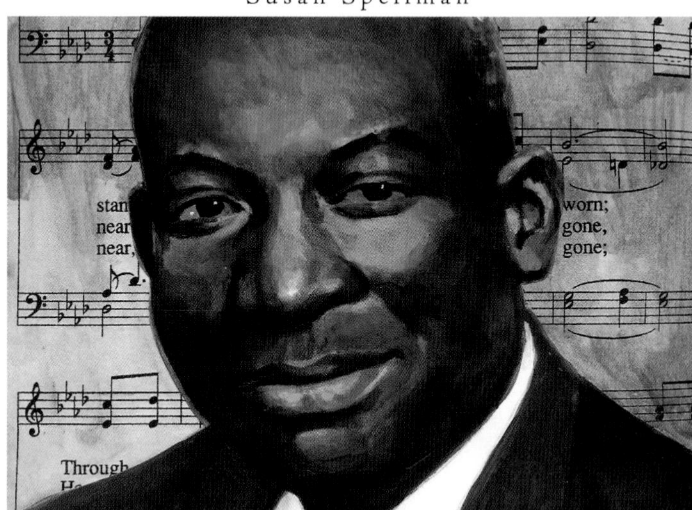
near
near,
worn;
gone,
gone;
Through

Larry Johnson

Laura Nikiel

Gerardo Suzan

ARTISTS' REPRESENTATIVE
· GWEN WALTERS ·
561-805-7739

ArtIncGW@aol.com
www.gwenwaltersartrep.com

Judith Pfeiffer

Rosario Valderrama

Linda Pierce

Pat Paris

Lane Gregory

Deborah White

amanda warren

teach
reach
feed.
lead

represented by harriet kastaris
www.kastaris.com | 314.249.1100

DAN COSGROVE

daniele collignon
200 W. 15th nyc 10011
212·243·4209
www.danielecollignon-reps.com
Chance
Chance
MONOPOLY
70
Community Chest
Community Chest
110 BREWS
OLD CHICAGO
PASTA & PIZZA
SUPER BOWL
XXXIX

POSTERS, ICONS, LOGOS AND PACKAGE DESIGN

CHICAGO, STUDIO
COSGROVEDESIGN.COM
312.609.0050

ANITA GRIEN
155 East 38th Street
New York, NY 10016
TEL: (212) 697-6170
FAX: (212) 697-6177
e-mail: agrien@aol.com
www.anitagrien.com

Representing:
Fanny Mellet Berry
Higgins Bond
Ron Carboni
Anthony Jenkins

Also Representing:
Alan Neider
Julie Johnson
Mona Mark
Alan Reingold
and Don Morrison

ANITA

6:30AM

Fanny Mellet Berry (digital art)

Higgins Bond

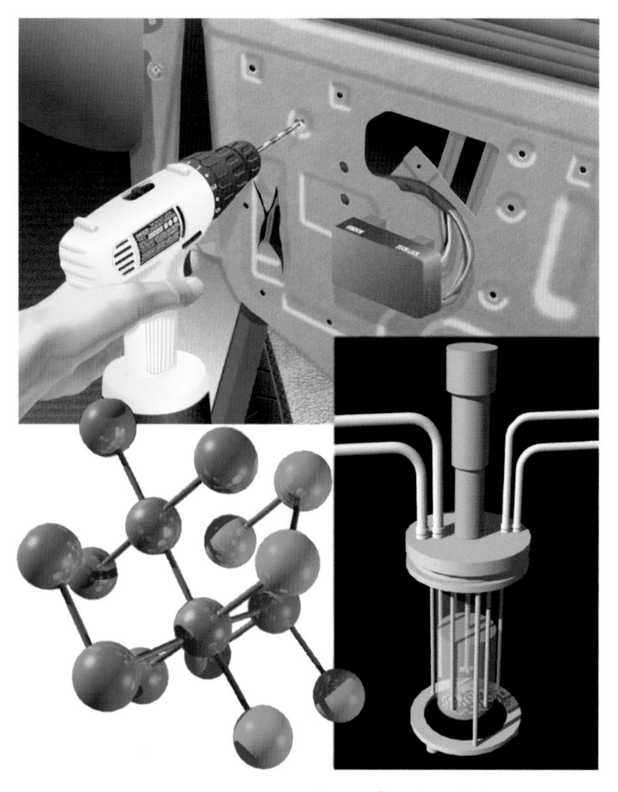

Ron Carboni (digital art)

Anthony Jenkins

ANITA GRIEN
155 East 38th Street
New York, NY 10016
TEL: (212) 697-6170
FAX: (212) 697-6177
e-mail: agrien@aol.com
www.anitagrien.com

Representing:
Alan Neider
Julie Johnson
Mona Mark
Alan Reingold

Also Representing:
Fanny Mellet Berry
Higgins Bond
Ron Carboni
Anthony Jenkins
and Don Morrison

ANITA

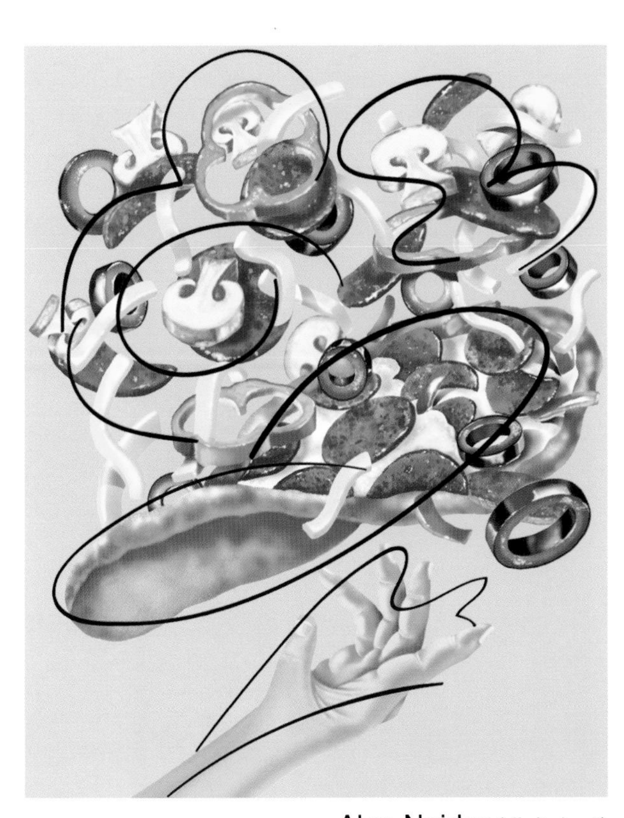

Alan Neider (digital art)

Julie Johnson

COOKING
AT
COOKTIQUE
Over 200 International Food Classics
from a Teaching Kitchen
Silvia Lehrer

Mona Mark

Alan Reingold

JON FLAMING
sun
jet airplane
ball player
gardener
princess
downtown
songbirds
tv cowboy
tree, flower, leaf
barn
campfire
pumpkin

4 BEARS

Peter Pahl

S. LEONG

Shelton Leong

deborah melmon

represented by

Sharon Morris associates 415.987.4517

www.sharonartrep.com www.debmelmonstudio.com

Flowers

Hello
INK

deborah melmon

represented by
Sharon Morris associates 415.987.4517
www.sharonartrep.com www.debmelmonstudio.com

Carole Newman & Associates
CREATIVE RESOURCE AGENCY

DIGITAL TRADITIONAL

ILLUSTRATION • DESIGN • PHOTOGRAPHY

Gino Hasler

Patrick Jones

John Rowe

Adrian Chesterman

Aa Bb Cc
23456

Ardvark

Adrian Chesterman

Tel 818.719.9933 www.carolenewman.com Fax 818.719.9922

CREATIVE CONNECTION, INC.
P.O. Box 253
Gibson Island, MD 21056
TEL: (410) 360-5981
FAX: (410) 255-8889
e-mail: mail@cciart.com
www.parkerfulton.com
www.theispot.com

Client List: Ceaco, Doubleday, Woman's Day, World Wildlife Fund, Prudent Publishing, National Wildlife Federation, McGraw Hill, The Bradford Exchange, All About Kids Publishing, The New York Times, Bits and Pieces, AMIA, Manual Woodworkers, Quarasan

See *Directory of Illustration #s 13-21* for additional work or call for portfolio.

PARKER FULTON ©05

PARKER FULTON

Peggy Turchette

Elizabeth Hinshaw

Jack Lutzow

Lindy Burnett

Thomas Gonzalez

Don Morris

Stanislawa Kodman

ALEXANDER-POLLARD INC.

ARTISTS' AGENT

www.alexanderpollard.com

800.347.0734

www.wandanow.com

INS
TITU
TION

FREDERIQUE BERTRAND

EMMANUEL KERNER

TIM ROBINSON

EMILIE CHOLLAT

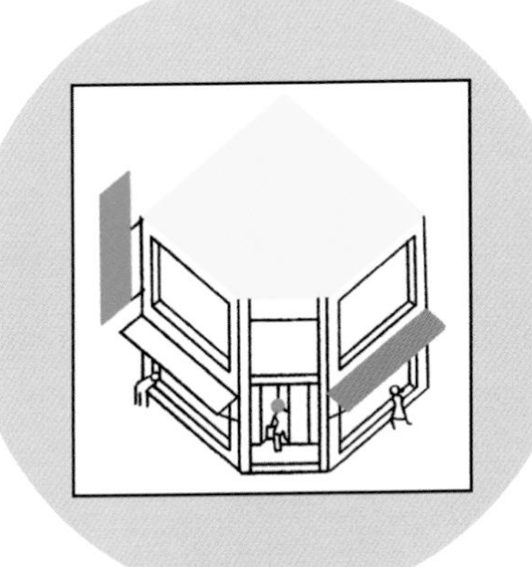

LAURENT CILLUFFO

BENOIT LAVERDIERE

BIRD
THE PARTS OF

DOUGLAS MULLEN

OLIVIER LATYK

MICHAEL MEISTER

REPRESENTED  WANDA NOWAK 
CREATIVE ILLUSTRATORS AGENCY

PHONE 212·535·0438 FAX 212·535·1624

INTERNATIONAL BUILDING . 630 FIFTH AVENUE. 20TH FLOOR
ROCKEFELLER CENTER . NEW YORK . NEW YORK 10111
ARTIST REPRESENTATIVES . CREATIVE CONSULTANTS
PHONE 212.332.3460 . FAX 212.332.3401

VICKI PRENTICE ASSOCIATES INC.

RIDDELL'S BAY
MIDDLE ROAD
GIBB'S HILL LIGHT HOUSE
PINK BUS STOP TO HAMILTON & ST. GEORGES
SOUTH ROAD
HAMILTON 8K →
PINK BUS
SOMERSET & DOCKYARD
SOUTH ROAD
PINK BUS STOP TO SOMERSET & DOCKYARD
SCOOTER RENTAL
SOUTH ROAD COTTAGES (FUTURE)
SHUTTLE BUS
BOAT BAY VILLAGE (FUTURE)
BAY CLUB
TENNIS COURTS (FUTURE)
DIVE SHOP
BOAT BAY
DOLPHIN BAY
PRIVATE
FISHERMAN'S POINT
CARLTON WING
SOUTHSHORE PRESERVE
HONEYMOON POINT
SINKY ROCK
ATLANTIC OCEAN
N
W
E
S
WYNDHAM BERMUDA RESORT & SPA
SOUTHAMPTON BEACH

"The new owners of the Wyndham Bermuda Resort & Spa knew they wanted to give their guests an illustrative 'site map' attached to their room key card so they would be able to navigate around the property, as well as providing a terrific keepsake. It was not until we found Andrew that I felt we could achieve what we were looking for. Working with photos, old advertisements, and narratives, Andrew was able to work through our design concepts and vision for the piece. The final product he created has exceeded our expectations in his level of detail, whimsy, and finally the choice of color palette. It is truly a beautiful piece of artwork we and all the guests will enjoy for many years."

Inga F. Hanks, Vice President of Marketing
The Southhampton Beach Resort

ANDREW SHIFF

 Image title: *Bermuda Resort Guest Map*

VickiPrenticeAssociatesInc.com

INTERNATIONAL BUILDING . 630 FIFTH AVENUE. 20TH FLOOR
ROCKEFELLER CENTER . NEW YORK . NEW YORK 10111
ARTIST REPRESENTATIVES . CREATIVE CONSULTANTS
PHONE 212.332.3460 . FAX 212.332.3401

VICKI PRENTICE ASSOCIATES INC.

NOBEL
PRIZE
A
B
C

"I believe there is a natural passion for art that begins early in our lives. For it is in us all — an instinct to create. With art serving as a divine state of both imagination and reality we are able to express the inexpressible." John Parra is an award winning illustrator and designer, working with such clients as United Airlines, Macmillan/McGraw-Hill, Virgin Records Inc., Jeep/DaimlerChrysler, Rising Moon Publishing and PBS. He has received accolades from New York's Society of Illustrators, *Print* Magazine. and the Art Directors Club of New York.

JOHN PARRA

"John Parra's artistic vision brought my words to life with images that are alive with color, spirit and a Latino flair. His brilliant illustrations and artistic vision enhance any writers work."

Monica Brown, Author,
My Name is Gabriela, the story of the first woman Latina to win the Nobel Prize for Literature

 Image title: *Gabriela, the Children, and the Rainbow*

VickiPrenticeAssociatesInc.com

www.buket.com 718·832·7720

GREG • NEWBOLD

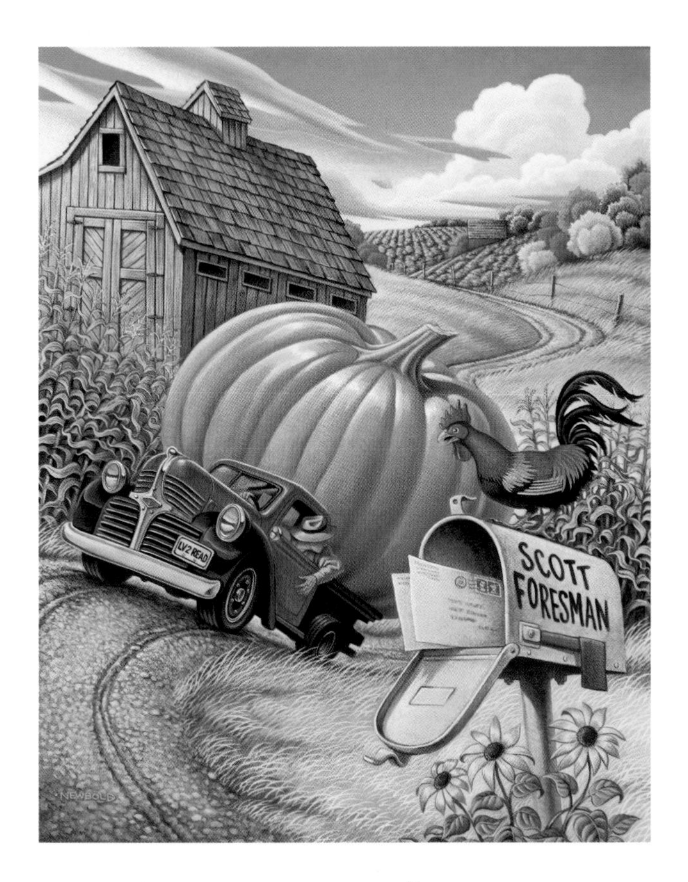
SCOTT
FORESMAN
LV2 READ
NEWBOLD

NEWBOLD

NY

801.274.2407 • WWW.GREGNEWBOLD.COM

BOB DOB

AMP HEAD
Marshall

WWW.BOBDOB.COM

310 / 480 / 6110

BOB DOB

38 YEAR OLD MAN-CHILD
ALIVE
RESIN HEAD
CANNON
NO SMOKING

WWW.BOBDOB.COM
310 / 480 / 6110

Tel 413•458-0056

JOHN MacDONALD

Fax 413•458-5379

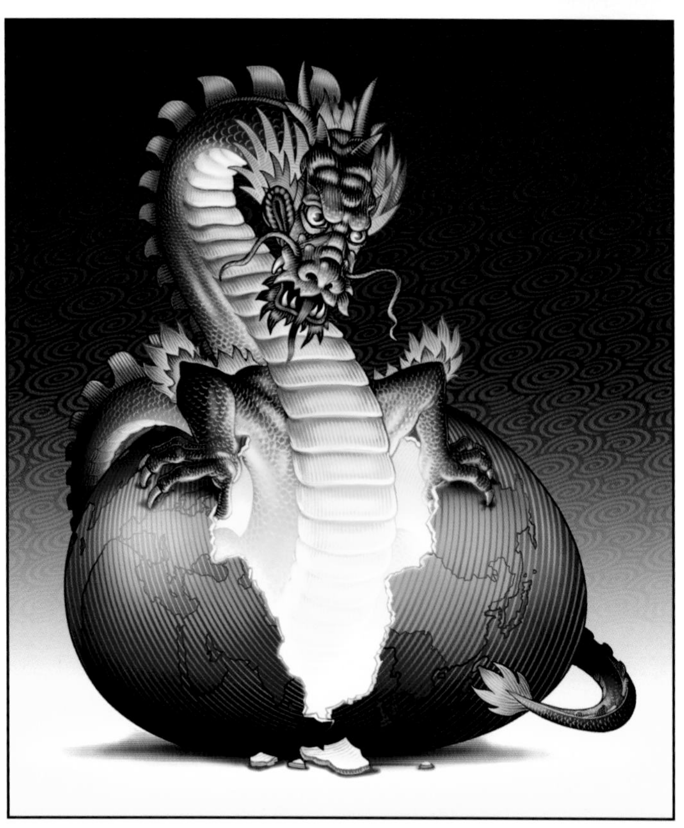

Der Spiegel • *cover*

Security Management • *feature*

VOTE

Outdoor Life • *feature*

Barrons • *cover*

on-line portfolio: www.jmacdonald.com // *e-mail:* john@jmacdonald.com

LUANA
LUANA
KAUFMANN
COLLAGE
DESIGNS

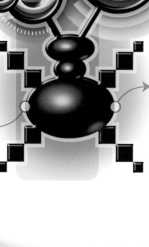

es copyright tom white.images
1 3 5 6 2 0 1
343
$ 50,000.00
April 8, 2000
Dollars
Electronic Frontier Foundation
twi

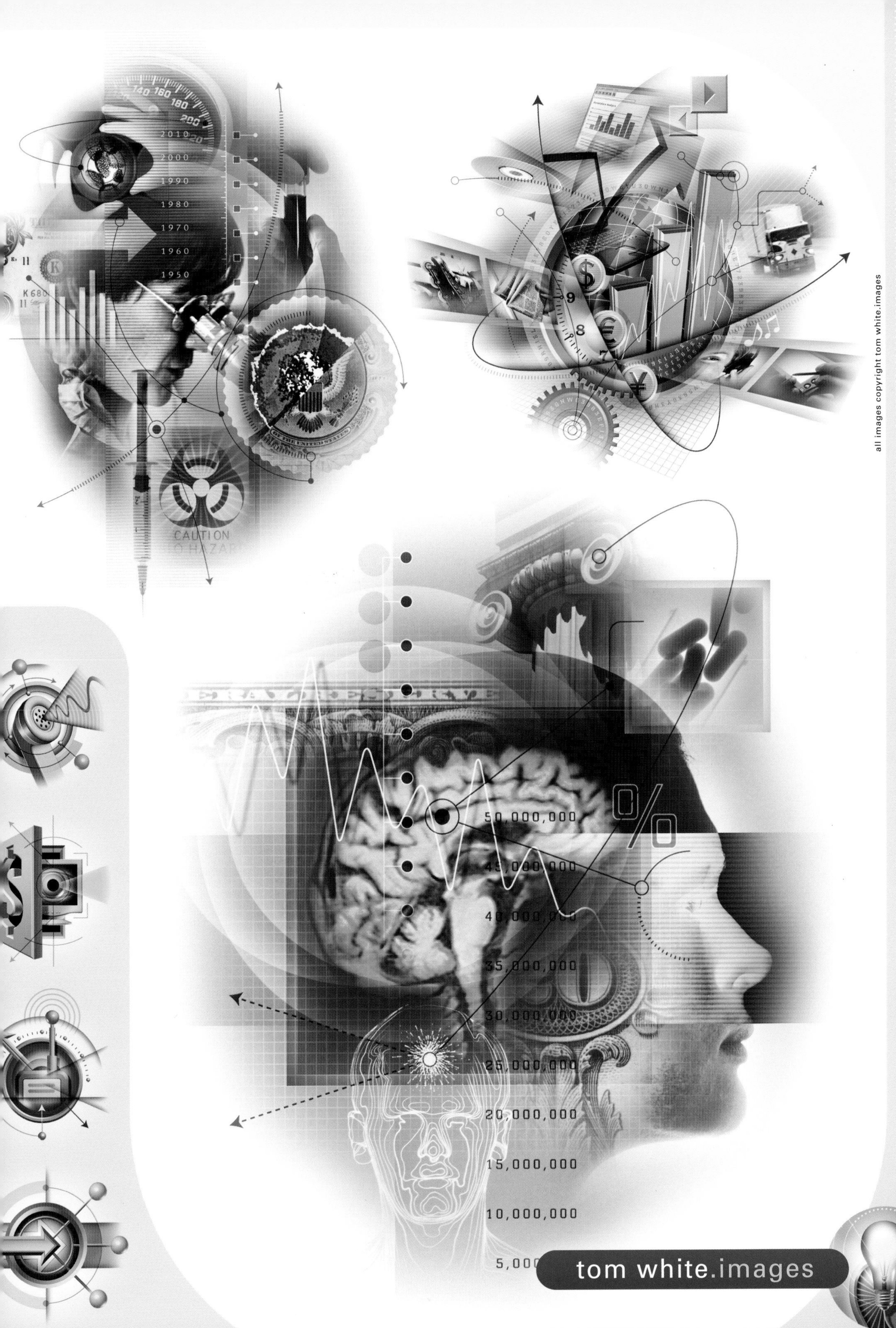
tom white.images
all images copyright tom white.images
CAUTION
50,000,000
45,000,000
40,000,000
35,000,000
30,000,000
25,000,000
20,000,000
15,000,000
10,000,000

STEVEN NOBLE

© CD & ME LOGO

© WELCH'S FUIT BARS

© LINDSEY COFFEE

JORDAN
HANDCRAFTED HOMES
a Tradition Since 1956

© FEDERAL RESERVE

TEL 415.897.6961 OR TEL 707.789.0166
www.stevennoble.com
nobleart@earthlink.net
Mead Show Award Winner 2001 • Featured in Communication Arts

STEVEN NOBLE
© GUARDIAN OF THE GRAPE IMPORTS
© JAKOB DEMMER
Garden of Life
ARTISAN
BLEND
© CELESTIAL SEASONINGS
© WILLIAM SONOMA
LE BEURRE
© MCDONALD'S CHICKEN STRIPS
TEL 415.897.6961 OR TEL 707.789.0166
www.stevennoble.com
nobleart@earthlink.net
Mead Show Award Winner 2001 • Featured in Communication Arts

Matthew G. Finger

Tel 401-421-0581
e-mail mattfinger@earthlink.net
www.fingerillustration.com
Also on the web at www.theispot.com/artist/mfinger

HAPPY
'S PLUMS

MICHAEL FORNALSKI
TEL (877) 252-0204
TEL/FAX (510) 252-0204
michael@fornalski.com

Traditional and digital art for collateral, packaging, web, advertising and editorial uses.

See the Directory of Illustration Volumes 13–15, 20 and 21 for additional work.

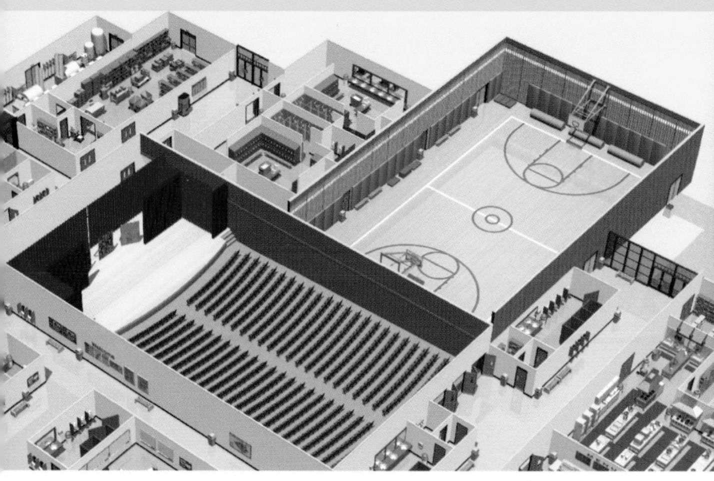

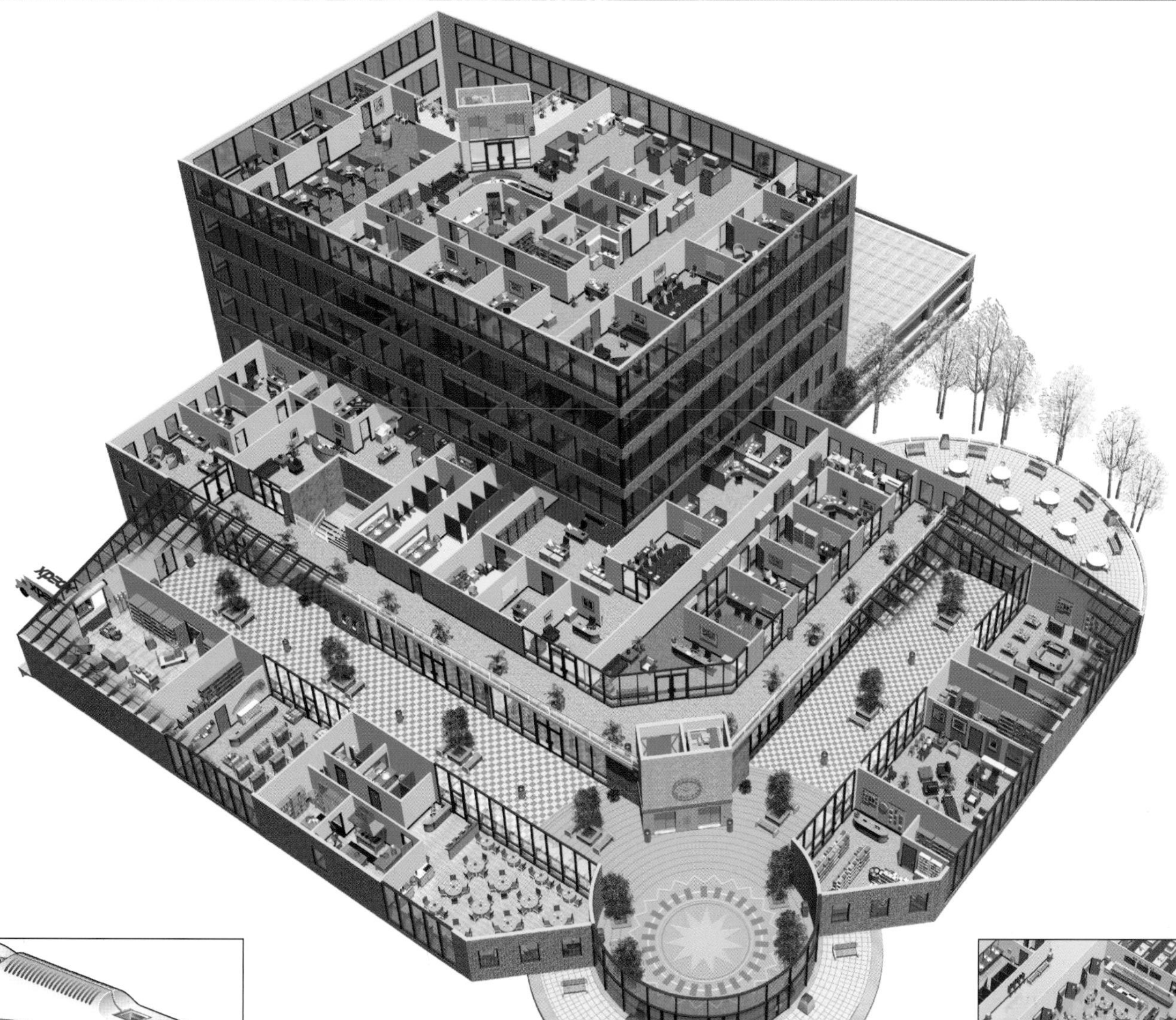

MICHAEL
FORNALSKI
ILLUSTRATION
877-252-0204

Rosemary McGuirk

PO Box 202 • Elkins, NH 03233

(603) 526-6798

rosemarym@tds.net

Paula Cohen
ILLUSTRATION

Monkeys swinging in the trees Eat scrambled eggs with cheddar cheese.

16 Laurel Place • Fanwood, N.J. 07023
ph 908.889.7656 • pcdrawme@earthlink.net

www.paulacohen.com

Sandy Chestnutt

Wildlife Illustration
and other fun stuff

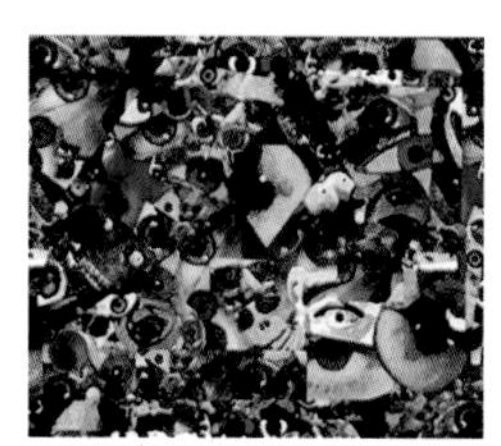

626-201-2573 • wuffdawg@earthlink.net • sandychestnutt.com
also see Directory of Illustration #21 pg. 278

Assignments ~ Prints ~ Original Paintings and Drawings

www.ryanetter.com

info@ryanetterillustration.com

816.228.9347
ryanetter.com

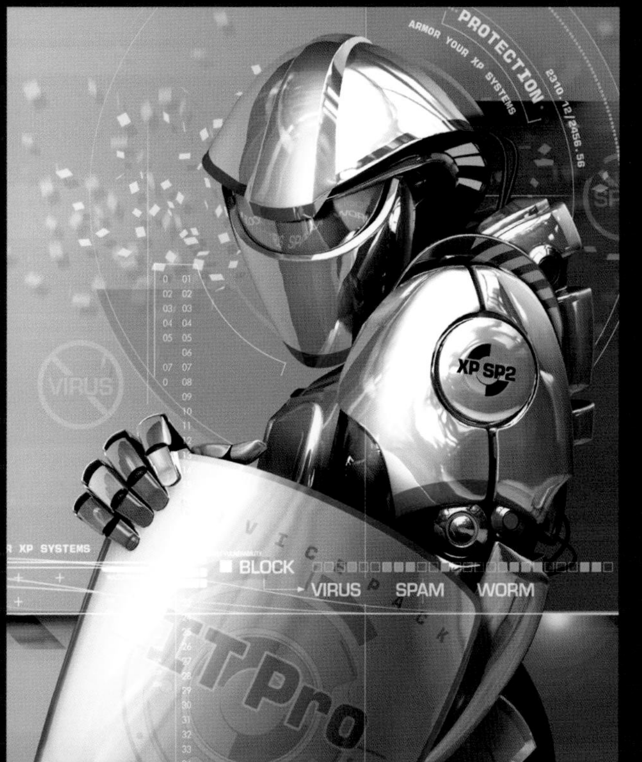
PROTECTION
ARMOR YOUR XP SYSTEMS
XP SP2
VIRUS
BLOCK
VIRUS SPAM WORM

See Also
DI 21 pg 431
DI 20 pgs 404-405

12 SOUTH MAIN STREET
PO BOX 356
STEWARTSTOWN, PA 17363

JIM STARR ILLUSTRATION

STUDIO: 717 993 6598
FAX: 717 993 9537
E-MAIL: jim@jimstarr.com
WEBSITE: www.jimstarr.com

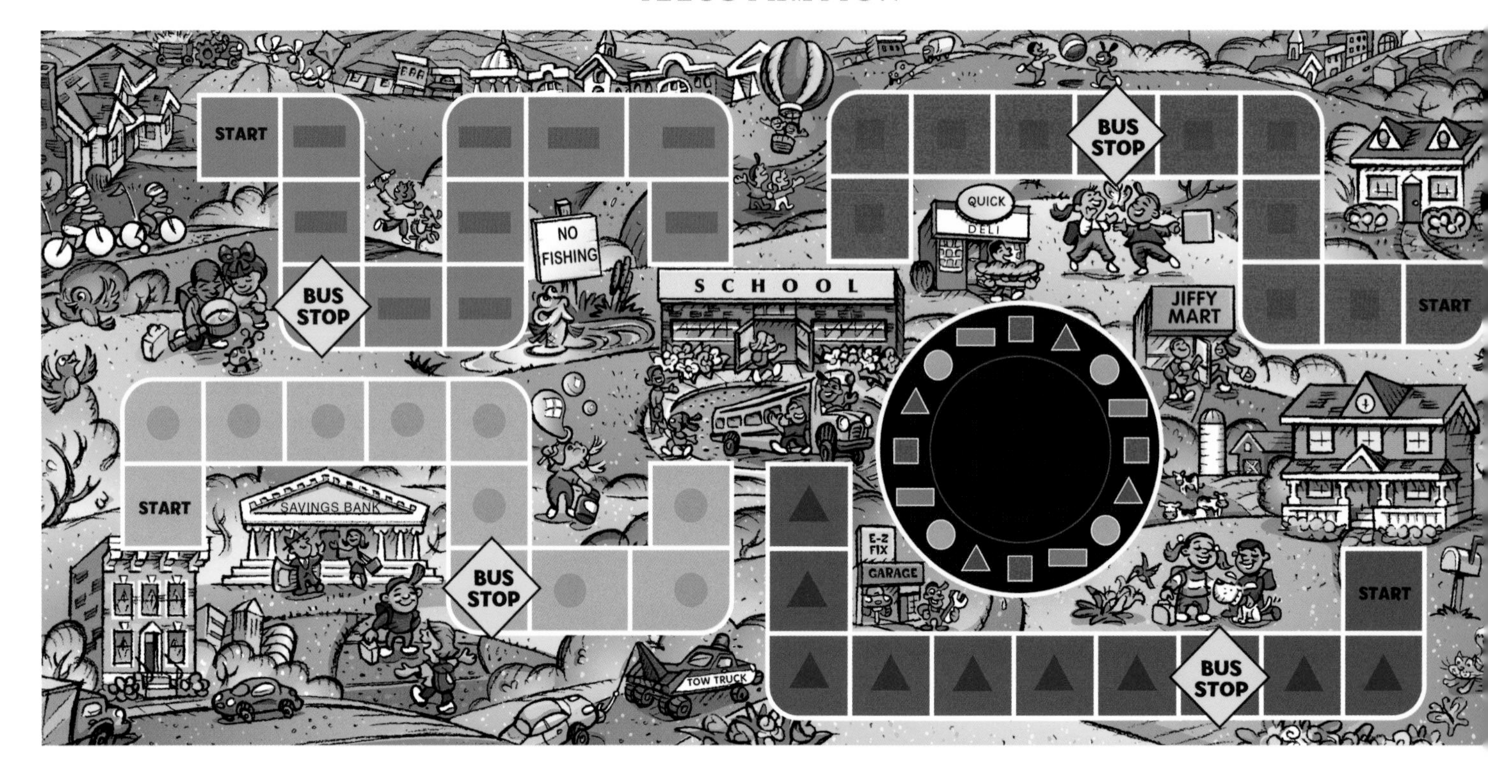
START
BUS STOP
NO FISHING
SCHOOL
QUICK
DELI
BUS STOP
JIFFY MART
START
START
SAVINGS BANK
BUS STOP
E-Z FIX
GARAGE
START
TOW TRUCK
BUS STOP

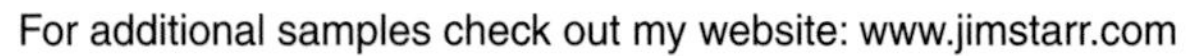
For additional samples check out my website: www.jimstarr.com

Jim's stock portfolio available @ www.stockart.com
800 297 7658

stockart.com

12 SOUTH MAIN STREET
PO BOX 356
STEWARTSTOWN, PA 17363

STUDIO: 717 993 6598
FAX: 717 993 9537
E-MAIL: jim@jimstarr.com
WEBSITE: www.jimstarr.com

JIM STARR
ILLUSTRATION

Whey Beyond
WALL STREET
BANK
Mortgage
PHILLIPS 66
conoco
76

Jim's stock portfolio available @
www.stockart.com
800 297 7658

stockart.com

For additional samples check out my website: www.jimstarr.com

Chicago Rocks!
Movie
Munchies
Recycling
McGraw -Hill

Laurie Hamilton *illustration*

312.944.3970 • 312.787.4700 *phone*
www.lauriehamiltonart.com *portfolio*
laurie.hamilton@rcn.com *e-mail*

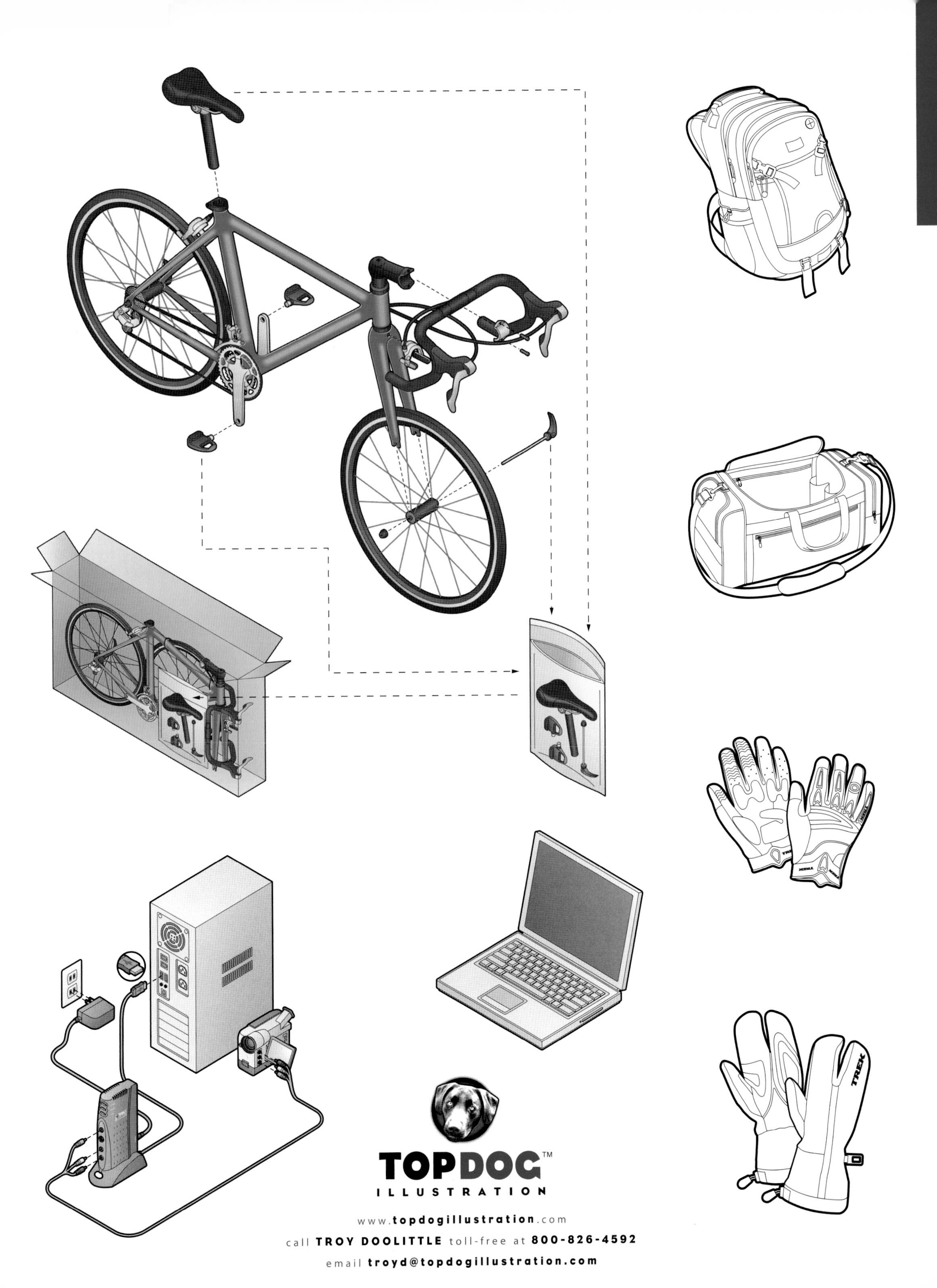
TREK
TOPDOG™
ILLUSTRATION
www.topdogillustration.com
call TROY DOOLITTLE toll-free at 800-826-4592
email troyd@topdogillustration.com

GOODNESS

4 images
©Disney

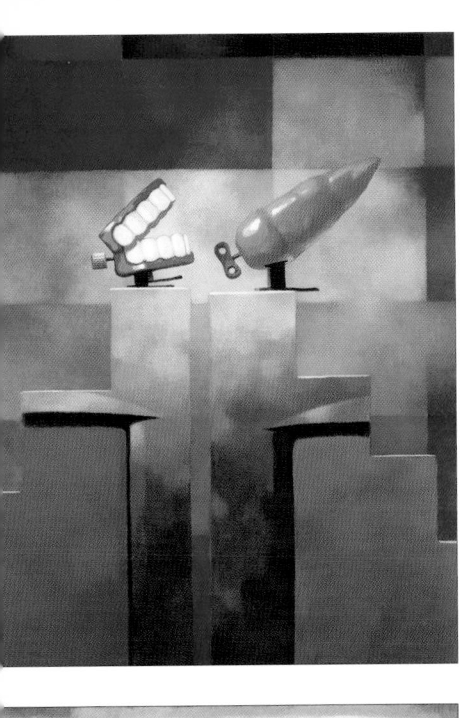

010 1011010
10100 01

ART VALERO

artvalero.com theispot.com artx12.com member IPA 843 856 0103

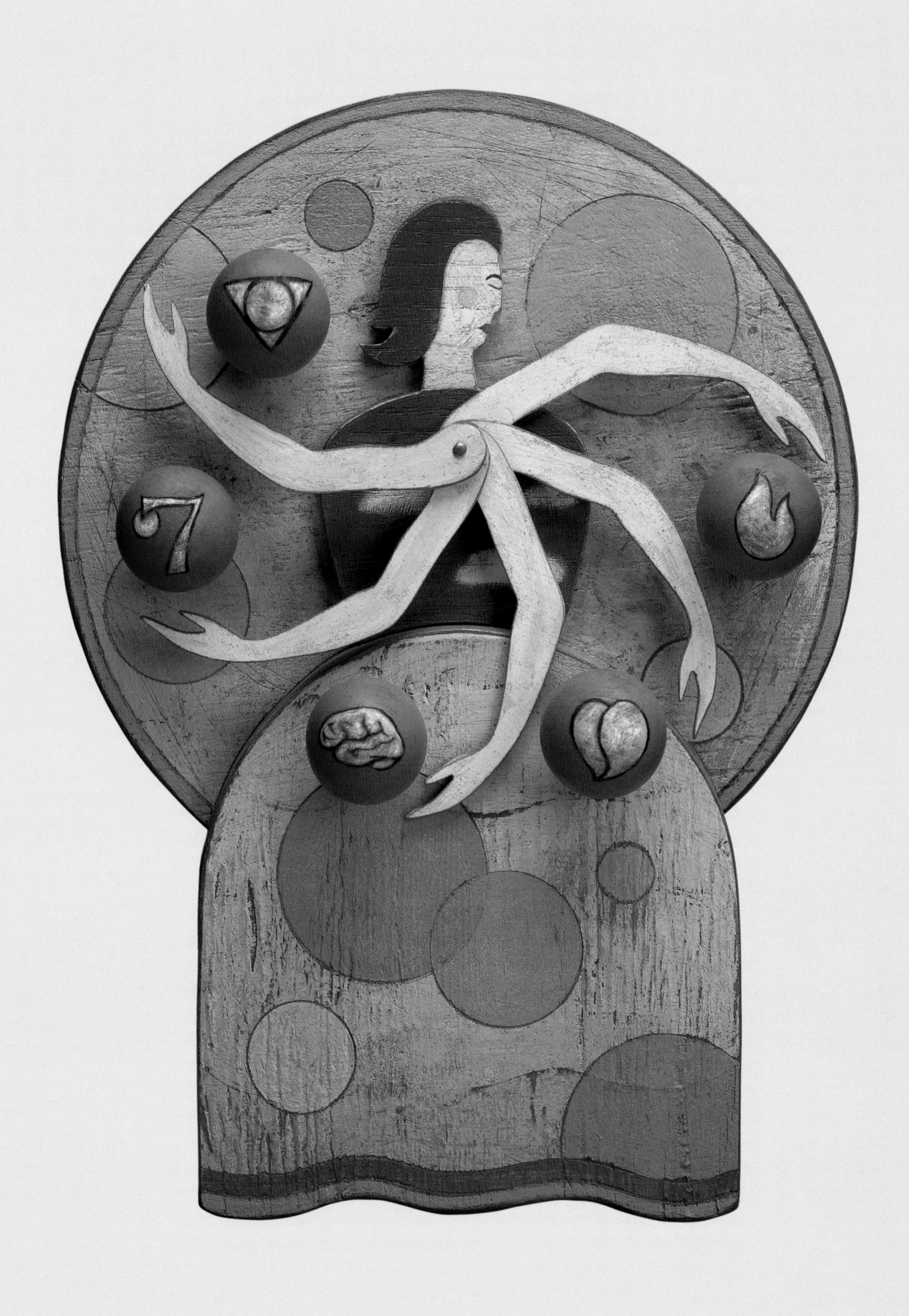

MARIARENDON.COM | T. 805 682 8816

Admission
$10.00
025849

WE SHOW IN THIS ILLUSTRATIO
A VERY COMPLETE OUTF
1,000,000
1/2
USEFUL INFORMATION PERTAINING

Objective
Actions
Situation

1292
Honey.
Extracted Honey.

L
P
M
F
N

FAN WORKS DESIGN®

Dawn Ripple McFadin Kevin McFadin

P 804.353.3060 E info@fanworksdesign.com I fanworksdesign.com

Colin Hayes

Fitness Magazine (Men's Health)

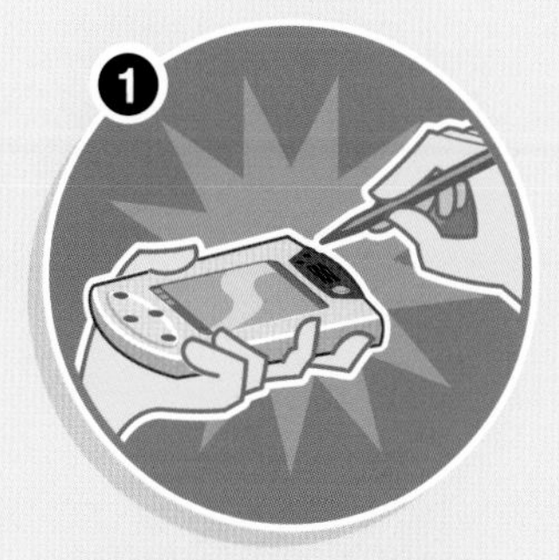

1. Select project name off pop-up list on wireless handheld.

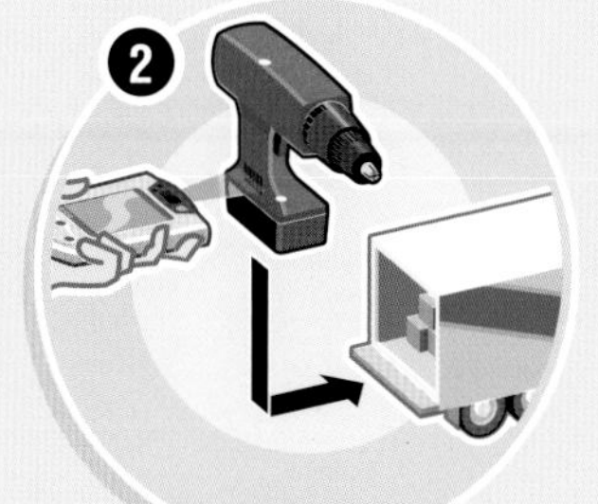

2. Scan tools with bar-code device on wireless handheld then load tools on truck.

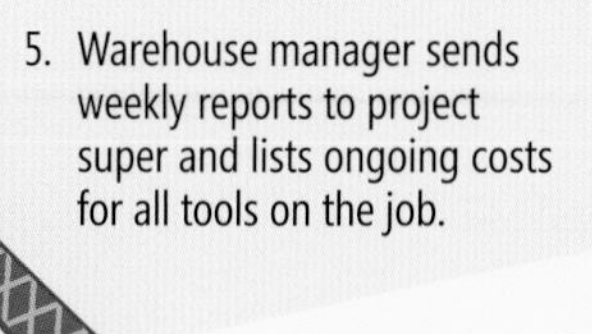

5. Warehouse manager sends weekly reports to project super and lists ongoing costs for all tools on the job.

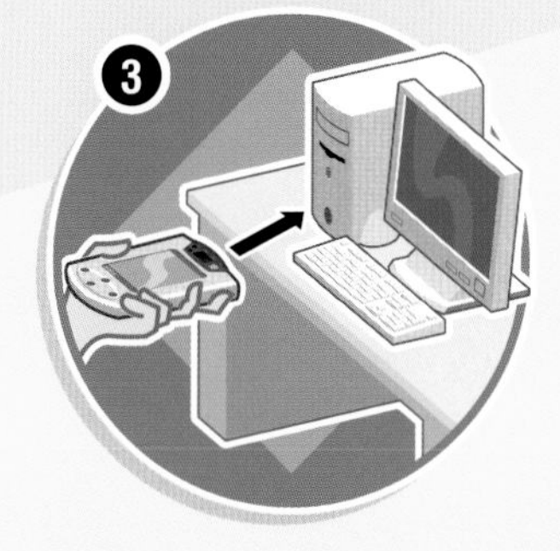

3. Send data to ToolWatch application on desktop in the tool area of warehouse.

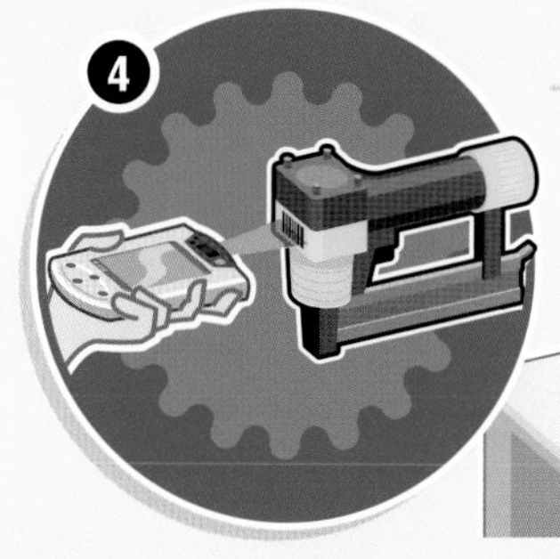

4. Tool warehouse manager goes out to jobsite with wireless handheld to take inventory.

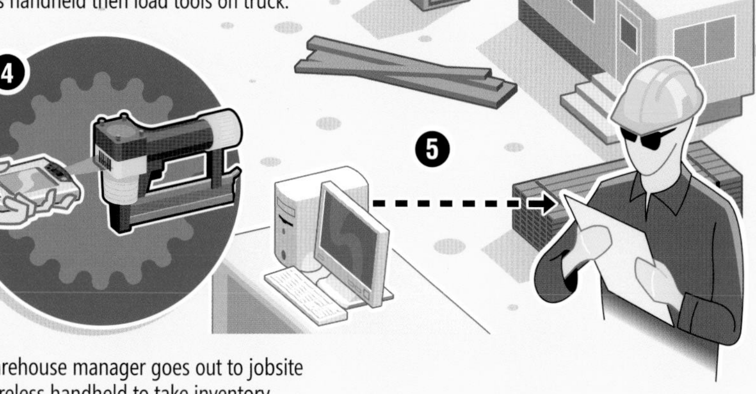

Builder Magazine

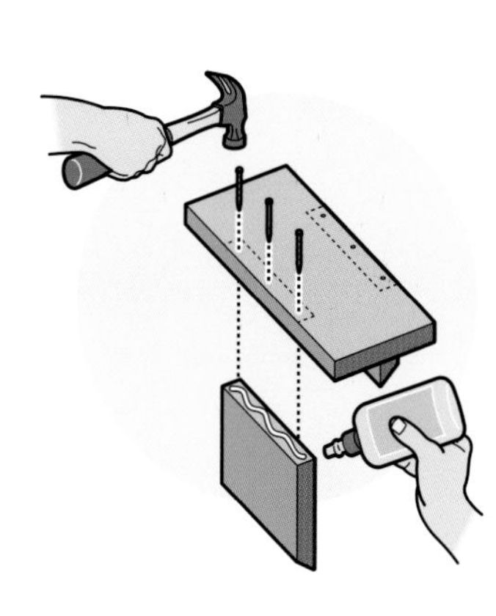
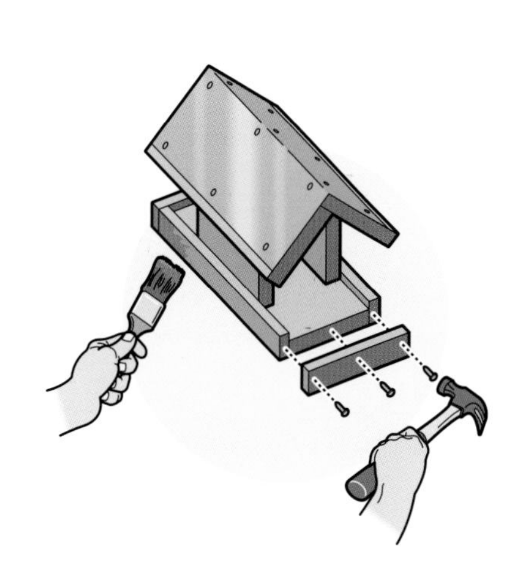
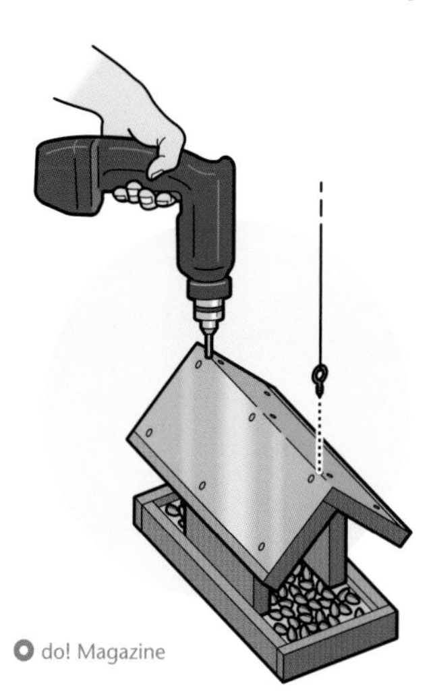

do! Magazine

425-338-5452 colin@colinthayes.com www.colinthayes.com

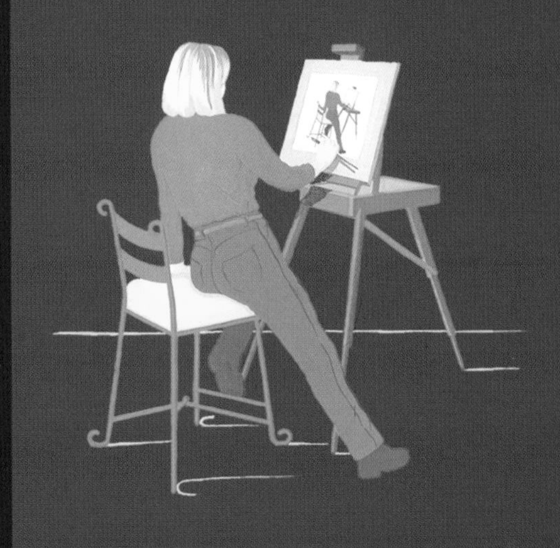

brucedayink.com

Bruce Day illustrations

(208) 888-1944

Fried Spuds
Carrots
CORN
Peas
HOT DOGS
ICE CREAM
Fruit
OJ
MILK
5
Yogurt

samuel a. minick
portfolio: www.saminick.com
e-mail: sam@saminick.com
phone: 260.420.6027

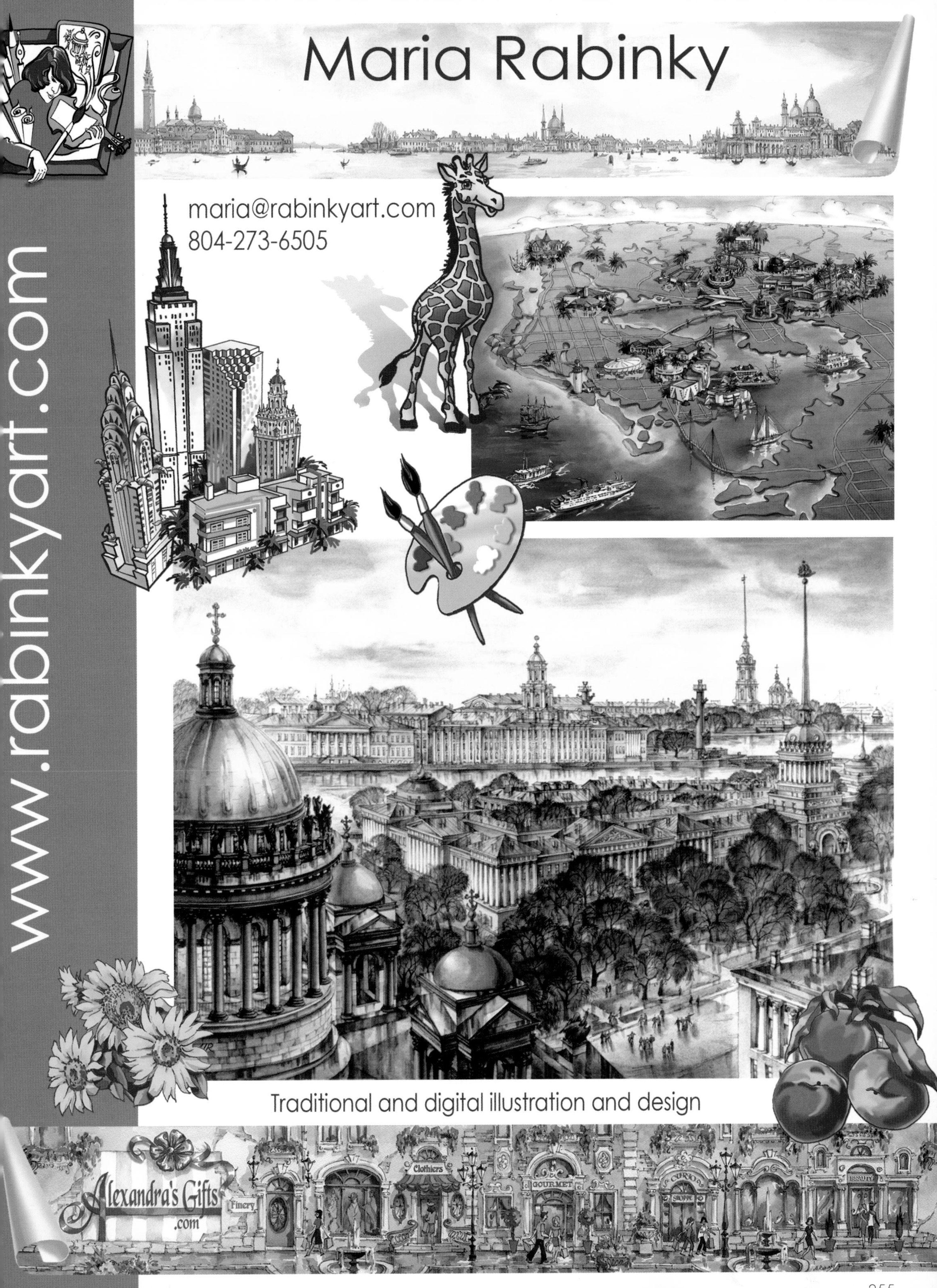
Maria Rabinky
maria@rabinkyart.com
804-273-6505
www.rabinkyart.com
Traditional and digital illustration and design
Alexandra's Gifts
.com
Finery
Clothiers
GOURMET
CURIO
SHOPPE
BEAUTY

MICHAEL AUGER

www.arty4ever.com
240-683-3987

DON QUIXOTE

PICK UP THE PIECES
By: R.W. Marino, Jr.
Illustrations By: Michael Auger

Jen Norton ART STUDIO

www.NortonStudio.com

408.626.8701 jen@nortonstudio.com

information graphics • technical • products • maps • charts
toll free
877-864-6472
BRYON THOMPSON
www.bthompson.net
bryon@bthompson.net

bran
don
reese
.com
BRANDON REESE ILLUSTRATION (704) 281-3472
brandon@brandonreese.com www.brandonreese.com

口 kuchi
mouth

雨 ame
rain

森 mori
forest

犬 inu
dog

Amy Bock

Phone: 203.431.1357 | Fax: 203.431.6249 | e-mail: arbock@aol.com | www.amybock.com

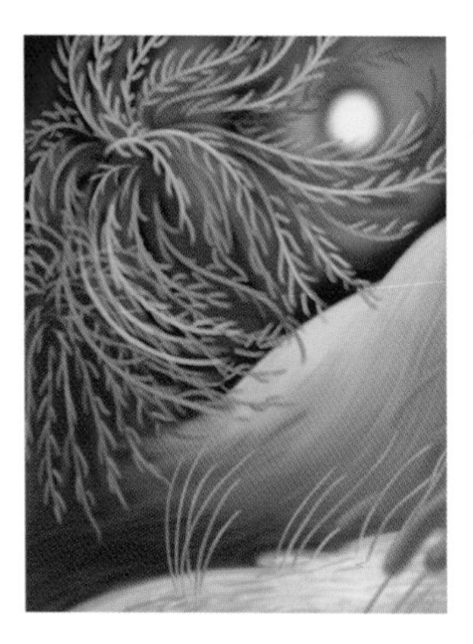

3
2
1

cyrus
deboo
illustrator
+44 (0)20 8788 8167 ph . f
cyrus.deboo@virgin.net
www.cyrusdeboo.com

Specialist in digital line and flat colour illustration

CALIFORNIA
SHO P12X

DANIELS & DANIELS
BEAUDANIELS.COM
14 South Madrid Avenue
Newbury Park, CA 91320
TEL: (805) 498-1923
e-mail: daniels@beaudaniels.com
www.beaudaniels.com

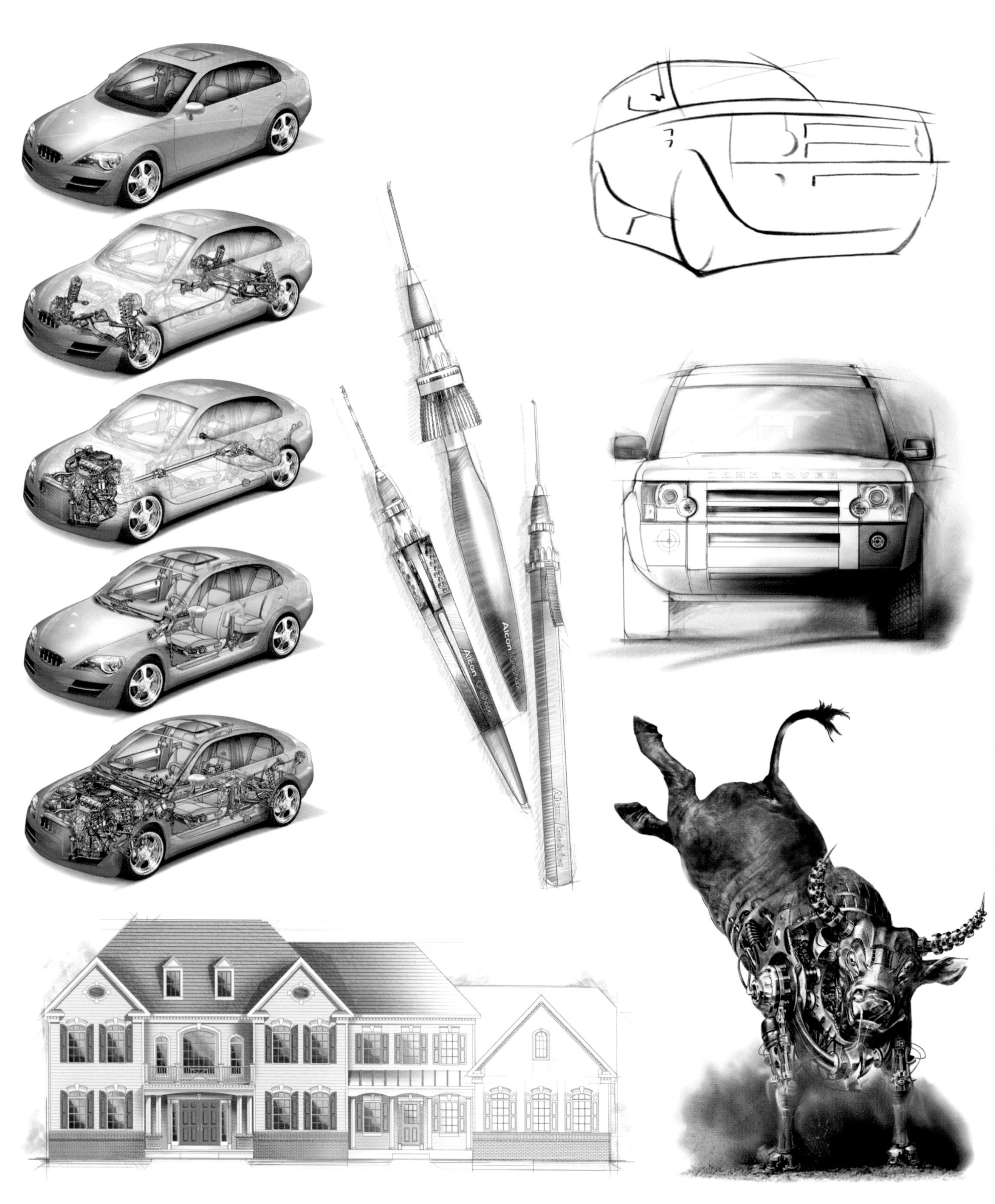
Alcon
Alcon
Alcon
LAND ROVER

DANIELS & DANIELS
BEAUDANIELS.COM
14 South Madrid Avenue
Newbury Park, CA 91320
TEL: (805) 498-1923
e-mail: daniels@beaudaniels.com
www.beaudaniels.com

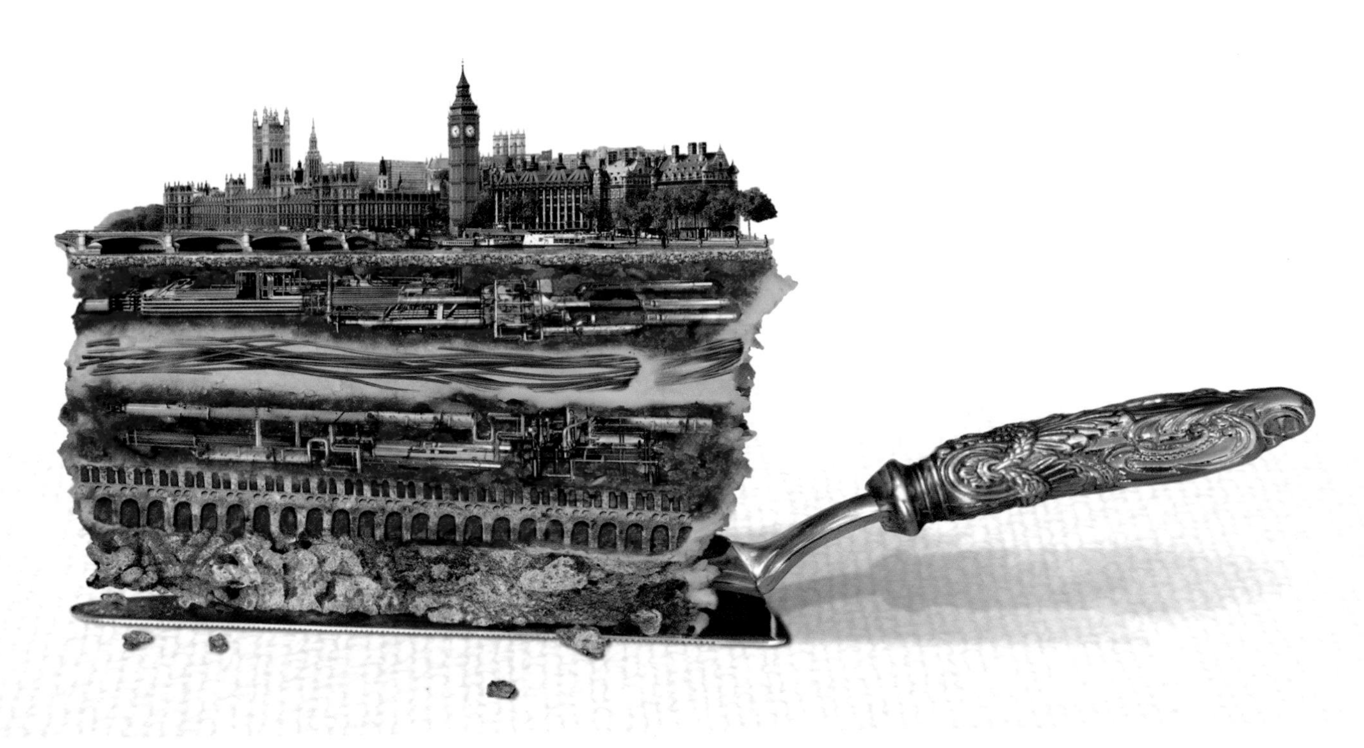

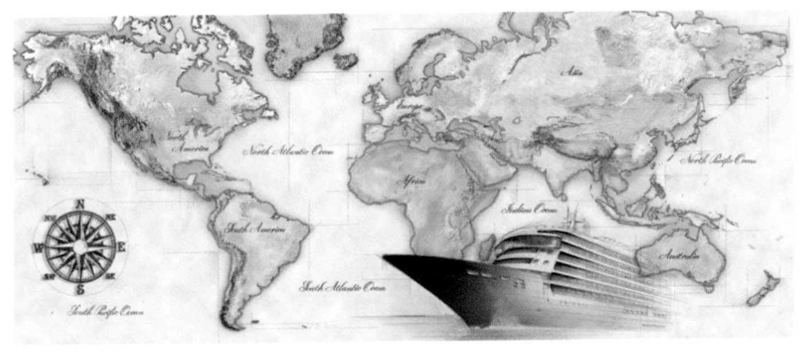

daryll collins
513.683-9335

USA
TO CHINA

www.daryllcollins.com

cynthia iannaccone

cynthia@cynthiasillustration.com 585 334-7255 www.cynthiasillustration.com

3rd Annual
Rosetta Festival
of New Works
LaChanse

FOOD Pyramid
Your Health
THE ENEMY

JT Morrow

tel: 800-466-4060
or 650-355-7899
fax: 650-355-8051
email: jt@j2morrow.com
www.j2morrow.com

FUTURES

FEDERAL RESERVE
1 2 3 4 5 6 7

DARIN OVERHOLSER
300 East 3rd Street #6
Newport, KY 41071
TEL: (859) 466-3946
e-mail: darin@illustratorguy.com
www.illustratorguy.com

Darin Overholser's illustrations uncover the humor of being human. Former CF Payne assistant, Darin is making a name for himself in the illustration industry. He delivers solid concepts and execution that is sure to please. Contact Darin for any editorial, packaging or book illustration projects.

Client list includes: Dallas Daily News, Cincinnati Enquirer, St. Martin's Press, Funny Bone Comedy Club, Ripple Junction, Late for the Sky Productions and others.

NEVERLAND
RANCH
Darin
Overholser

Alan Witschonke (617) 744-1930 www.alanwitschonke.com alanwits@comcast.net

jackdesrocher.com
479 · 925 · 7810

401 E 86th Street
New York, NY 10028

Sonja Lamut

http://members.aol.com/slamut/

212-831-4634
slamut@aol.com

lampe

PHONE: 312 735 2077 EMAIL: TRAVISLAMPE@YAHOO.COM
WWW.TRAVISLAMPE.COM

lampe

Fig. 1.
decision support
core clinical
core clinical
best of breed
best of breed
best of breed
core clinical
Making a Choice
aVF

www.
dianefenster.com

diane@dianefenster
.com

650.355.5007

REVENUE PROCEDURES
IRS NOTICES
ROTH IRA
Publication 590
Individual Retirement Arrangements (IRAs)
Publication 575
Pension and Annuity Income
Instructions for Forms 1099-R and 5498

Dorothy Stott

Little Duck Productions
Dorothy Stott
212 - 591 - 1004
www.littleduckproductions.com
email: dorothy@littleduckproductions.com

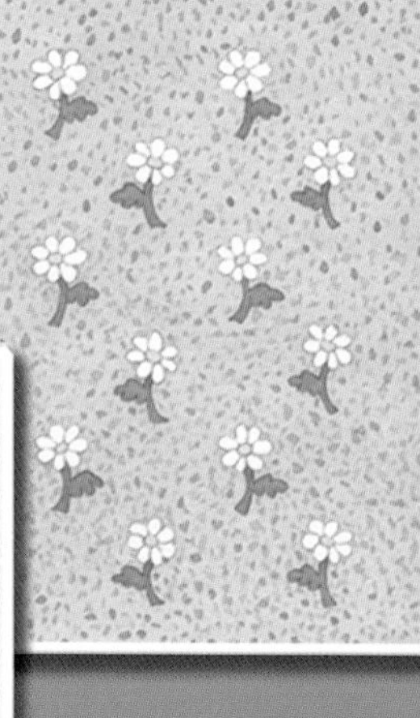

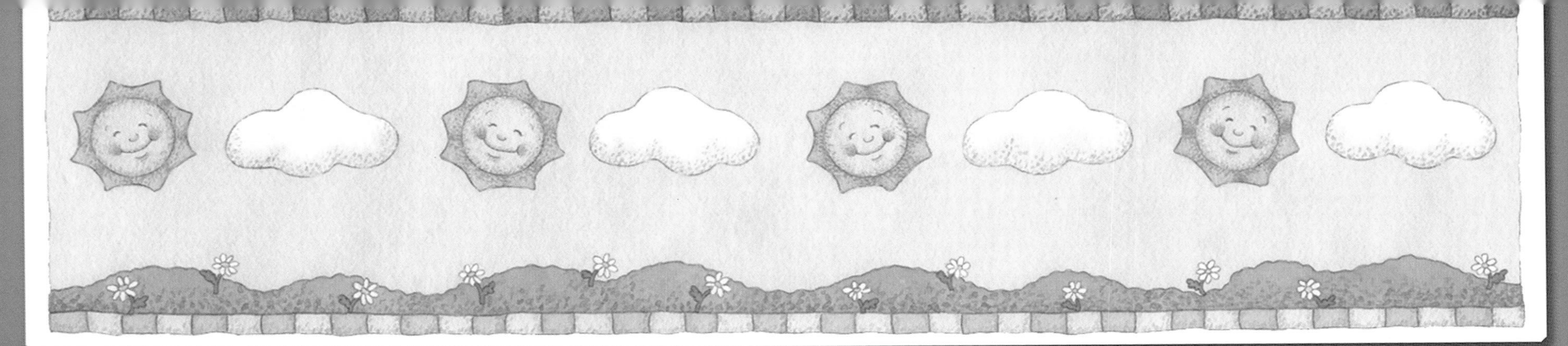

Little Duck Productions • Dorothy Stott • 212-591-1004 • www.littleduckproductions.com

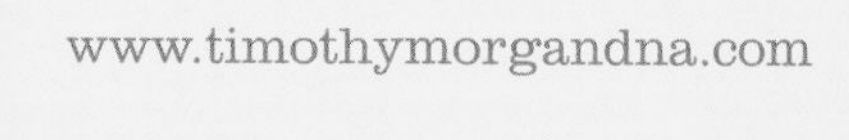

www.timothymorgandna.com

TIMOTHY MORGAN

tmorgan1@pacbell.net

(415) 387-7831

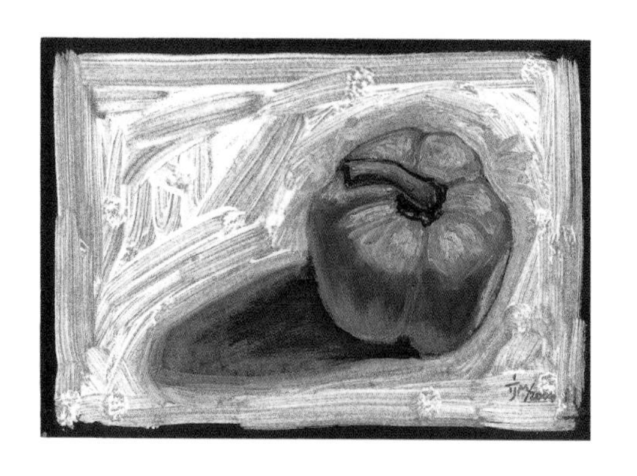

Rank
Chain
% Sales Growth
1996 U.S. Sales ($ Millions)
1 Einstein's/Noah's 439% $146
2 Bruegger's Bagels 80% $226*
3 Fazoli's 71% $204
4 Landry's 64% $170
5 Don Pablo's 50% $133
6 Boston Market 47% $1,167
7 Starbucks 45% $622*
8 Schlotzky's 41% $198
* Estimate
Only chains with $100 MM or more were eligible for ranking.
Source: '97 Technomic Top Report
Straight 25%
Flavored 30%
Blends 15%
Decaf 15%
Organic 5%
Dark Roast 10%
What's Brewing?
Chart Graphics!
Icons! Fun Stuff!
Sarah Edgar
Illustrator/Graphic Artist
62-65 Saunders Street #3C
Rego Park, New York 11374
(718) 896-2812

Pat Byrnes www.patbyrnes.com

The New Yorker

Eli Lilly & Co.

Harvard Business Review

Johns Hopkins

Boston Globe

Illinois Tourism

Wall Street Journal

Screen Actors Guild

Barron's

Jim Beam

Reader's Digest

Rich Foods

773.472.3649 pjb@patbyrnes.com

NOW SHOWING!
THE PASSION OF THE CHRIST

"I thought the book was better."

P. BYRNES.

Courtesy of The New Yorker

"Put the punster in with the mime."

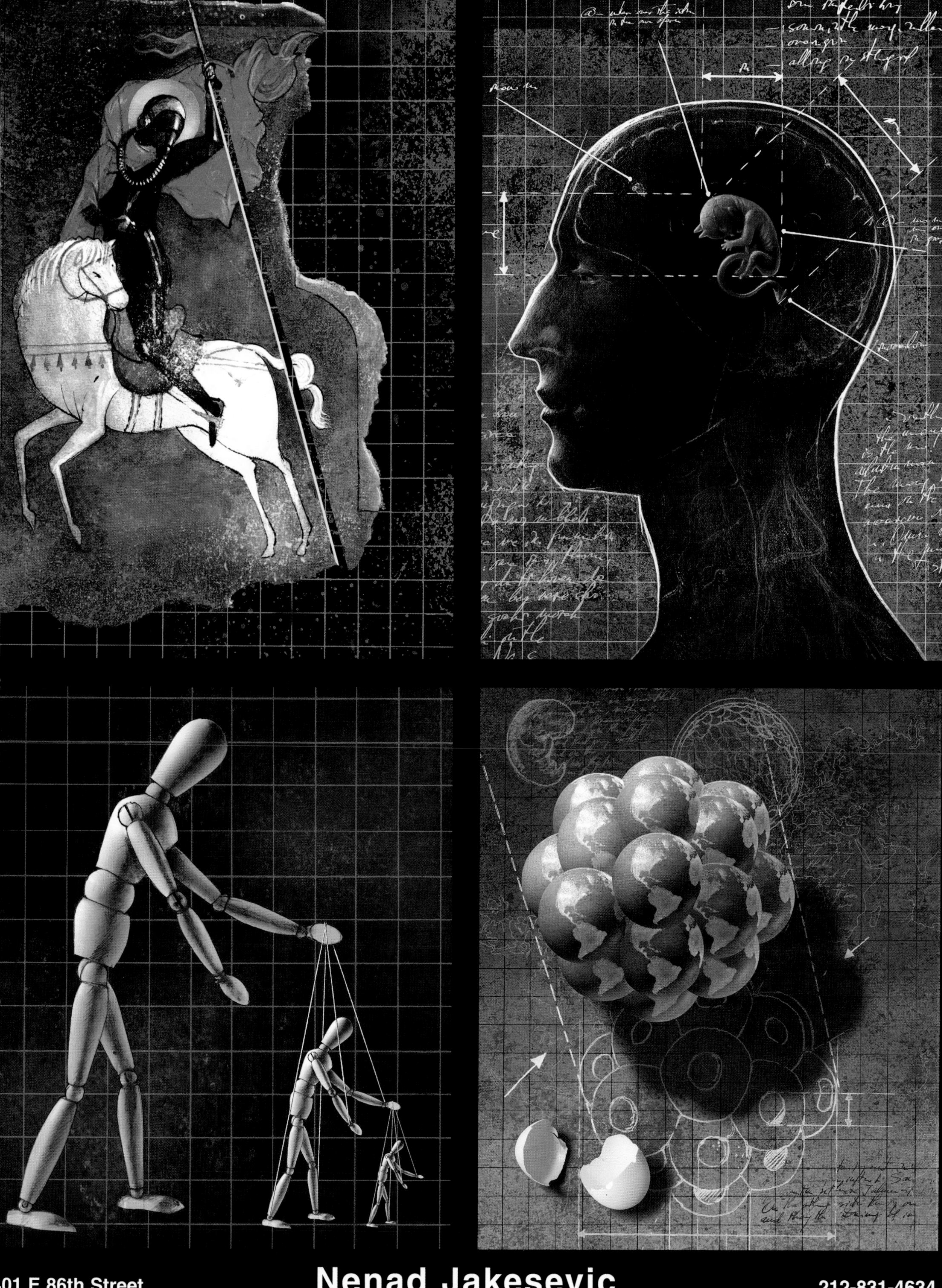

01 E 86th Street
New York, NY 10028

Nenad Jakesevic

http://members.aol.com/nenadj/

212-831-4634
nenadj@aol.com

Chad Wallace
www.chadwallace.com
(914) 962-6472

S. LARSON

JOURNAL
Dad

S. LARSON

UNITED STATES OF AMERICA

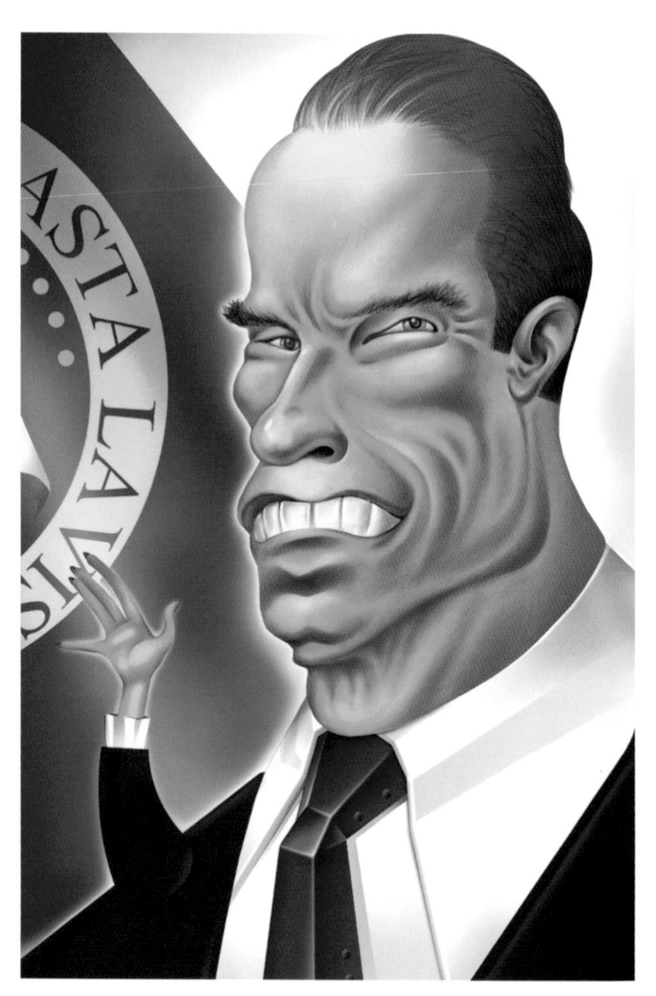
ASTA LA

P U T I N

WWW.VADIMART.COM TEL 415 307 3177 FAX 415 751 1766

Amy Vangsgard

CLAY ILLUSTRATIONS

PHONE: 323-461-3094

PORTFOLIO: AmyVangsgard.com

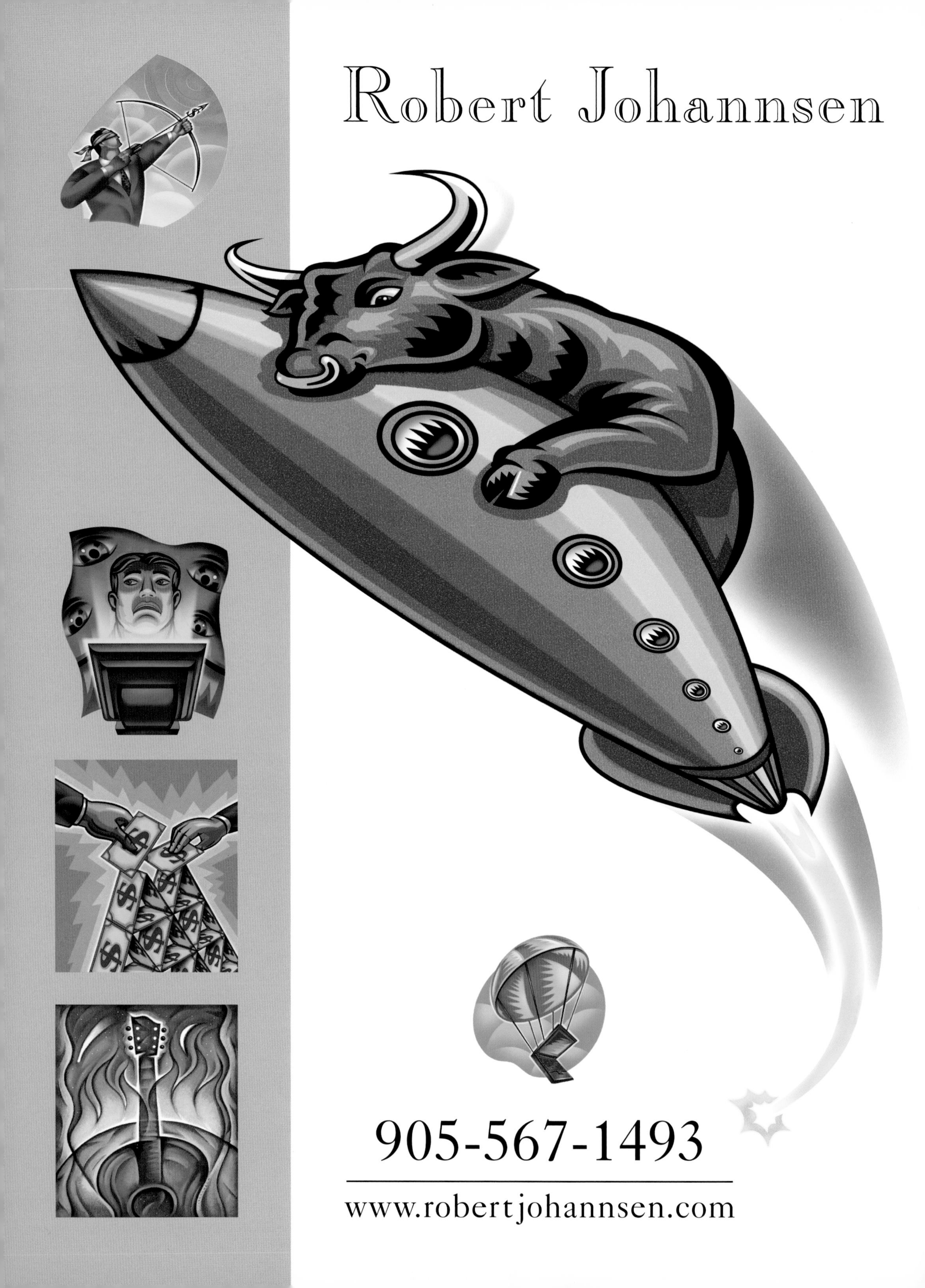
Robert Johannsen
905-567-1493
www.robertjohannsen.com

UZANE LANGLOIS
EL: (514) 526-2600
-mail: pif@cam.org
www.cam.org/~pif

Children's Books:
Weighing the Elephant (image below), *Share the Sky*, *The Birthday Book*, Publisher: Annick Press, Toronto, Canada

First Novels (15 titles):
Pourquoi le monde est comme il est?
Mr. Christie Book Award 2002
Publisher: Éditions de la courte échelle, Montréal, Canada, *Pinocchio*,
Publisher: CTW (Children's Television Workshop), New York, U.S.

Commercial book project:
A Rosie Summer, Client: Nestlé

Happy
Halloween
T.A.B.T.T.

Peace
Groovy Chick

Peace
Groovy Chick

Love
G.C.A.T.B.C.

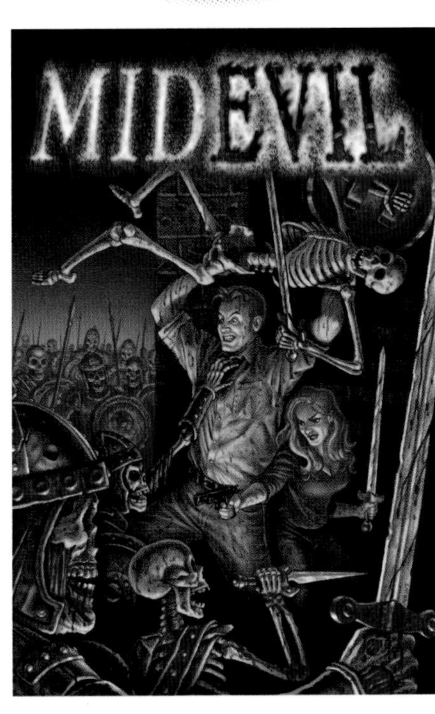
MIDEVIL
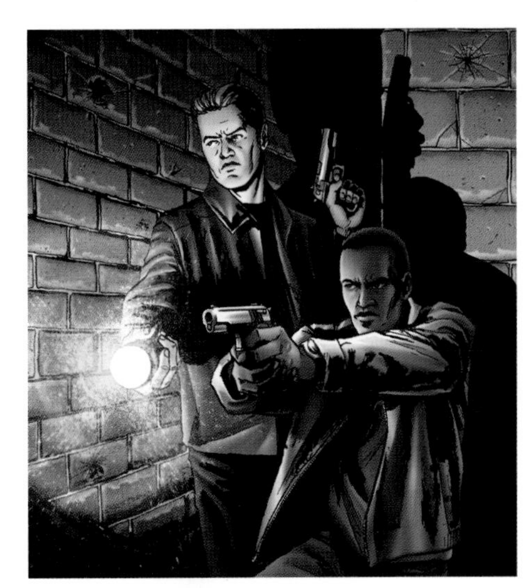

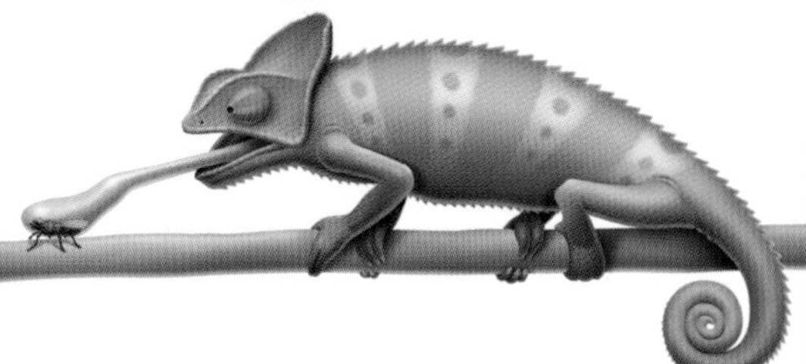

mary peterson illustration

OPEN

mary@marypeterson.com www.marypeterson.com 323-669-0381

steve austin illustration

BED #1
FORDGT
THE CLUNK STOPS HERE
I. CLUNK
AIR BAGS
U SAVE
559 323 6939 austinart@comcast.net stevetheartist.com

patton brothers illustration

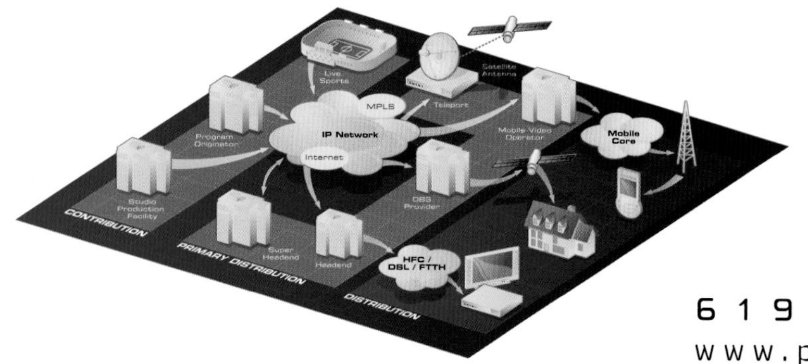
Live Sports
Satellite Antenna
MPLS
Teleport
Program Originator
IP Network
Mobile Video Operator
Mobile Core
Internet
Studio Production Facility
DBS Provider
CONTRIBUTION
Super Headend
Headend
HFC / DSL / FTTH
PRIMARY DISTRIBUTION
DISTRIBUTION

619.463.4562
www.pattonbros.com

Kenneth Spengler

Spengler Creations Inc.
2668 17th Street Sacramento, CA 95818
phone 916.441.1932
fax 916.441.3490
kenspengler.com
email: thespenglers@sbcglobal.net

craig howell
716 860 9286

cheeba productions

CREATIVE ★ THINK ★ TANK...

WWW.CHEEBAPRODUCTIONS.COM
email: craig@cheebaproductions.com

ALBUMS | POSTERS & AD DESIGN
BOOK & EDITORIAL ILLUSTRATION
PACKAGING | LOGOS & MORE

CLIENTS INCLUDING:
LUCASFILM
RANDOMHOUSE PUBLISHING
UNIVERSAL MUSIC
INTERSCOPE RECORDS
WARNER BROS
CLEAR CHANNEL
ELEKTRA RECORDS
SONY / SIGNATURES

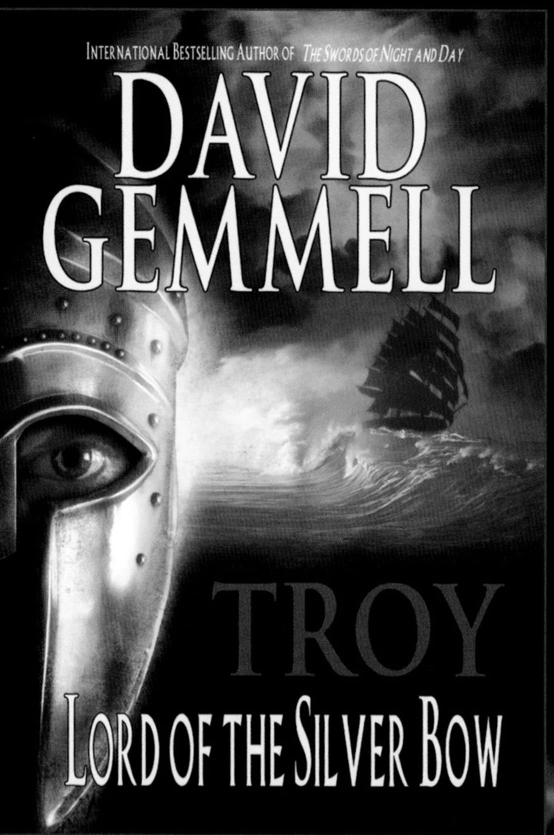

International Bestselling Author of The Swords of Night and Day
DAVID GEMMELL
TROY
LORD OF THE SILVER BOW

DARTH VADER

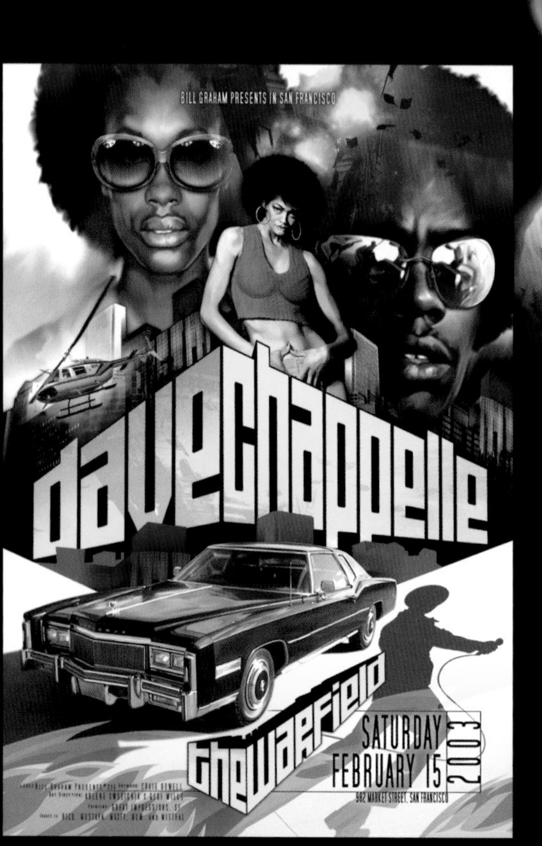

BILL GRAHAM PRESENTS IN SAN FRANCISCO
dave chappelle
the warfield
SATURDAY FEBRUARY 15 2003
982 MARKET STREET, SAN FRANCISCO

JEDI

Bill Graham Presents in San Francisco
Gillian Welch
Old Crow Medicine Show
Friday and Saturday
October 8 and 9
the Fillmore
20
04

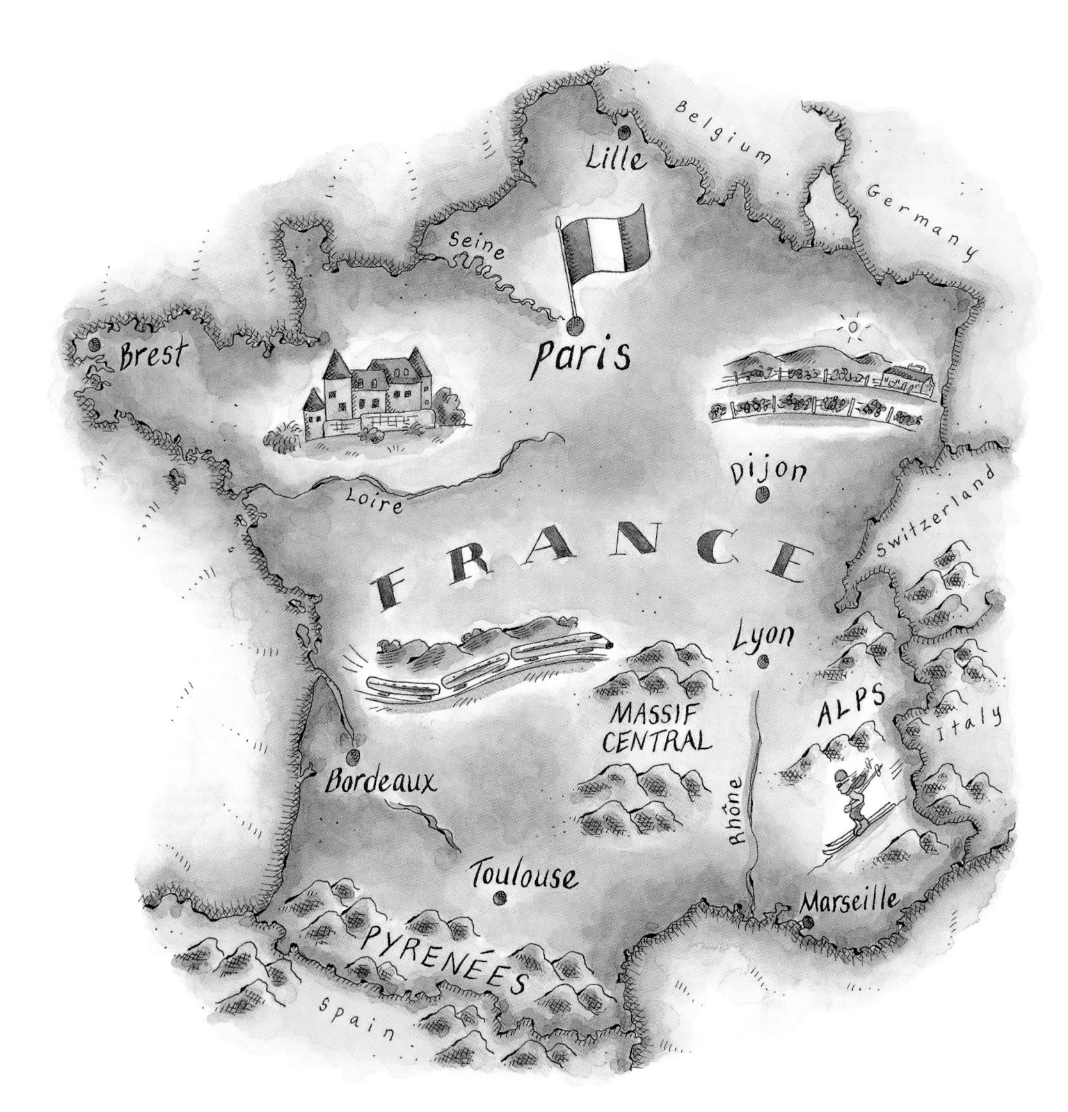
Lille
Belgium
Germany
Seine
Brest
Paris
Dijon
Loire
Switzerland
FRANCE
Lyon
MASSIF
CENTRAL
ALPS
Italy
Bordeaux
Rhône
Toulouse
Marseille
PYRENÉES
Spain

Long Beach, Wash.
to
Cannon Beach, Ore.
Nov. 11-15, 2005
Lewiston and
Lapwai, Idaho
JUNE 14-17, 2006
Fort Benton and
Great Falls, Mont.
JUNE 1 - JULY 4, 2005
New Town, N.D.
AUG. 17-20, 2006
Bismarck, N.D.
OCT. 22-31, 2004
Billings, Mont.
JULY 22-25, 2006
St. Louis, Mo.
SEPT. 23-24, 2006
Route West
Return Route
N
W
E
S

GUATEMALA
HONDURAS
N
W
E
S
SAN
SALVADOR
Cuscatlán
EL SALVADOR
Pacific Ocean

Jennifer Thermes

phone 203.270.0539
email jennifer@jenniferthermes.com
website www.jenniferthermes.com

GATE

Plein Air Painting in
TUSCANY
ARCIPELAGO
Siena
Montepulciano
TOSCANO
to Rome

PERSONAL 2005

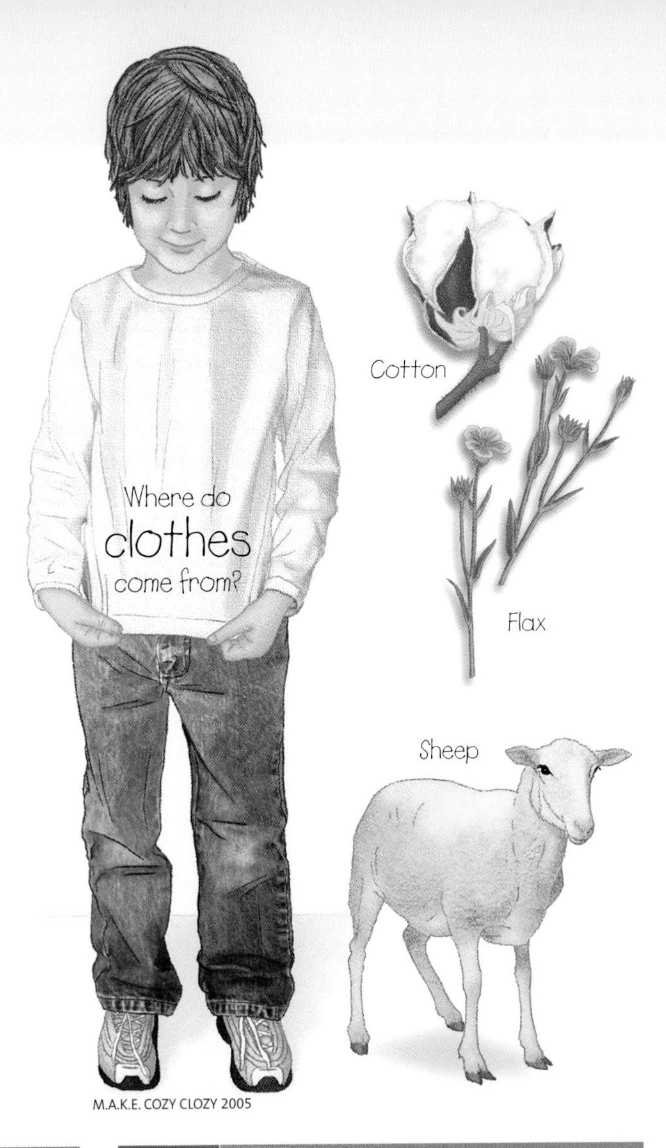
Where do
clothes
come from?
Cotton
Flax
Sheep

M.A.K.E. COZY CLOZY 2005

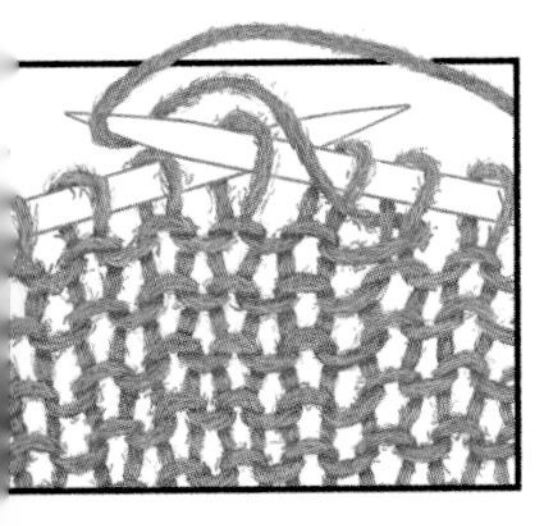

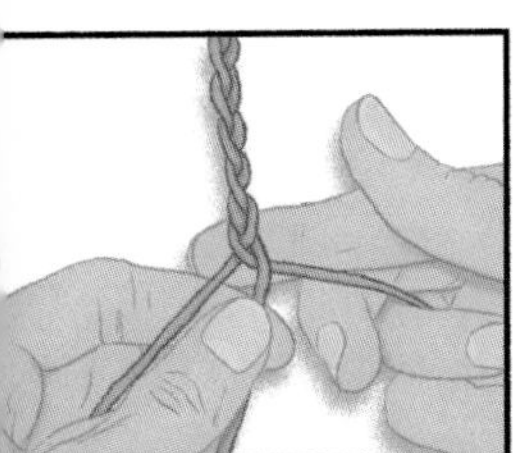

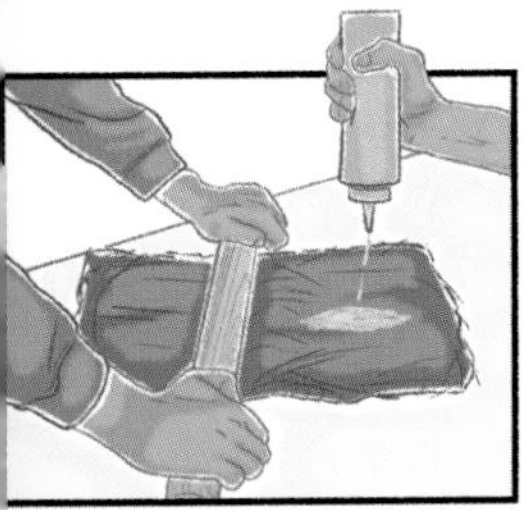

M.A.K.E. COZY CLOZY 2005

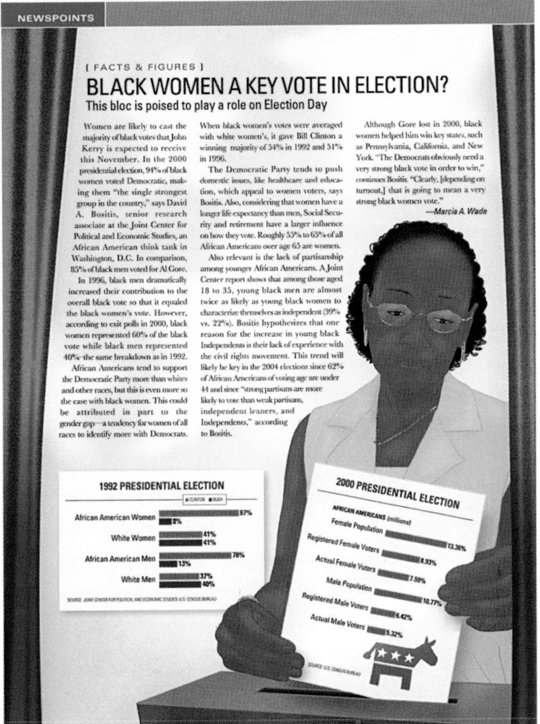

NEWSPOINTS

[FACTS & FIGURES]

BLACK WOMEN A KEY VOTE IN ELECTION?

This bloc is poised to play a role on Election Day

Women are likely to cast the majority of black votes that John Kerry is expected to receive this November. In the 2000 presidential election, 94% of black women voted Democratic, making them "the single strongest group in the country," says David A. Bositis, senior research associate at the Joint Center for Political and Economic Studies, an African American think tank in Washington, D.C. In comparison, 85% of black men voted for Al Gore.

In 1996, black men dramatically increased their contribution to the overall black vote so that it equaled the black women's vote. However, according to exit polls in 2000, black women represented 60% of the black vote while black men represented 40%—the same breakdown as in 1992.

African Americans tend to support the Democratic Party more than whites and other races, but this is even more so the case with black women. This could be attributed in part to the gender gap—a tendency for women of all races to identify more with Democrats.

When black women's votes were averaged with white women's, it gave Bill Clinton a winning majority of 54% in 1992 and 51% in 1996.

The Democratic Party tends to push domestic issues, like healthcare and education, which appeal to women voters, says Bositis. Also, considering that women have a longer life expectancy than men, Social Security and retirement have a larger influence on how they vote. Roughly 55% to 65% of all African Americans over age 65 are women.

Also relevant is the lack of partisanship among younger African Americans. A Joint Center report shows that among those aged 18 to 35, young black men are almost twice as likely as young black women to characterize themselves as independent (39% vs. 22%). Bositis hypothesizes that one reason for the increase in young black Independents is their lack of experience with the civil rights movement. This trend will likely be key in the 2004 elections since 62% of African Americans of voting age are under 44 and since "strong partisans are more likely to vote than weak partisans, independent leaners, and Independents," according to Bositis.

Although Gore lost in 2000, black women helped him win key states, such as Pennsylvania, California, and New York. "The Democrats obviously need a very strong black vote in order to win," continues Bositis. "Clearly, [depending on turnout,] that is going to mean a very strong black women vote."

—Marcia A. Wade

1992 PRESIDENTIAL ELECTION

	CLINTON	BUSH
African American Women	87%	8%
White Women	41%	41%
African American Men	78%	13%
White Men	37%	40%

SOURCE: JOINT CENTER FOR POLITICAL AND ECONOMIC STUDIES, U.S. CENSUS BUREAU

2000 PRESIDENTIAL ELECTION

AFRICAN AMERICANS (millions)	
Female Population	13.36%
Registered Female Voters	8.93%
Actual Female Voters	7.59%
Male Population	10.77%
Registered Male Voters	6.42%
Actual Male Voters	5.32%

SOURCE: U.S. CENSUS BUREAU

AUGUST 2004 · BLACK ENTERPRISE · WWW.BLACKENTERPRISE.COM · ILLUSTRATION BY BETSYHAYES.NET

BLACK ENTERPRISE MAGAZINE AUGUST 2004

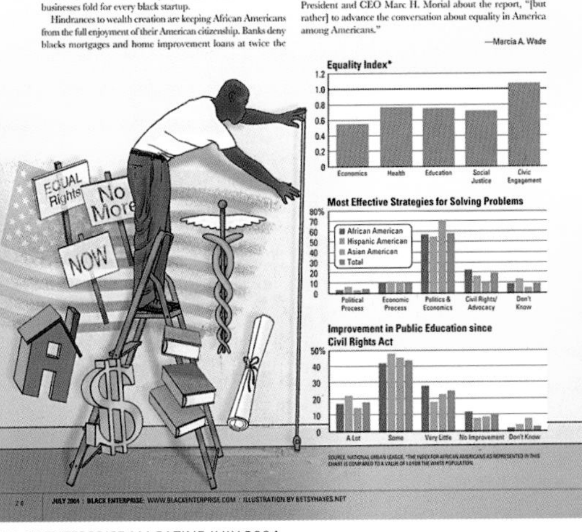

NEWSPOINTS

[FACTS & FIGURES]

NATIONAL URBAN LEAGUE: STATE OF BLACK AMERICA

Report shows African American status is less than that of whites in economics, housing, education, and healthcare

If African Americans were considered three-fifths (60%) of a person in 1788 when the framers of the Constitution counted slaves for tax purposes, then their economic value in 2004 amounts to less than three-fourths (73%) when compared to their white counterparts, states the National Urban League in its State of Black America 2004 Equality Index.

The Equality Index measures disparities between blacks and whites in economics, housing, education, health, social justice, and civic engagement. Of those six categories, civic engagement was the only area where blacks outranked whites, partly due to the number of blacks who volunteer in the military.

According to the report, leveling the playing field would require that an additional 23,698 black students earn bachelor's degrees from four-year colleges every year. It would also require that 751,000 blacks find employment and that three white businesses fold for every black startup.

Hindrances to wealth creation are keeping African Americans from the full enjoyment of their American citizenship. Banks deny blacks mortgages and home improvement loans at twice the rate of whites. According to the report, less than 50% of black families own their homes, versus 70% of whites. Moreover, black homes are valued, on average, at $42,800 less than white homes.

Also in the Urban League's report is a national poll that examines the attitudes of African Americans, Hispanic Americans, and Asian Americans pertaining to the quality of life in their communities and pertinent social, economic, and political issues. Fifty-four percent of the African Americans surveyed said that things will remain the same or get worse for them, identifying race as the key concern. Fifty-one percent of the African Americans surveyed were more optimistic about the quality of life improving for Latinos and Asian Americans.

"This is by no means to deny—or not to celebrate—the progress [blacks have] made," says National Urban League President and CEO Marc H. Morial about the report, "[but rather] to advance the conversation about equality in America among Americans."

—Marcia A. Wade

EQUAL Rights
No More
NOW
Equality Index*
1.2
1.0
0.8
0.6
0.4
0.2
0
Economics
Health
Education
Social Justice
Civic Engagement
Most Effective Strategies for Solving Problems
80%
70
60
50
40
30
20
10
0
African American
Hispanic American
Asian American
Total
Political Process
Economic Process
Politics & Economics
Civil Rights/ Advocacy
Don't Know
Improvement in Public Education since Civil Rights Act
50%
40
30
20
10
0
A Lot
Some
Very Little
No Improvement
Don't Know

JULY 2004 · BLACK ENTERPRISE · WWW.BLACKENTERPRISE.COM · ILLUSTRATION BY BETSYHAYES.NET

BLACK ENTERPRISE MAGAZINE JULY 2004

www.betsyhayes.net 508.785.1659

Koerber

nora koerber illustration
626-791-1953 * land
626-375-5637 * cell
www.norakoerberillustration.com

www.theispot.com
www.folioplanet.com

REDNECK

© Mattel

MARY ROSS

RHYTHM
& BLUES

Women's Health

BREED

It's a GIRL!

POP!

Poet's Leap

Electric
Reindeer

Tutti
Frutti!

PHONE/FAX: 415 661-2930 **WEB:** maryrossillustration.com

ARTIST
JEFFREY J RANDAL
401 - 762 - 490
112 SAYLES HILL RD. N. SMITHFIELD R.I 0289
jrandall-studios@cox.net - View more of jeffs work at portfolios.co
GOLF

DAN LISH
?1 South 2nd St., #1L
Brooklyn, NY 11211
TEL: (718) 486-0119
e-mail: dan@danlish.com
www.danlish.com

Clients include:
Barnes & Noble, Sony,
Rockstar Games, Motorola,
Official Playstation Magazine,
Take 2 Interactive, Playlounge,
The People's Publishing Group

chili's
Corona Clipper
Corona Extra
ROADSIDE AMERICA
VACATION
Playlists
Browse
Extras
Settings
Backlight
MENU
SONY
Robots The Movie
G2
ILLUSTRATIONS INC
GLENNGUSTAFSON.COM 630.243.9972

A balanced diet is
a cookie in each hand!

namista

Clients include:

- Hasbro
- The Time Factory
- Anagram
- Day Dream, Inc.
- The Rug Barn
- Erlanger Fabrics
- Kurt S. Adler, Inc.

joy JOY joy
JOY
Scatter Joy!

Blessed are those who
can give without
remembering and take
without forgetting.

Imaginative Illustration of Heart & Soul

www.nanettehilton.com
(702) 454-2661
singingbrush@hotmail.com

Nanette Hilton™

Expect a Miracle
Miracle Mail
Delivery
Service
FOR U
OPEN 24/7
JUST LOOK
UP
DOWN
ALL AROUND
Nan

www.nanettehilton.com
(702) 454-2661
singingbrush@hotmail.com

JAMES A. TRAVERS ©
Happy Halloween

www.traversstudio.com

JAMES A. TRAVERS
VISUAL ARTIST

(603) 623-6549

LOEL BARR
[cut off] Boxwood Court
[cut off]augerties, NY 12477
[cut off]EL: (845) 246-3765
[cut off]-mail: loel@loelbarr.com
[cut off]www.loelbarr.com

MFA-Drawing, Painting
Clients include: The Washington Post, Time-Life Books, USA Today, National Geographic, New York Times

VIN

STUDIO FORONDA

anthony foronda
www.studioforonda.com
anthony@studioforonda.com
301.538.2344

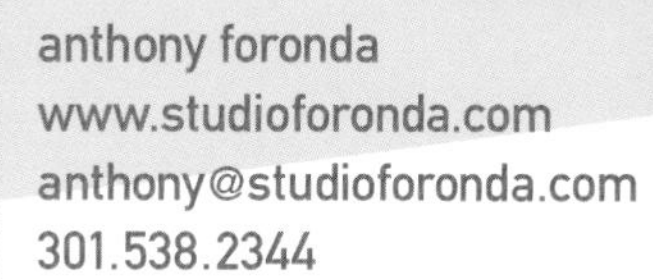

801 274-8828
www.bobcommander.com

Jeff Grunewald

digital illustration

773-281-5284

www.jeffgrunewald.com

realistic architectural rendering
retail and trade show visualization
conceptual illustration

2120
2120

java
joint

Life with
MAX
Max, isn't that a cute dog!
I know dogs and that's no dog!!!

2D AND 3D ILLUSTRATION

Skyhook Studios

William Lombardo

37 West 28th Street 4th Floor
NYC, New York 10001
212 292 2630 • fax 212 292 2624
email:skyhook@dti.net • http://www.skyhook-art.com

Karen Greenberg

212. 645. 7379
www.karengreenberg.com
karen@karengreenberg.com

Chosen: AI21, AI23 & AI24
Big Book of Illustration, 2004

Digital illustration | Hand lettering

tres jolie
splendid

EXPERIENCE THE WORLD
AT CENTRAL PARK
SUMMERSTAGE

parfum

Glow Guide
Yoga
Simple Steps for Health and Well-Being
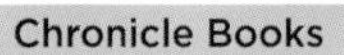

HEMISPHERES
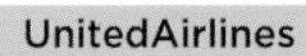

ens Club | Tokyo Central Park SummerStage Ritz Carlton Magazine Chronicle Books UnitedAirlines Natural Health

David Deen

Illustration
(617) 718-2855

36 Curtis St. No. 2
Somerville, MA 02144

email@daviddeen.com
www.daviddeen.com

WINNER
2001
T-SHIRT
CONTEST
HOWARD
REUNION
AT LAKE HUGO

DEEN ©'04

DEEN © '05

DEEN ©'01

Chris Butler
PHONE: (303) 530-4695
FAX: (303) 530-5036
For additional samples of more than 180 illustrations, call or fax your request.

LTL-CAR

Living With SUVs

Late for School

Jacob Lambert·Humorous Illustration

1202 Pine St. Philadelphia, PA 19107 www.JacobLambert.com (215) 893-3534

416-699-1525 DAN FELL dfell@sympatico.ca

Travel
ITALIA

BRITISH COLUMBIA
Agritourism

TORONTO

MINNEAPOLIS
FALL
2005

www.danfell.com

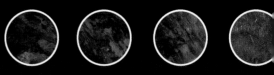

JUDITH MOFFATT
Cut Paper Illustration
13 Charles St. Medway MA 02053
Phone: 508-533-4496
Web: judithmoffatt.com

©SHELLY O HAAS 2001

www.shellyohaas.com
SHELLY O HAAS
(509) 253-4752
P O Box 333
Harrington, WA
99134

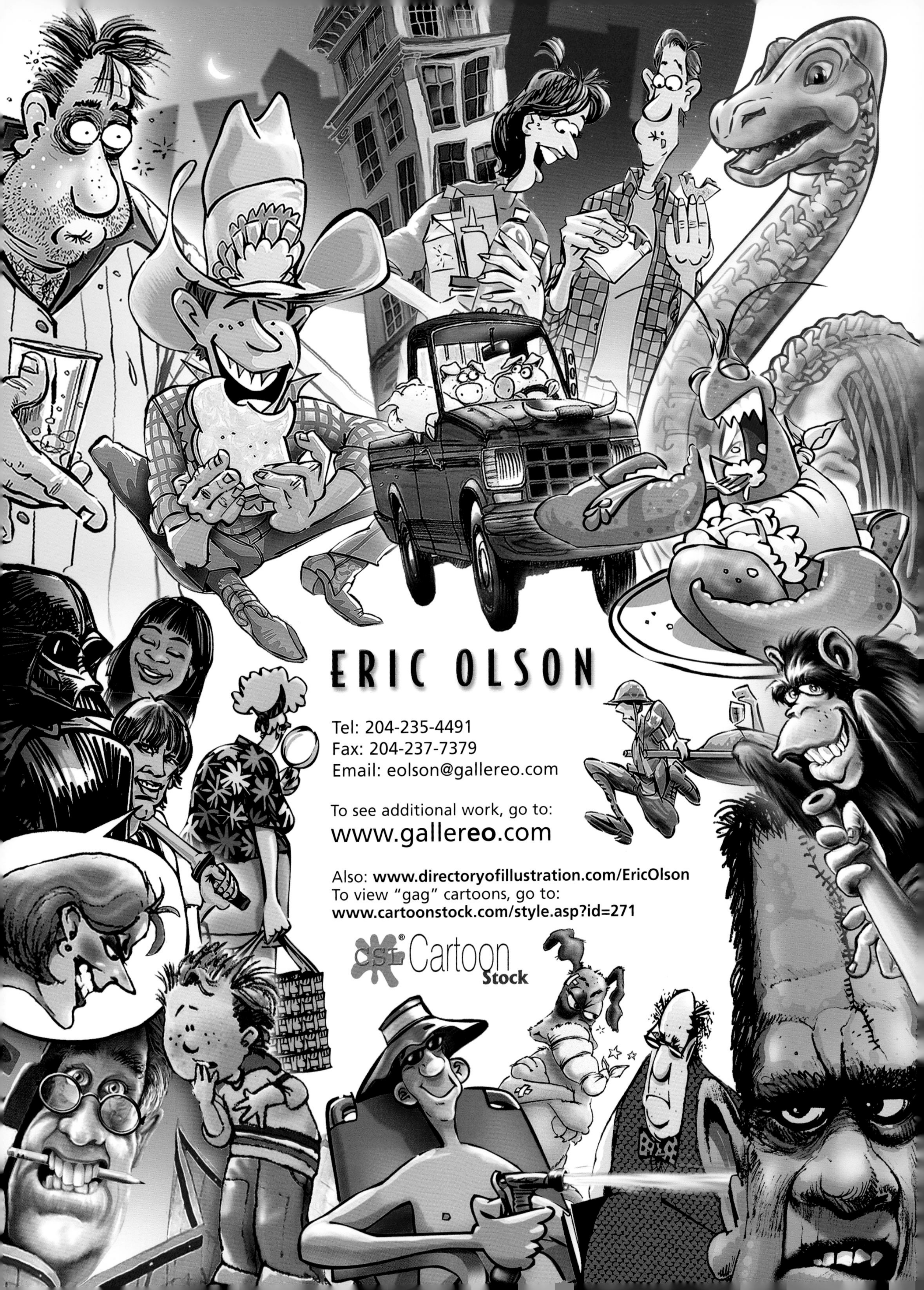
ERIC OLSON
Tel: 204-235-4491
Fax: 204-237-7379
Email: eolson@gallereo.com
To see additional work, go to:
www.gallereo.com
Also: www.directoryofillustration.com/EricOlson
To view "gag" cartoons, go to:
www.cartoonstock.com/style.asp?id=271
CSL® Cartoon Stock

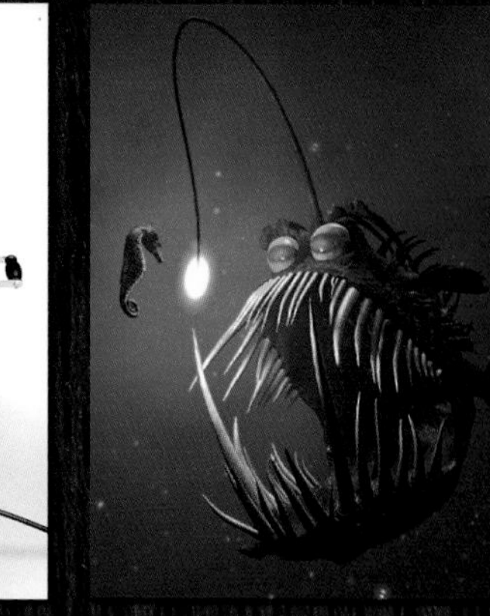

MADE IN USA KOHRMAN GRAPHICS DIGITAL PENCIL
MADE IN USA

* illustration * **Lisa K. Weber** * character design *

* 381 Atlantic Avenue, #2 * Brooklyn, NY 11217 * ph: 718-243-2914 * e: lisa@creatureco.com *

NOD
LKW
* www.creatureco.com *

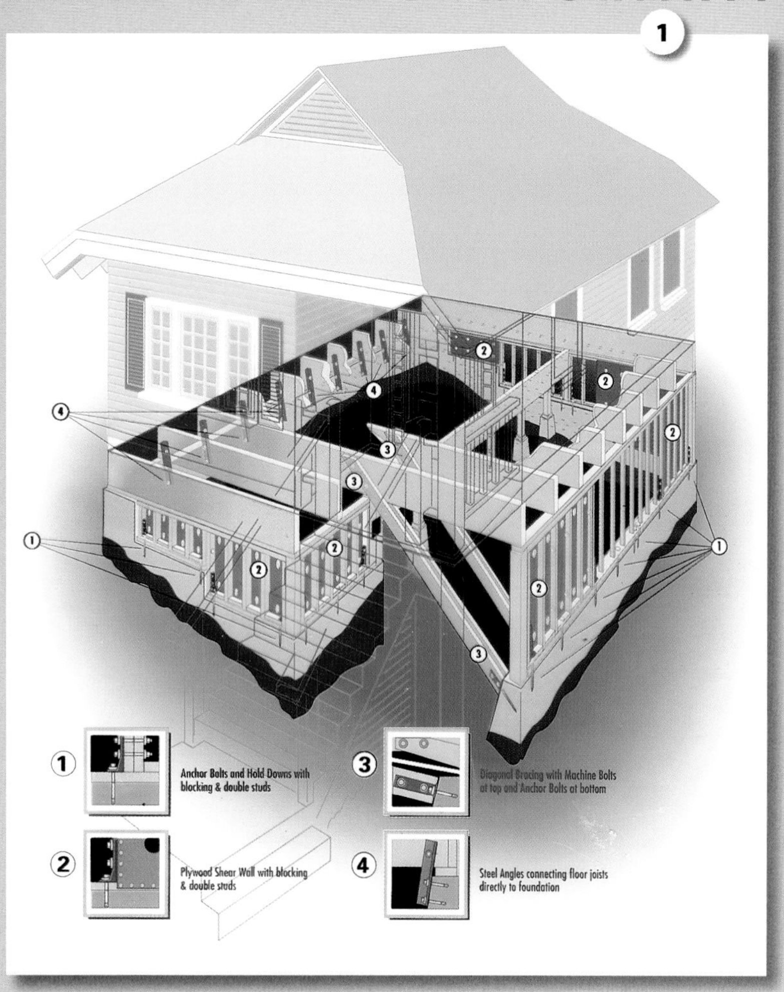
1
Anchor Bolts and Hold Downs with blocking & double studs
2
Plywood Shear Wall with blocking & double studs
3
Diagonal Bracing with Machine Bolts at top and Anchor Bolts at bottom
4
Steel Angles connecting floor joists directly to foundation

2
MED LAB
HOSPITAL

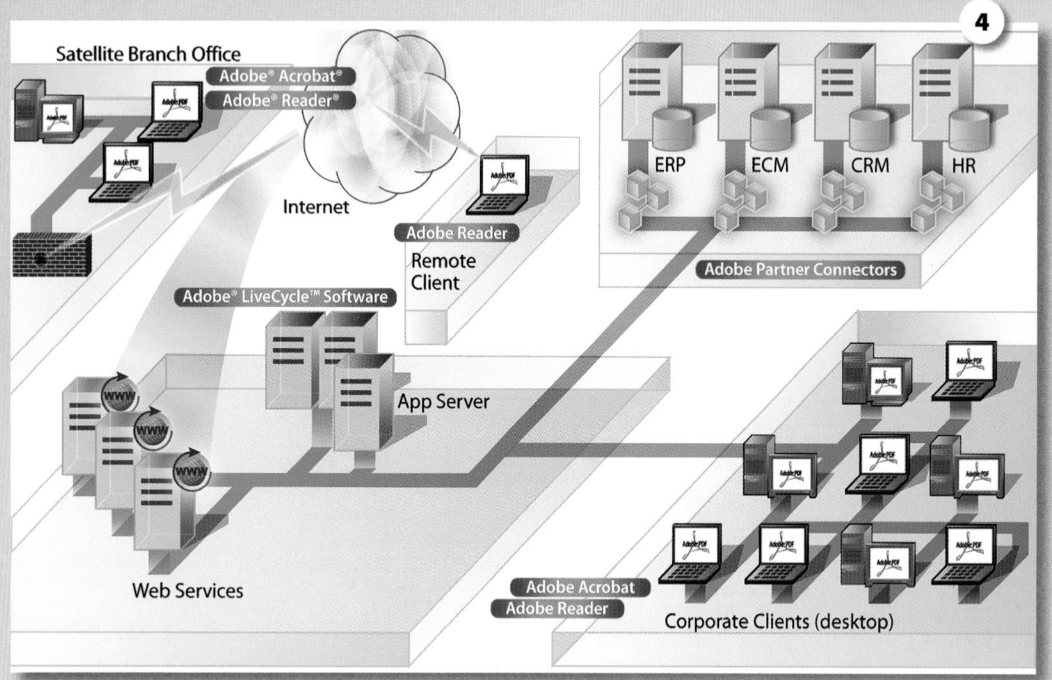
4
Satellite Branch Office
Adobe® Acrobat®
Adobe® Reader®
Internet
Adobe Reader
Remote Client
ERP
ECM
CRM
HR
Adobe Partner Connectors
Adobe® LiveCycle™ Software
App Server
Web Services
Adobe Acrobat
Adobe Reader
Corporate Clients (desktop)

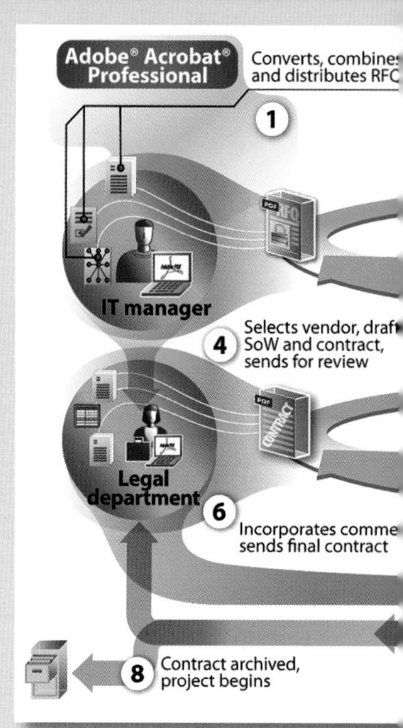
Adobe® Acrobat® Professional
1
IT manager
4
SoW and contract,
sends for review
Legal department
6
sends final contract
8
Contract archived,
project begins

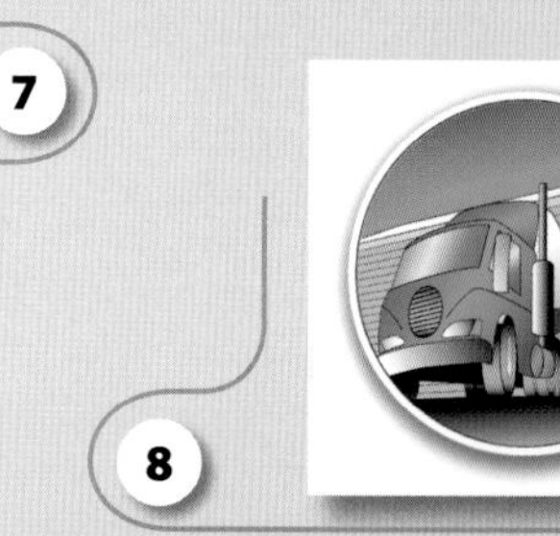
7
8

The
ric Berendt
Studio

925.462.6809
c@berendtstudio.com
w.berendtstudio.com

ally compelling
gery to illustrate
iness and marketing
cepts, products,
processes

3

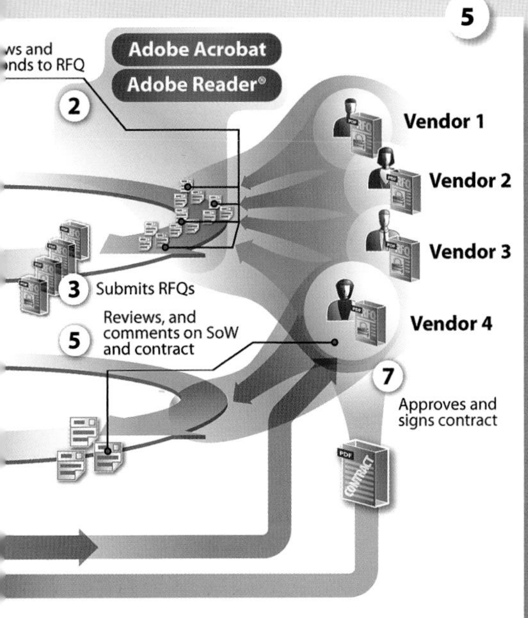
5
ws and
nds to RFQ
Adobe Acrobat
Adobe Reader®
2
Vendor 1
Vendor 2
Vendor 3
Vendor 4
3 Submits RFQs
5 Reviews, and comments on SoW and contract
7 Approves and signs contract

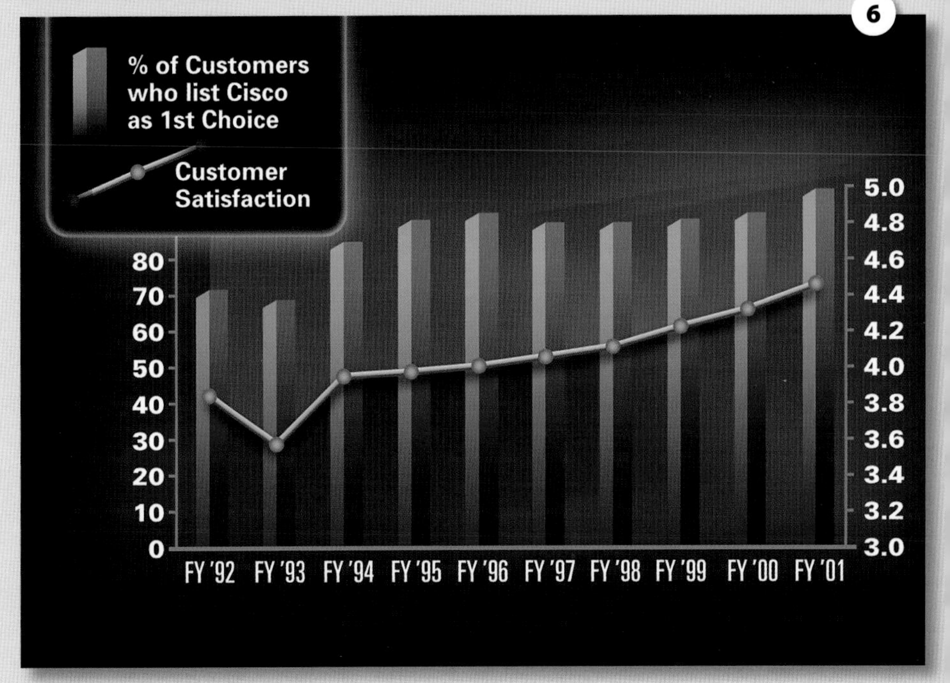
6
% of Customers who list Cisco as 1st Choice
Customer Satisfaction
80
70
60
50
40
30
20
10
0
5.0
4.8
4.6
4.4
4.2
4.0
3.8
3.6
3.4
3.2
3.0
FY '92
FY '93
FY '94
FY '95
FY '96
FY '97
FY '98
FY '99
FY '00
FY '01

1. Cut-away Bungalow. Earthquake Safety, Inc., ©1994, The Eric Berendt Studio
2. Asterion.com in the medical records and billing cycle-capabilities brochure. Asterion.com, © 2000, The Eric Berendt Studio
3. Brochure Cover with medical records theme. QuadraMed. ©1998, The Eric Berendt Studio
4. Cable and internet network topology map using Adobe® Acrobat® technology. ©2004, Adobe Systems, Inc.
5. The IT Contract Cycle using Adobe Acrobat technology. ©2004, Adobe Systems, Inc.
6. Customer Satisfaction Bar Chart. ©2002, Cisco Systems, Inc.
7. Seventeen of over 140 presentation component graphics on Adobe company technology themes. ©2003-5, Adobe Systems, Inc.
8. Three of six printing industry themed illustrations for Collabria.com online print broker website. Collabria.com, ©2000, The Eric Berendt Studio

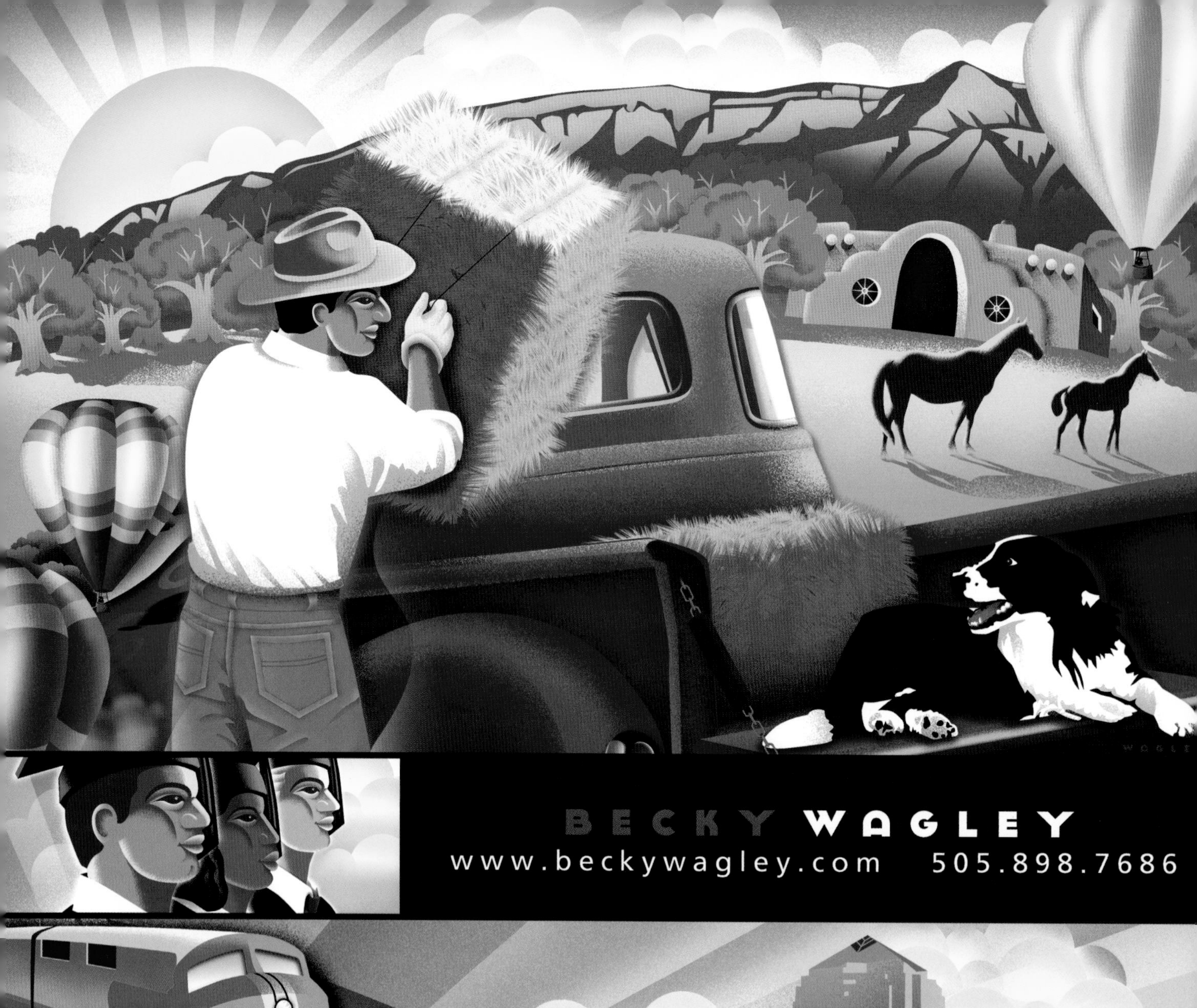
BECKY WAGLEY
www.beckywagley.com 505.898.7686

SANTA FE
ALBUQUERQUE
NEW MEXICO
US
66

GARY OVERACRE

770-973-8878
www.GaryOveracre.com

2D
Photography
Photoshop
3D
Bill Frymire
VISUALS
billfrymire.com
250-851-8791
http://www.
INVESTING

Clients Include:

Bebop Books
Dogs in Hats Publishing
Duos and Trios Cards
Fishs Eddy
Godiva Chocolatier
Oxford University Press
Scribblemats

Susie Lee Jin

www.susieleejin.com (212) 252-1072 www.susiestudio.com

MARK EVAN WALKER

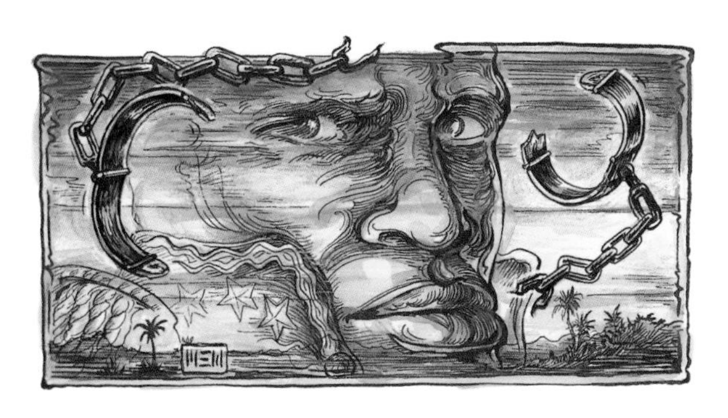

T.: 817-905-0057 F.: 817-924-8905 E.: mevanw@earthlink.net
www.markevanwalker.com

BAILEY DESIGN
Stephen Bailey
phone/fax (716) 745- 3341
mobile (716) 807-6713
web site sbaileyillustration.com
MONSTER TRUCK
Racing
BIGFOOT
ADAM RYAN
Bear Foot
GUN SLINGER
RIP
DENNIS ANDERSON
EQUALIZER
SELECT
Orange
Cola
Roasted & Salted Almonds
CHEDDAR CHEESE
TUXEDOS
mini twist pretzels
TONY
Grave Digger Racing

Safeway Foods

Kelloggs

Stratosphere Resort

YOU'VE
GOT
MAIL...

THE PALM

LEE COBURN

CO

COBURN CREATIVE
1-888-LCOBURN
WWW.LEECOBURN.COM

NoBens
• C.A. Nobens •
Illustration & Design, Inc.
If you see someone jumping rope,
and you like jumping rope, too,
skip right over and jump along.
Together make up
a jump-rope song.
© 2005
Creative Teaching Press
© 2005
McGraw-Hill
Publishers
1
Sad
Bear's
Day

• Contact Cheryl Nobens • Phone & Fax (952) 935-9130 • Voicemail (612) 599-7570 •
• canobens@uscorp.net • 3616 Rhode Island Avenue South, Saint Louis Park MN 55426-4031 •

CHILDREN • NATURE • COMMERCIAL • SEASONAL • TEXTILE EFFECTS • GRAYSCALE
ILLUSTRATION • MIXED DIGITAL MEDIA • CUSTOM TEXTURES • TYPE TREATMENT • BACKGROUNDS

TINA FIELD HOWE

PO BOX 762, CORNING, NY 14830 • 607-936-1455
INFO@TINAFIELDHOWE.COM • WWW.TINAFIELDHOWE.COM/ILLUSTRATIONS

Giacomo Marchesi
is pronounced "JOCK-o-mo mar-KAY-zee"
Telephone: 718.832.7376
e-mail: bucket@earthlink.net
website: www.GiacomoMarchesi.com

Taia Morley
651.436.8855
taia@taiamorley.com

SCOTT ANNIS

.O. Box 575
onifer, CO 80433
EL: 303-816-1300
AX: 303-838-8263
ww.SCOTTANNIS.com
A@SCOTTANNIS.com

Some ideas are difficult to come up with.

Double Your Monkey
TM

Double Your Monkey is a Trade Mark of Vista Gaming Corp.

Some ideas are good but could be a lot better.

Some ideas are great!

Patricia Raun Craig

425-644-5676 www.rauncraig.com patcra@rauncraig.com

All By Myself,
color pencil

Sisters Playing,
color pencil

Rebecca skillfully guides Mary,
digital illustration

Casey's Tender Caress,
color pencil

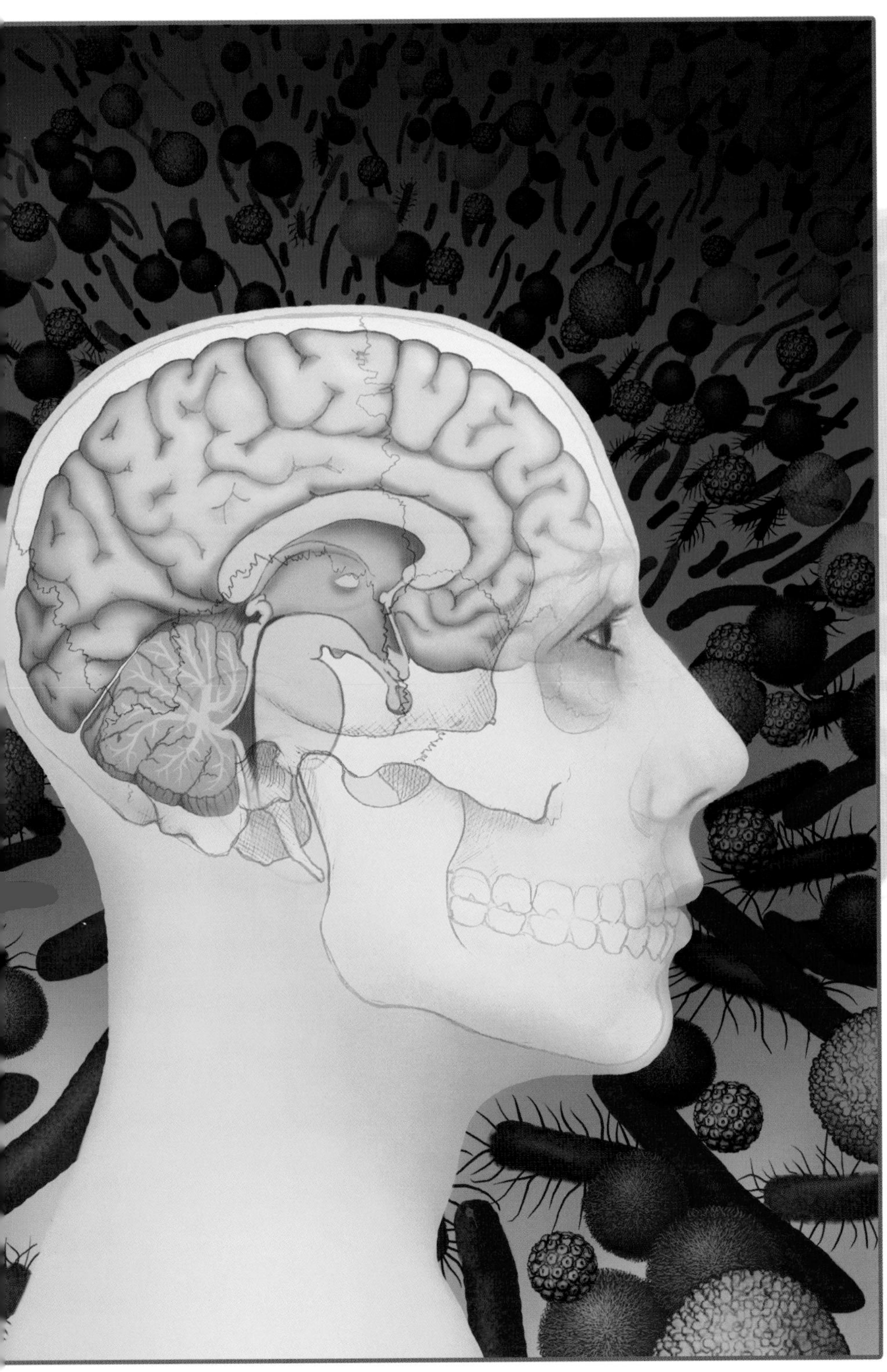

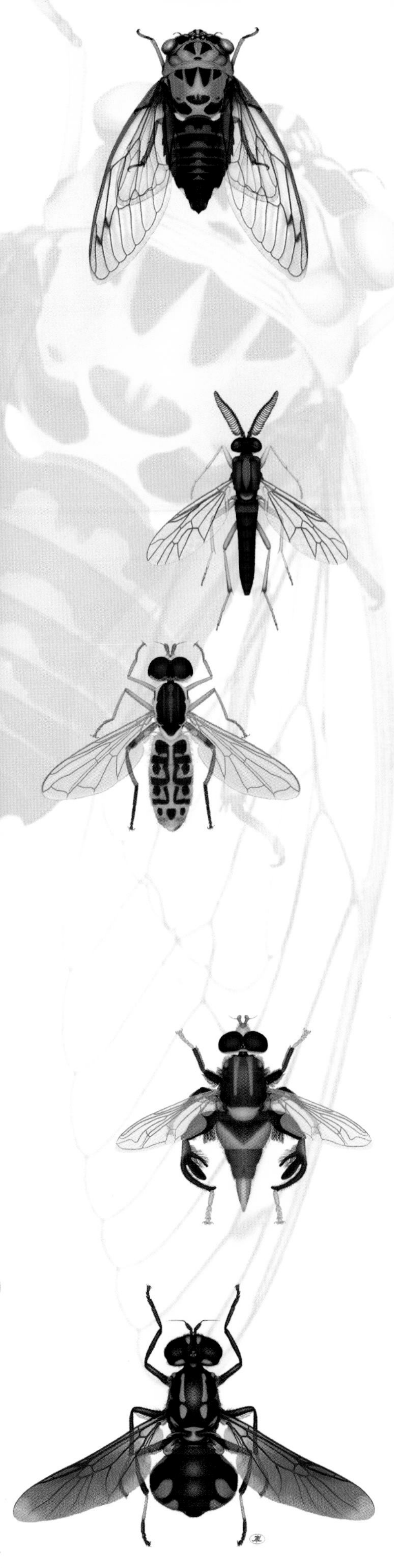

LITWAK ILLUSTRATION STUDIO

Taina Litwak, CMI
taina@litwakillustration.com
301-977-5203
www.science-art.com
www.portfolios.com

Clients include: Smithsonian Institution, National Institutes of Health, Center for Disease Control, McGraw-Hill Companies, StackPole Books, Chanticleer Press, Interlink Healthcare Inc., Nichols-Dezenhall, Cystic Fibrosis Foundation

JOHN DYESS
727 Top Notch Lane
Eureka, MO 63025
TEL/FAX: (636) 938-1200
e-mail: jcdyess@swbell.net
www.studiodyess.com

I am a professional illustrator with 40 years in the business and a vast list of clients. In this ad, I have included work done (left to right) for Pearson Education, *L– (Lawyer) Magazine, Medical Economics* and a self-portrait (bottom right). This group of images combines traditional and digital methods, incorporating typography, texture, photography, drawing and painting. Please view more of my work online at studiodyess.com, stl-illustrator.com or directoryofillustration.com. I welcome the opportunity to work with you.

Civil rights struggle
MARIAN
WRIGHT
EDELMAN

UNITED STATES OF AMER
LIBERTY
QUARTER DO
Corporate Income Tax
Sales and Use Tax
Individual Income Tax
Capital Gains Tax
tax increase
tax cut
government
Department of the Treasury
Internal Revenue Service
Checking.
Savings.
the AMOUNT YOU OWE.
tax (taks) n. 1. an enforced contribution to the public funds, levied on persons, property, or income by governmental authority.

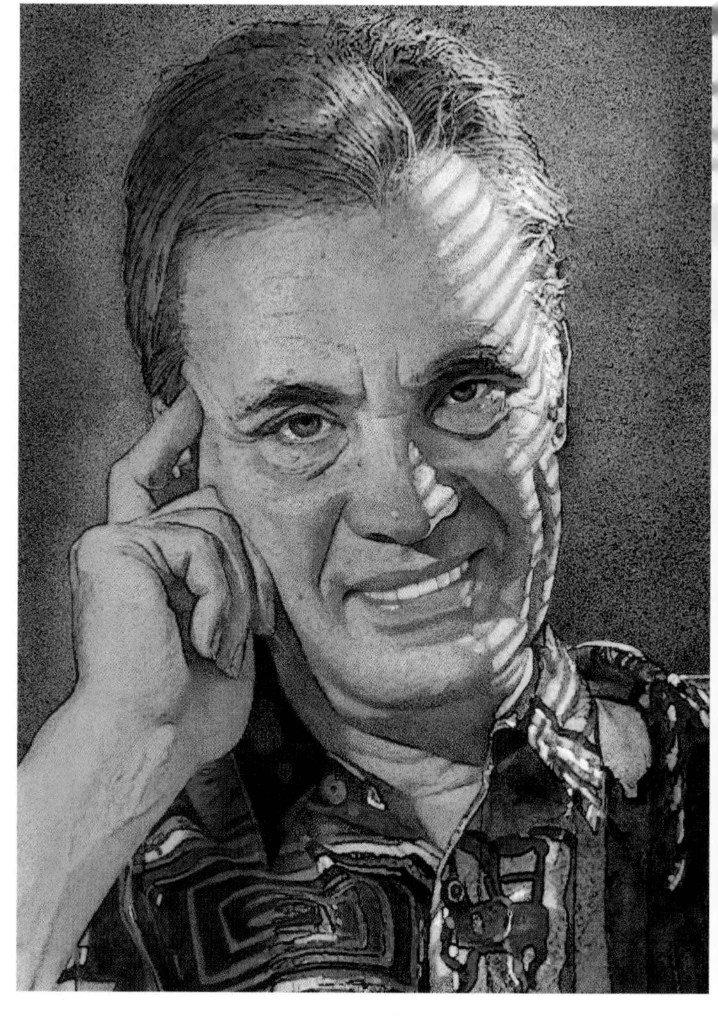

ERRY PACZKO
01 Brecksville Road
dependence, OH 44131
L/FAX: (216) 447-8864
mail: terrypaczko@ameritech.net
ww.terrypaczko.com

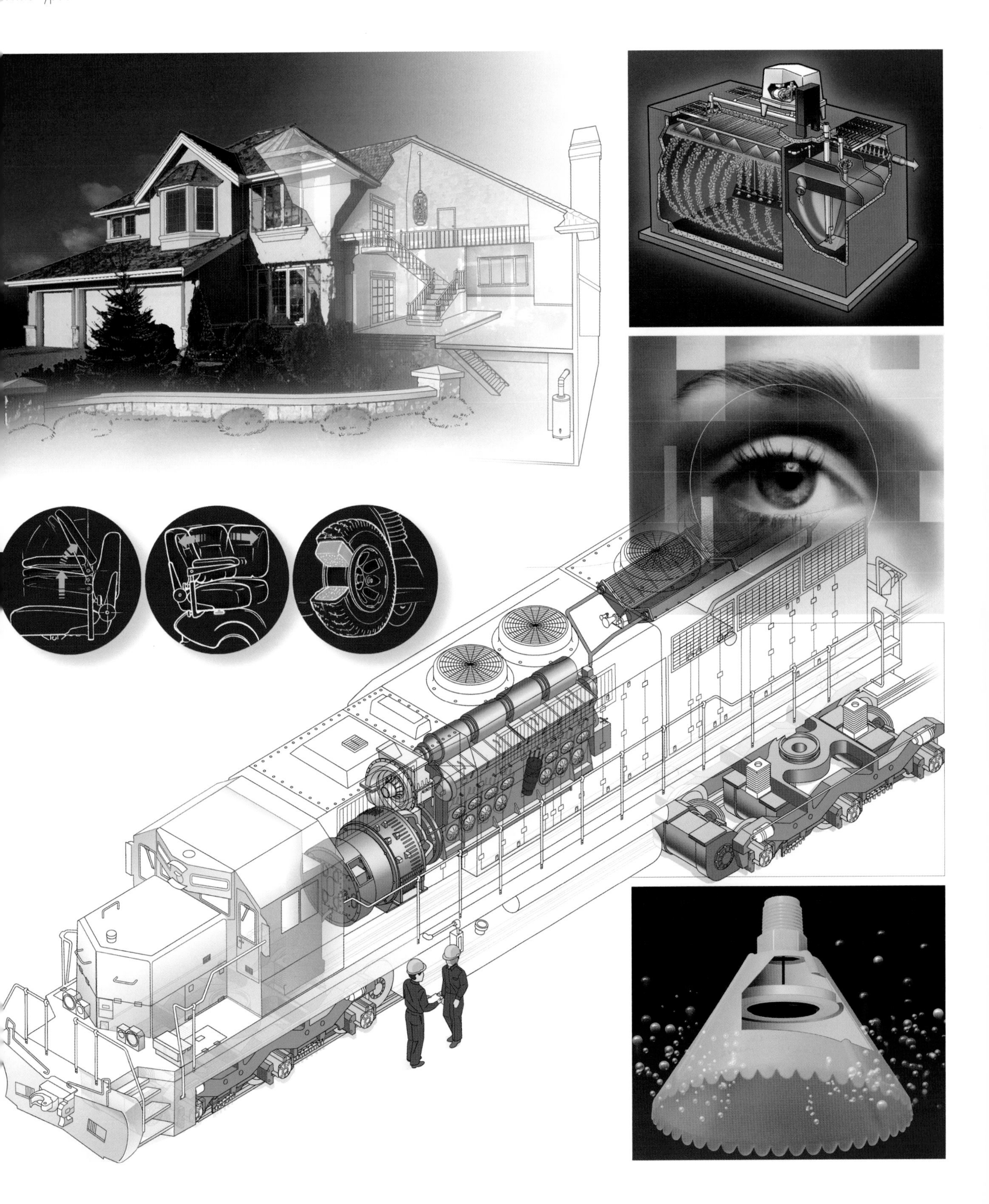

PAULA GOODMAN KOZ
306 Indian Springs Road
Williamsburg, VA 23185
TEL: (757) 253-8950
FAX: (757) 253-8982
e-mail: vitabreve@cox.net
www.paulagoodmankoz.com

Publication: *Shlemiel Crooks*, Text ©2005 by Anna Olswanger, Illustrations ©2005 by Paula Goodman Koz, Junebug Books, an imprint of NewSouth, Inc., Montgomery, Alabama, 2005.

VIRGINIA SHAKESPEARE
FESTIVAL 2005
THE TEMPEST · THE CMPLEAT WKS OF WM SHKSPRE (ABRGD) · CANDIDA
JULY 7-AUGUST 14 · (757)-221-2674
PBK HALL · WILLIAMSBURG
04/PKOZ

Christy Hand
illustrator

www.christyhand.com
me@christyhand.com

Style:
Humorous
Colorful
Whimsical

Market:
Editorial
Children's book
Educational
Toy & game

Media:
Watercolor
Pen & ink
Digital

PICKLES

THE CREATIVE CIRCUS COMPANY
BRAVE
THE MOST FEARLESS FLEAS
COME ONE. COME ALL.
Before you awaits a carnival of characters.
They will CAPTIVATE you with their TALENTS
Enchant you with their HIGH-FLYING CONCEPTS
For behind every illusion
LIES AWESOME ACTS OF
ILLUSTRATION
PRINT & WEB DESIGN
Elegant
STRONG
FLEXIBLE
WELL-TRAINED
WIS
You will find great happiness at the Creative Circus Company
Carlyn Cerniglia | Ring Leader
558 N. Saint Asaph Street
Alexandria, VA 22314
P: 781-910-7381 F: 703-299-3409
Carlyn@CircusCo.com
THE CREATIVE CIRCUS COMPANY
WWW.CIRCUSCO.CO

Michael Krider

voice (800) 557-6206
ACCESS CODE 06

all original, all digital illustration | worldwide web www.michaelkrider.com | electronic mail info@michaelkrider.com

BRANDING
MARKETING STRATEGY
CONTRACT NEGOTIATION
MEDIA DISTRIBUTION
ENDORSEMENT DEALS
TULANE

BUY
TEL PLAZA
CIVIC PROGRESS

TEAM 100

TEAM 100

GREG WRAY

ILLUSTRATION

SECRET SAUCE
SPECIAL BLEND
BREW
DRINK UP... HAVE A NICE DAY... AND LEAVE
DRIVE THRU
TIPS
HAIR OF THE DOG
CAFE CON TWEETY
TODAY'S SPECIAL
ONION LATTE
NUTTY BUNNY MOCHA

40681 Via Diamonte • Murrieta, CA 92562 • 951-696-3560 • greg@gregwray.com • www.gregwray.com

www.travisfoster.com phone (615) 876-2331

KEV BROCKSCHMIDT

(253)856-7026
KEV@KEVSCARTOONS.COM
WWW.KEVSCARTOONS.COM

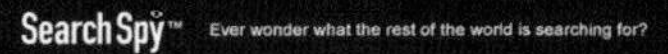
SearchSpy
Ever wonder what the rest of the world is searching for?

Filtered
View family-friendly real-time searches.
Unfiltered
View unedited real-time Web searches. Consider yourself warned.

© 2004 Infospace, Inc. Arfie is a trademark of Infospace, Inc.

EXPLORERS

DK JUNGLE
NOA HQ
POKÉCENTER

Nintendo Camp
Hyrule 2004
© 2004 Nintendo

RENTALS
CAMPS
STAFF
STORE
DEVELOPMEN
RESOURCES

www.LakeRetreat.org

© 2005 Infospace, Inc.
Arfie is a trademark of Infospace, Inc.

Darin Owen

(714) 376-1698

403 Robinson Drive Tustin, CA 92782

www.darinowen.com

TERRY COLON
3839 Toepfer Road
Warren, MI 48091
TEL: (877) 600-9667
e-mail: tmcolon@gogreatlakes.com
www.terrycolon.com

MARSHALL NOKIA
CALLING:
555-7789

SEARCHING DESKTOP...

dave walston

digital illustration

[714.527.8246]

www.davewalstonillustration.com

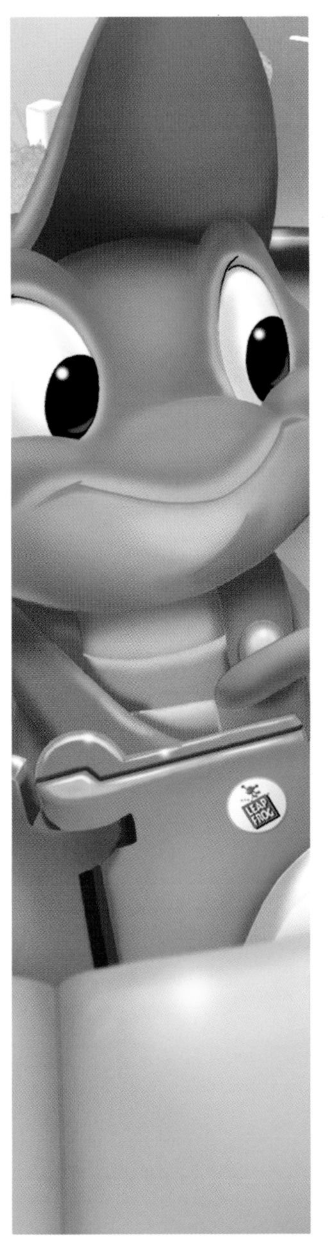

TAMARA GUION ILLUSTRATION

WWW.TAMARAGUION.COM

626·798·8878

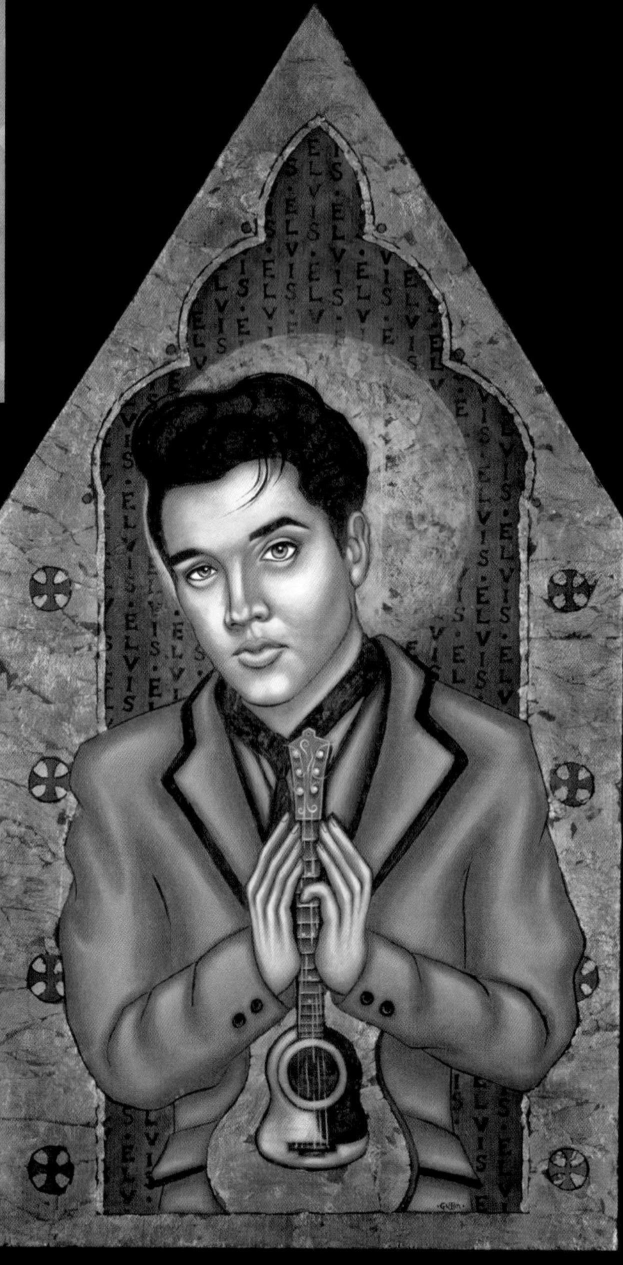

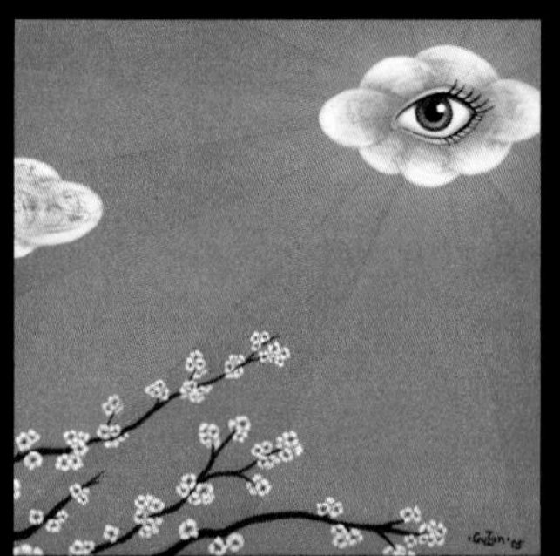

Quality & Service
...ALWAYS WITH A SMILE!

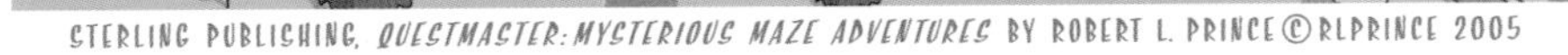
STERLING PUBLISHING, QUESTMASTER: MYSTERIOUS MAZE ADVENTURES BY ROBERT L. PRINCE © RLPRINCE 2005

willie
Houston ★ Public Library ★ Texas
PROPERTY
MR

MICHAELRULAND.COM T. 713 863 0315 F. 713 426 6455

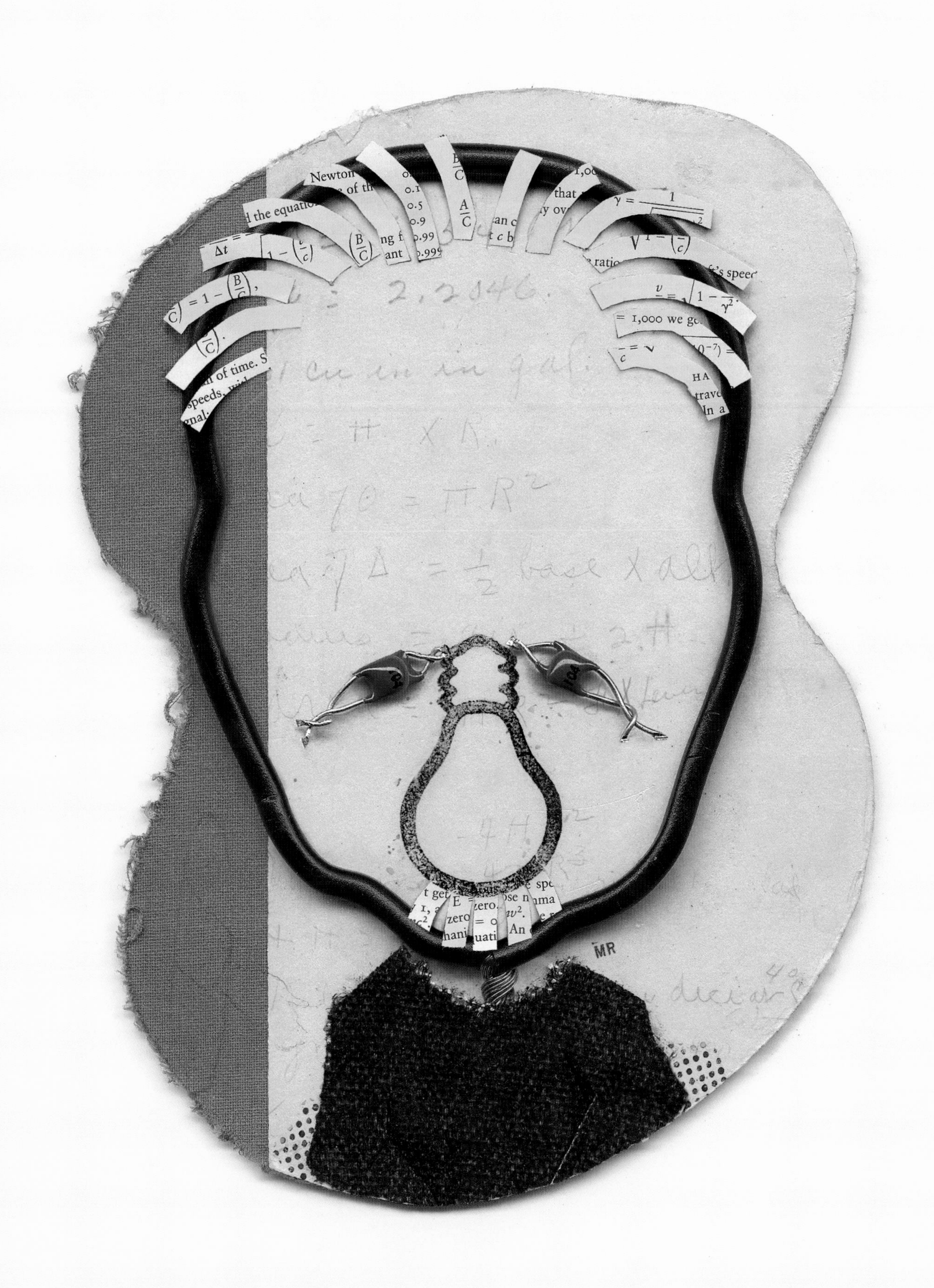

TIM SPOSATO
5 Lucina Terrace
Gorham, ME 04038
TEL: (207) 839-8404
FAX: (207) 839-6464
e-mail: timsposato@earthlink.net
www.timsposatoart.com

tad herr
Stephan & Herr
Illustration and
Graphic Design
717·426·2939
www.stephanherr.com
Directory of Illustration
16-21
"Germs" for Scholastic Library Publishing

ounce of prevention is worth a pound of cure
Rx Calculate endurance aloft

cathy
gendron

www.cathygendron.com

734-971-7341

cathy@cathygendron.com

Ghouls and Dolls

P. 619-238-4537 F. 619-238-1725
www.sveach.com steve@sveach.com

STEVEN VEACH

USAF
U.S. Air

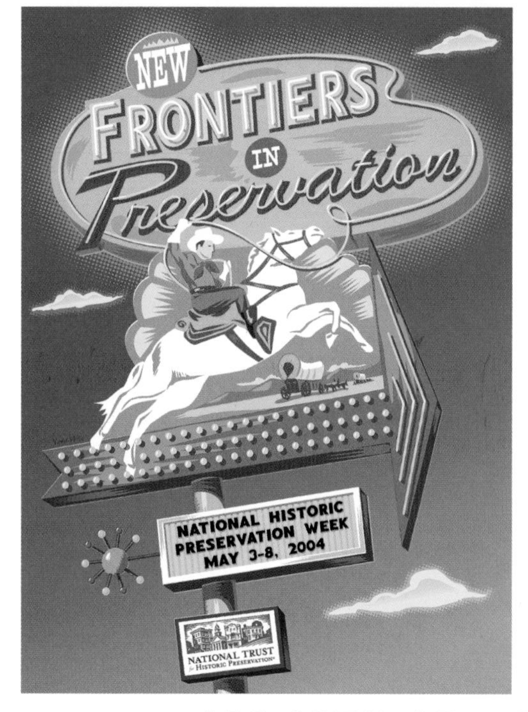
NEW
FRONTIERS
IN
Preservation
NATIONAL HISTORIC
PRESERVATION WEEK
MAY 3-8, 2004
NATIONAL TRUST

VEACH

657 20TH ST • SAN DIEGO • CA • 92102

Anna Veltfort

Digital Illustration
212 877 0430 • AVeltfort@aol.com • www.annaillustration.com
www.theispot.com/artist/aveltfort

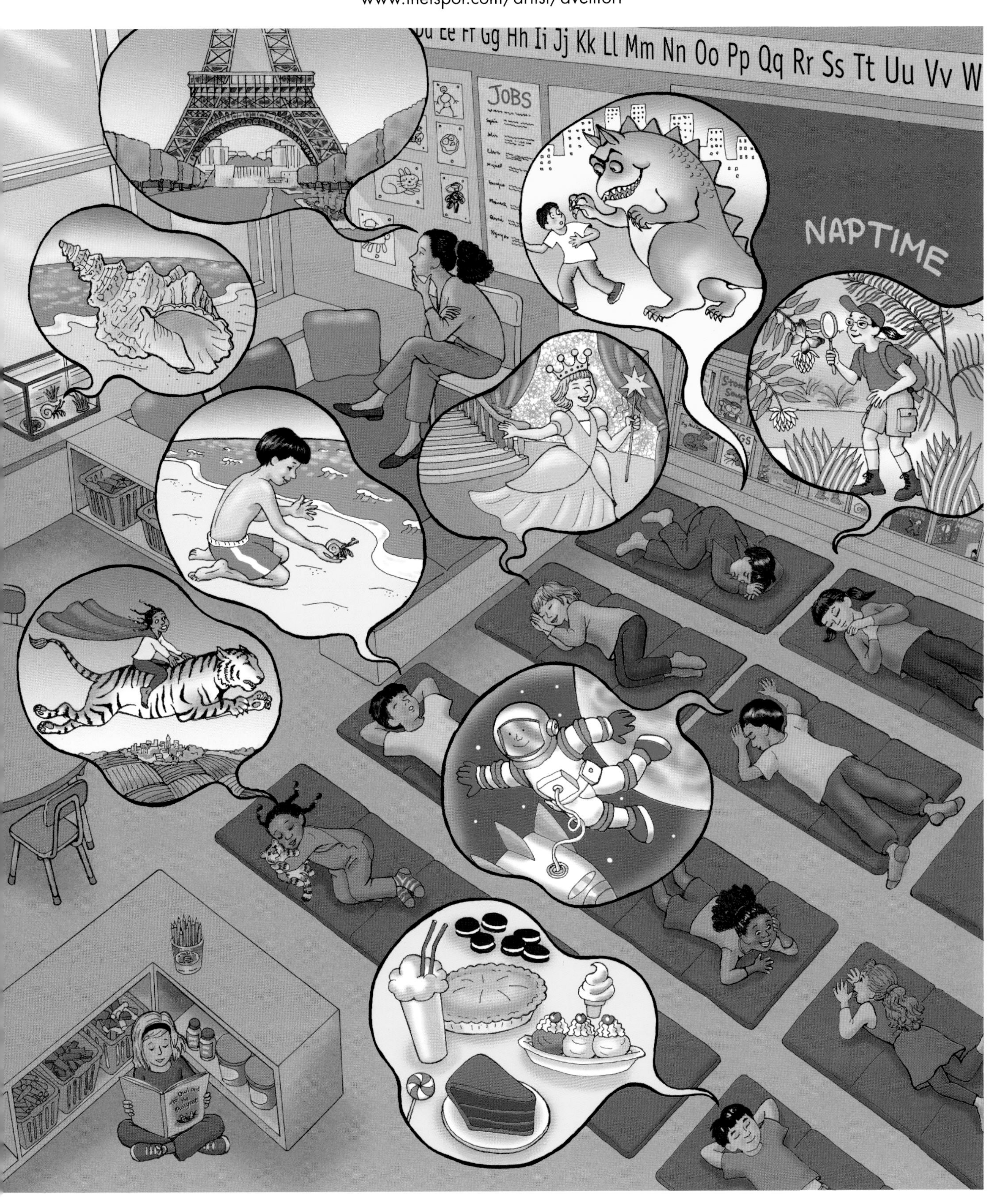
Dd Ee Ff Gg Hh Ii Jj Kk Ll Mm Nn Oo Pp Qq Rr Ss Tt Uu Vv W
JOBS
NAPTIME

STEVE McAFEE
13960 Fletchers Mill Drive
Tampa, FL 33613
TEL: (813) 963-1565
e-mail: mcafees@mindspring.com
www.stevemcafee.com

Specializes in digital/mixed media collage, photo illustration, photo manipulation and alternative photographic processes.

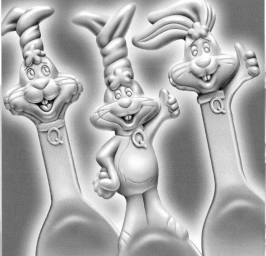

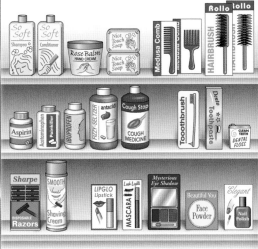

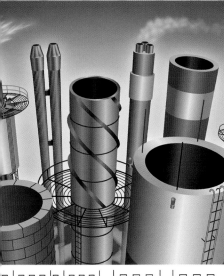

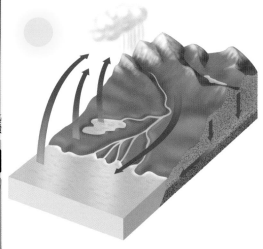

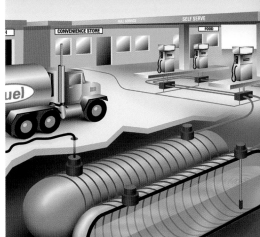

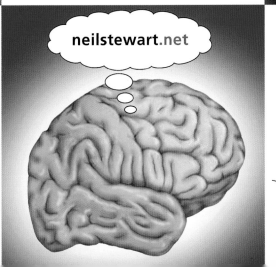

Old Brookville Winery

HOWLING MONKEY
BLACK AND TAN BEER
STEEL BREWING
LONGVIEW TEXAS
12
5%
MOOTH BLEND OF TRADITIONAL DARK PORTER
REFRESHING LAGER, BREWED FOR EXCEPTIONAL FLAVOR
HOWLING MONKEY
12 FL.OUNCES
BOTTLES: 6
BLACK AND TAN BEER

U.S. First Federal Credit Union

Mazda USA

Bridgeport Ebenezer Ale

Self-Promotion

Howling Monkey Black & Tan Beer

Tom Hennessy Illustrations - T 415 388-7959 - hennessyart.com - hennessyart@hotmail.com

TIMPER ARTS
TOLL FREE 1 877 539 8622
PHILLIP TIMPER · ILLUSTRATOR · 2015 YAMPA DR. PRESCOTT, AZ 86305
WWW.TIMPERARTS.COM PHIL@TIMPERARTS.COM

The Mid-Life Chryslers
DING
TIMPER

John Worthen

N
W
E
S

mark stephen ph: 310.450.4336 email: mstephenart@verizon.net web: theispot/stock.com

SMOKEY
STEVIE
DIANA
MARVIN
GORDY, JR.

PLINIO M. PINTO
illustrator

702 51st ST E, 902B
Bradenton - FL 34208
Tel.941-524-0744
pintopms@uol.com.br
www.grapesodastudio.com/pmpinto

Recent Clients
Jazziz Magazine
Playboy Enterpises, Inc.
Playboy Jazz Festival

That's not funny, young man.
MOMMY
Yikes!!
My kid can do better than that.
I just don't get it.
Smaller.
The nose is way too small.
Bigger.
Ever since he was little, Uncle Mike has loved to draw funny pictures.
And now that he's all grown up, Uncle Mike has drawn hundreds and hundreds of funny pictures for hundreds and hundreds of lovely clients.
I don't like the color.
Not funny enuf.
Too funny.
Make it dull.
Just change it.
Ok.
Ok?
Would you like Uncle Mike to draw a funny picture just for you?
It's easy! Just contact Mike Phillips at...
678.513.1768!!
unclemik@bellsouth.net
And have a nice day.

Jose Cuervo
ROCKS
THE
HOUSE
MARGARITA

PIRELLI
PRIVATE
Paradise

Clients include:

se Cuervo • Hewlett Pakard
Kentucky Fried Chicken
Pirelli • Toshiba • Intel
NFL • AAA • 3M

the johnee bee show!

Flash sites and
presentations too!

Studio 949 642 2789 e-mail jb at johneebee.com www.johneebee.com

Leaving Home/*watercolor*

Afternoon Dunes/*watercolor*

Two Toes: The Coyote Legend of Green River/Black Rock Press/*watercolor & gouache*

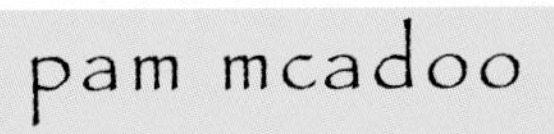
pam mcadoo

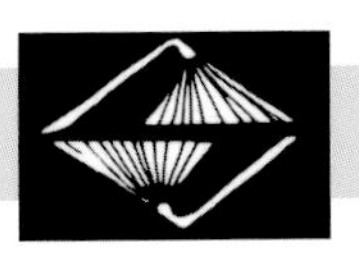

illustration

mcadent@jps.net 530/587-2388 www.pmcadoo.com

Adam Gustavson

Illustrator

www.adamgustavson.com
69 Rollinson Street, West Orange, NJ 07052
973.736.2909
adam@adamgustavson.com

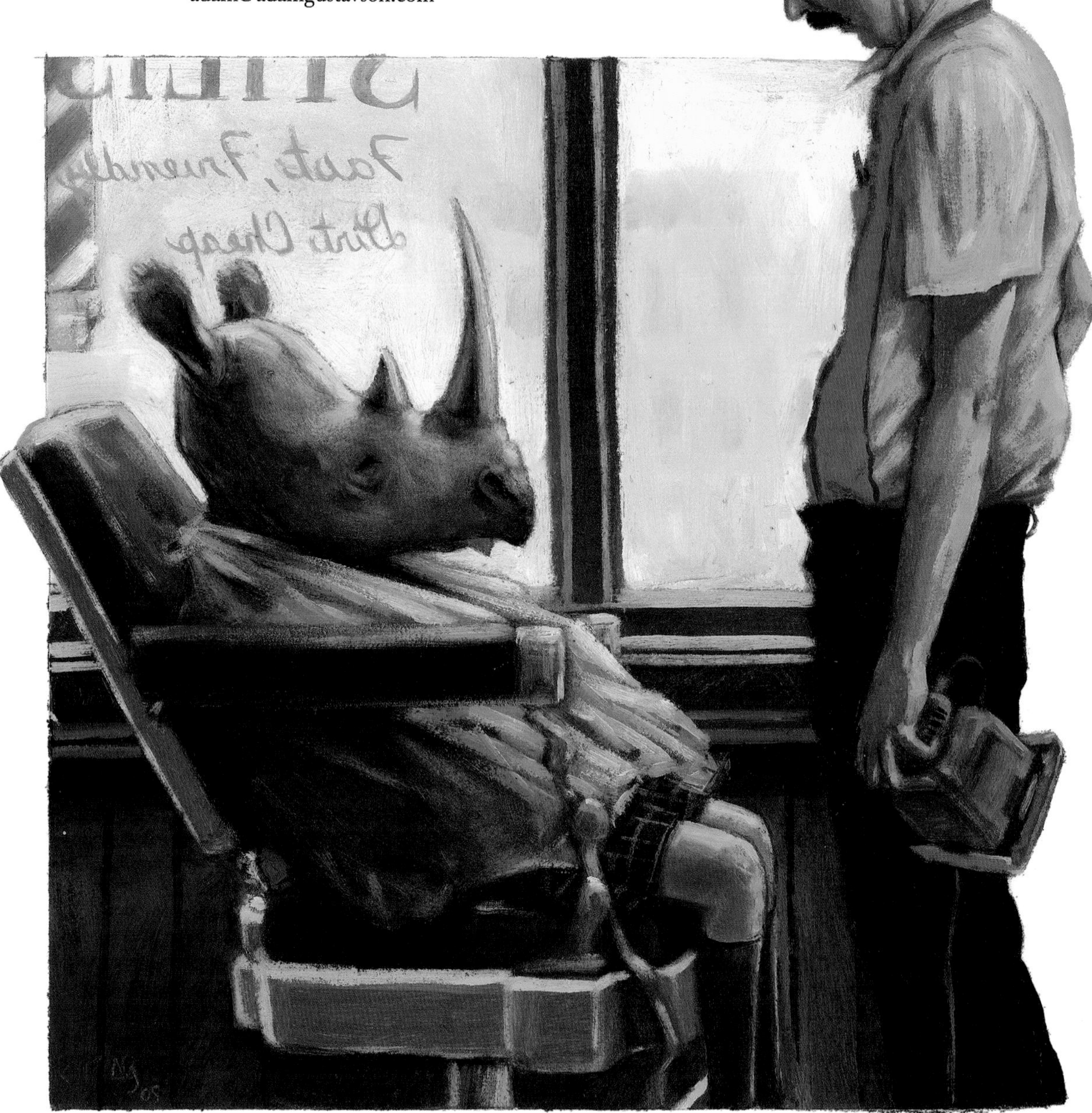

Knowing his horn was comprised entirely of hair, Jimmie decided that a trip to the barber would be the best solution to his predicament.

CDZ
technical illustrations
1-877-317-5894
© Craig Zolman 2005
BOSS
©Craig Zolman 2005
© Craig Zolman 2005
It is said in the advertising industry:
“You have only a few seconds to capture
the attention of the average consumer...”
The clock is ticking!

Sherri Johnson

www.enigmagraphics.com • sjohnson@enigmagraphics.com • 215.362.1586

50

Member of the Society of Children's Book Writers and Illustrators
Client list includes National Geographic, Weekly Reader, Winner Magazine, Cousteau Kids Magazine, Boy Scouts of America, American Cancer Society

RICHARD
EWING
DRAWINGS

40

I CAN MAKE ANYONE DO ANYTHING YOU WANT THEM TO DO!

888•403•1004 F - 562•989•9539 carickature@aol.com • www.theispot.com/artist/rewing

Bill Jaynes
Illustration
(562) 420-7209
www.billjaynes.com
2924 Ostrom Ave.
Long Beach Ca. 90815
willieworks@billjaynes.com

SHEFF

SHEFF
www.sheff.com
702.731.5889

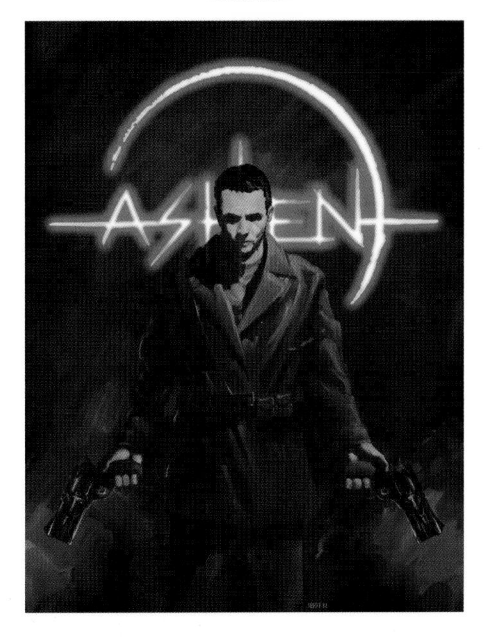

TODD KALE

todd@toddkaleart.com
www.toddkaleart.com

410.236.1762

AM

antonia manda 503/236/5826 antmanda.com

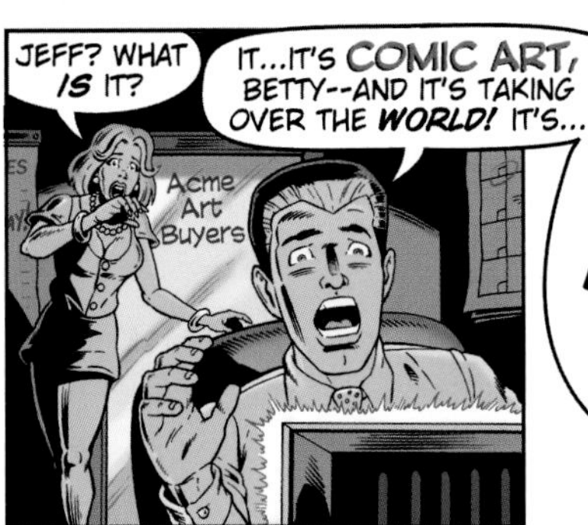

JEFF? WHAT *IS* IT?
IT...IT'S COMIC ART, BETTY--AND IT'S TAKING OVER THE *WORLD!* IT'S...
Acme Art Buyers

ACTION IMPULSE
STUDIOS
™

YES, REPORTS SHOW THAT *ACTION IMPULSE* HAS LAUNCHED A *FULL-SCALE GRAPHICS INVASION!* WATCH FOR THEM IN THE FOLLOWING AREAS:
Spot Illustration
Comps
Concept Art
Storyboards
GNN
GRAPHICS NEWS NETWORK

ILLUSTRATION! CARTOONS, COMIC ART, 3D, AND DIGITAL PAINTING FOR PRINT OR ELECTRONIC MEDIA!
FOX KIDS
I'LL NEVER *FORGET* YOU, MARY.
MY NAME IS ALICE.
WHATEVER.
CARTOON NETWORK
SCOOBY-DOO!
THE MYSTERY MACHINE

ANIMATION! FLASH TOONS FOR THE WEB *AND* FULL BROADCAST VIDEO!
K'NEX REKONSTRUCTORS

OH, JEFF--WHAT SHOULD WE *DO?*
DO? WE *CALL* ACTION IMPULSE ABOUT *OUR* NEXT PROJECT! BUT...*HOW?*
DEADLINES DUE YESTERDAY!
Acme Art Buyers

OUR SOURCES HAVE FOUND *CONTACT INFO* FOR ACTION IMPULSE! PLEASE SEE THE CRAWLER AT THE BOTTOM OF THIS PAGE. BUT PLEASE--APPROACH THEM WITH CAUTION! THEY ARE *DANGEROUSLY* TALENTED! AND...
Storyboards

HEY, WAIT A SEC! THIS ISN'T NEWS--IT'S JUST AN *ADVERTISEMENT!*
Illustration
Concept Art
CUT!

CALL: 402-884-3908 VISIT: WWW.ACTIONIMPULSE.COM

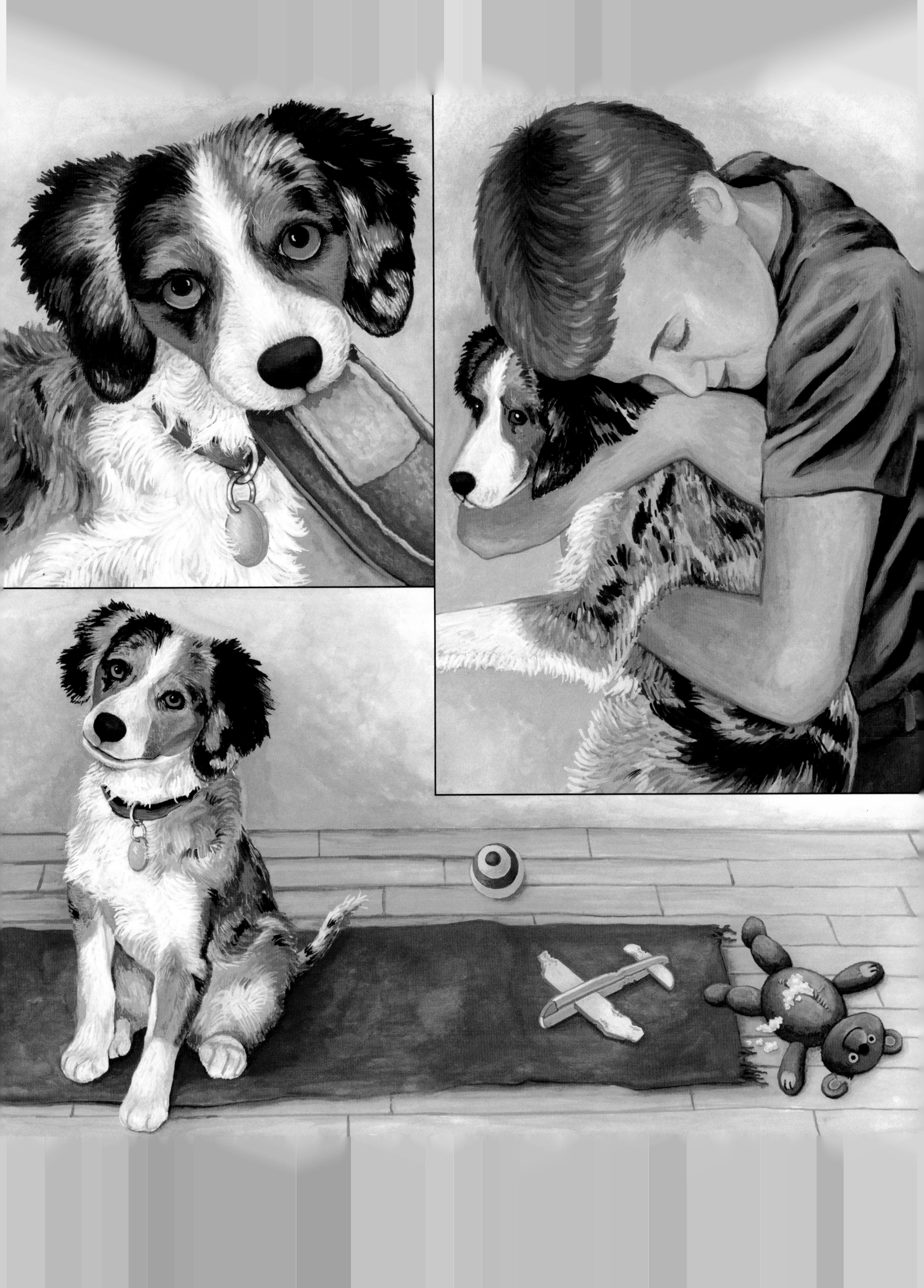

UFO
CCCP
CCCP
CCCP
USA

DANIEL GUIDERA
MODERN ILLUSTRATION

877 * 268 * 5120
or **413 * 585 * 9150**

daniel@danielguidera.com

www.danielguidera.com

Schaefer
AT BAT BALL STRIKE OUT
HOME
VISITOR

CAFE-TERIA
Menu

H
Li Be
Na Mg
K Ca Sc Ti V Cr Mn
Rb Sr Y Zr Nb Mo Tc
Cs Ba L Hf Ta W Re
Fr Ra A
L La Ce Pr Nd Pm

a film by
TODD SOLONDZ
PALINDROMES
WELLSPRING presents an EXTRA LARGE PICTURES production "PALINDROMES"
ELLEN BARKIN, STEPHEN ADLY GUIRGIS, RICHARD MASUR, DEBRA MONK
casting by ANN GOULDER music supervisor SUSAN JACOBS music by NATHAN LARSON
associate producer TIMOTHY BIRD editors MOLLIE GOLDSTEIN, KEVIN MESSMAN
costume designer VICTORIA FARRELL production designer DAVE DOERNBERG
director of photography TOM RICHMOND producers MIKE S. RYAN, DERRICK TSENG
written and directed by TODD SOLONDZ

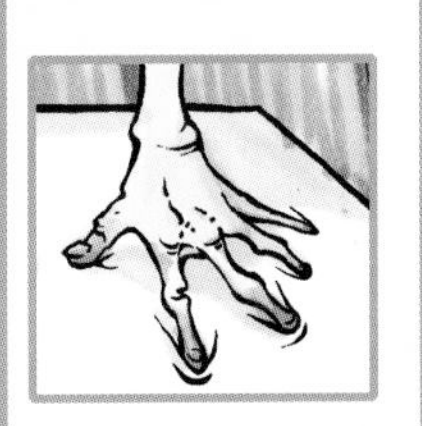

KATHRYN RATHKE
krathke@comcast.net (206) 760-9440

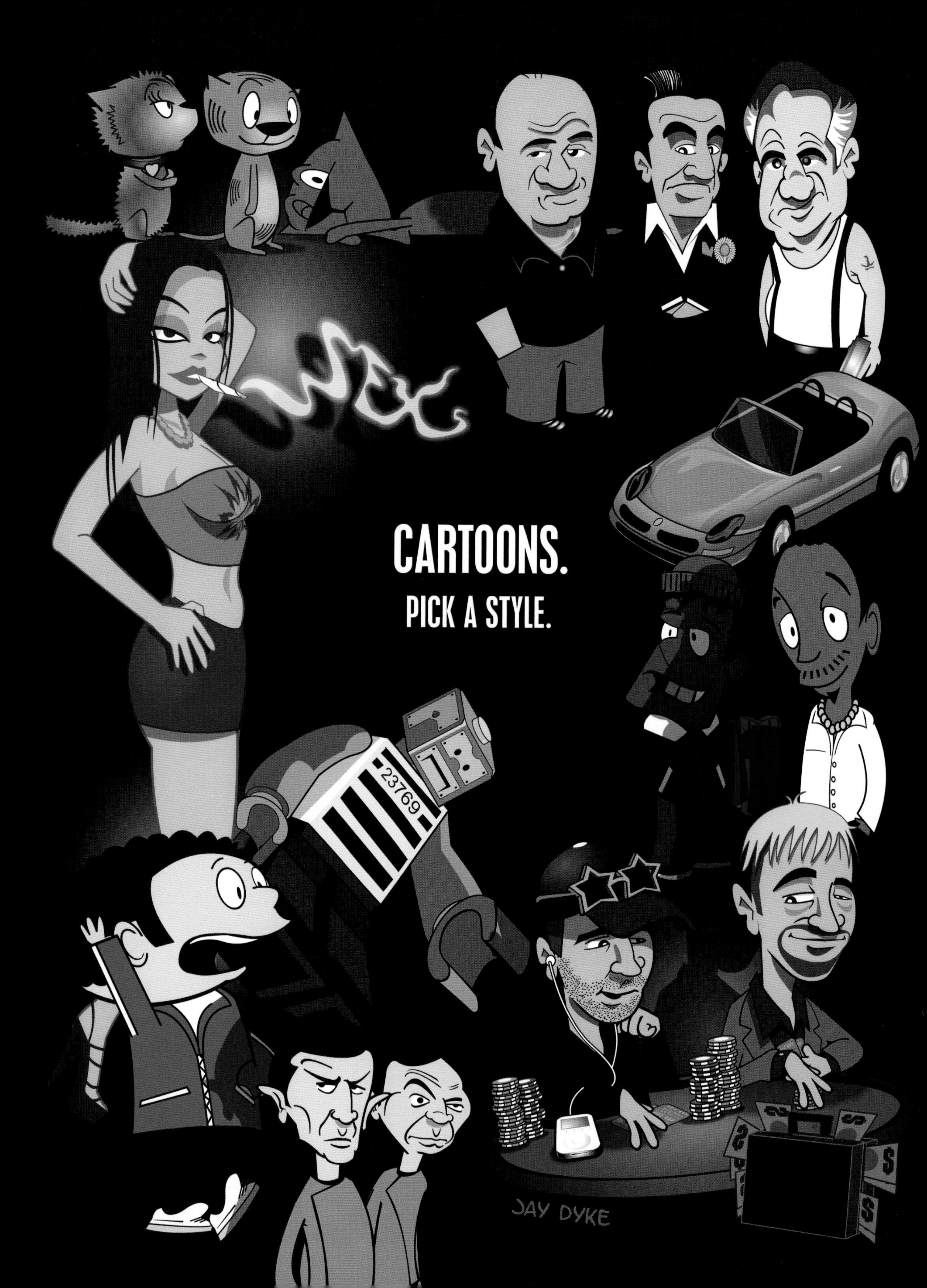
CARTOONS.
PICK A STYLE.
23769
JAY DYKE

DEBBY FISHER

Music Over Jacksonville/Acrylic

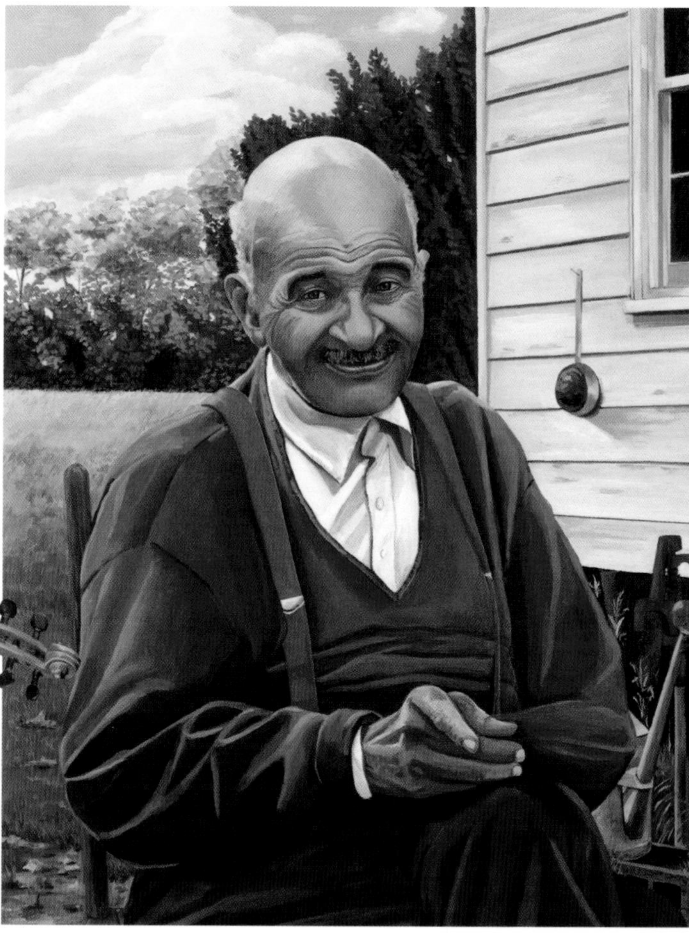
Willy's Memories/Acrylic

Spring Chores/Acrylic

541.665.2034

www.debbyfisher.com

MEILIN

Elesavet

www.elesavet.com
905-741-7167

ROD LITTLE • 712 10 TH ST. N.E. WASHINGTON, D.C. 20002 • TEL•202•543•1180

Inside an Allergic Reaction

Allergens are foreign substances that are not harmful to your body, but which your immune system has learned to attack anyhow. Once an allergen is detected by your immune system, a fast but complicated process begins that leads to the sneezing, congestion, and other symptoms of allergies.

Nasal Cavity

Allergen

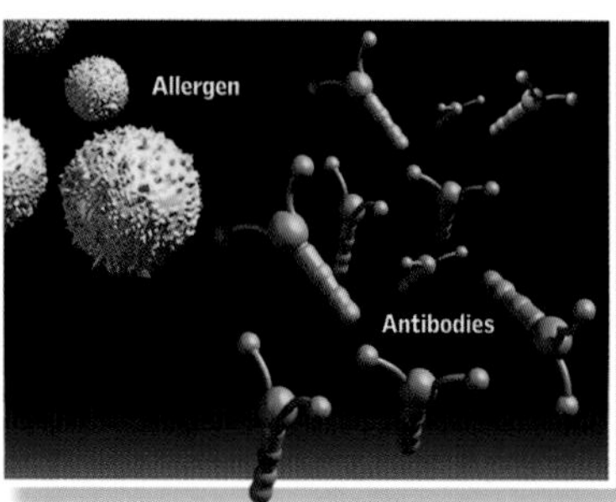

Allergen
Antibodies

1. Initial exposure to an allergen causes your body to create Y-shaped antibodies unique to that allergen. These antibodies then stay in your body, ready to pounce if the allergen shows up again.

2. On the next exposure to the allergen (which could occur years or even decades later), the antibodies discover it and immediately lock onto it.

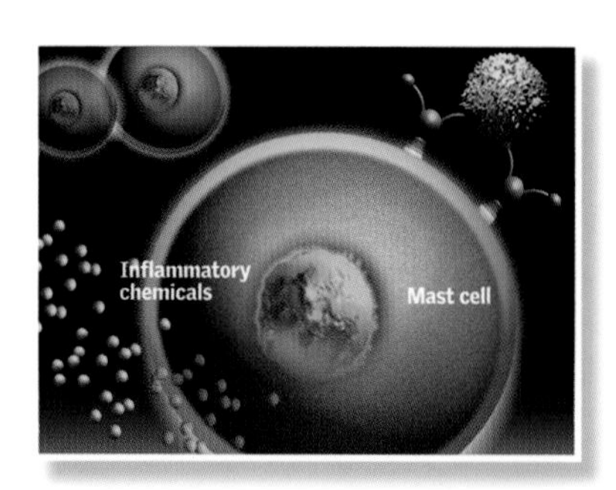

Inflammatory chemicals
Mast cell

3. The antibody then attaches to a mast cell lining your nose, throat, lungs, or elsewhere, which in turn triggers the release of inflammatory chemicals. The inflammatory process begins, with swelling, creation of mucus, reddening, heat, and vessel constriction. Voilá—an allergic reaction.

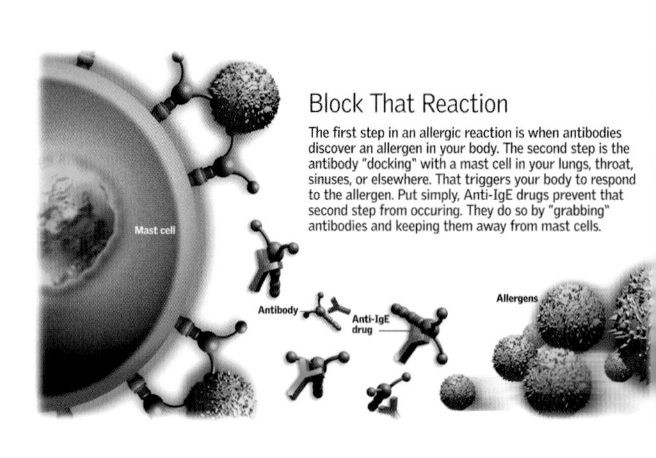

Mast cell
Antibody
Anti-IgE drug
Allergens

Block That Reaction

The first step in an allergic reaction is when antibodies discover an allergen in your body. The second step is the antibody "docking" with a mast cell in your lungs, throat, sinuses, or elsewhere. That triggers your body to respond to the allergen. Put simply, Anti-IgE drugs prevent that second step from occuring. They do so by "grabbing" antibodies and keeping them away from mast cells.

Constricted Airways

An irritant lands in one of the bronchioles. For a person with healthy lungs, a cough moves it on, or cilia sweep it away. But for a person with asthma, the irritant causes the release of histamines and other chemical responses that start the domino chain of an asthma attack.

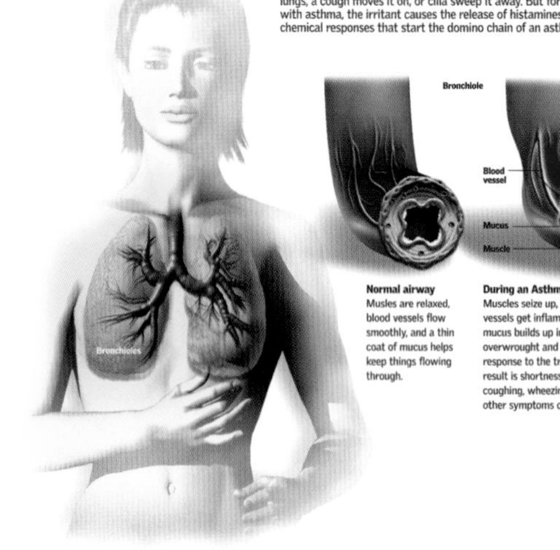

Bronchioles

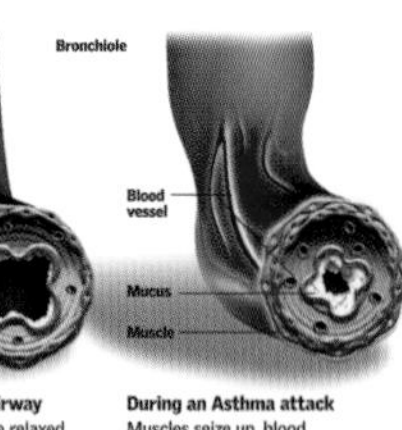

Bronchiole
Blood vessel
Mucus
Muscle

Normal airway
Musles are relaxed, blood vessels flow smoothly, and a thin coat of mucus helps keep things flowing through.

During an Asthma attack
Muscles seize up, blood vessels get inflamed, and mucus builds up in an overwrought and cascading response to the trigger. The result is shortness of breath, coughing, wheezing, and other symptoms of asthma.

How Inflammation Works

To most of us, "inflammation" means that a body part has become red, hot, and swollen. That's true, but the fascinating story lies in the "how" and "why." In fact, inflammation is your body's quick response mechanism for repairing tissue that is injured or infected.

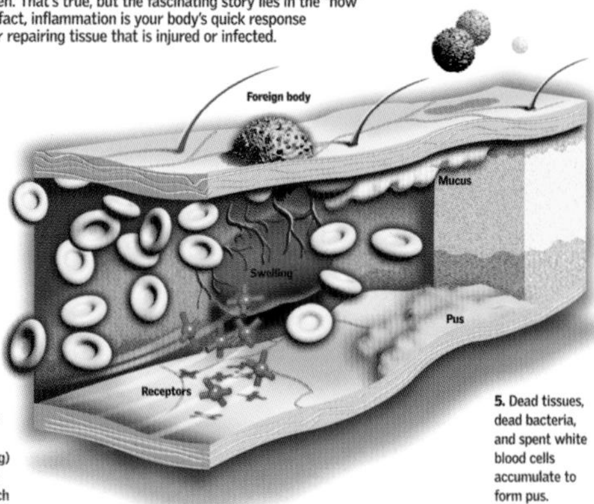

Foreign body
Mucus
Swelling
Pus
White blood cell
Receptors

1. A foreign body (germ, splinter, or allergen) is detected by white blood cells, which release several chemicals to launch a healing response.

2. Small blood vessels near the site leak fluid (causing swelling) and other white blood cells (which attack the foreign body). In addition, blood flow to the area increases, causing it to redden and heat up.

3. Tissue damage and signals from white blood cells trigger nerve pain receptors, increasing the pain of the injury. The goal: to make it difficult for you to use the hurt body part until it heals.

4. In addition, the body creates extra mucus in the area to help wash away foreign bodies. This is the reason for the runny nose, watery eyes, and congestion that occur with colds and allergies.

5. Dead tissues, dead bacteria, and spent white blood cells accumulate to form pus.

INFORMATION ILLUSTRATION

ROD LITTLE • 712 10TH ST. N.E. WASHINGTON, D.C. 20002 • TEL • 202 • 543 • 1180

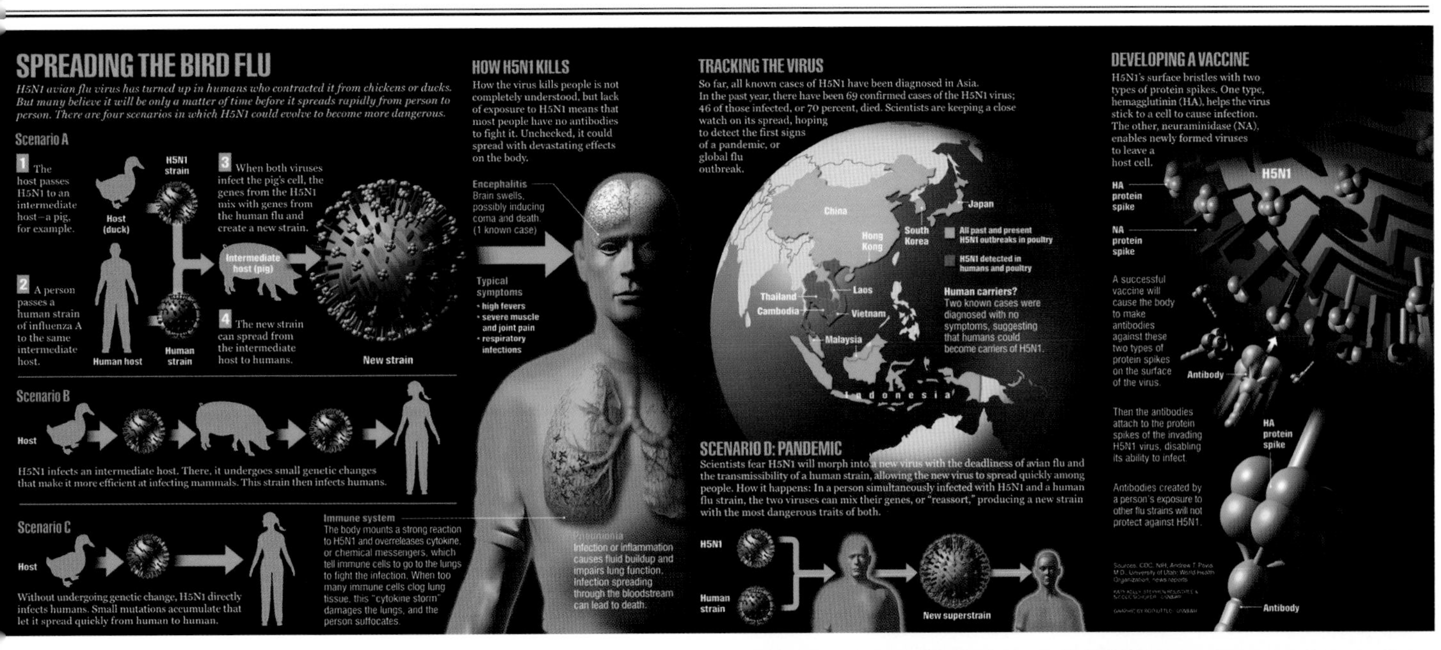

SPREADING THE BIRD FLU
H5N1 avian flu virus has turned up in humans who contracted it from chickens or ducks. But many believe it will be only a matter of time before it spreads rapidly from person to person. There are four scenarios in which H5N1 could evolve to become more dangerous.
Scenario A
1 The host passes H5N1 to an intermediate host – a pig, for example.
H5N1 strain
Host (duck)
3 When both viruses infect the pig's cell, the genes from the H5N1 mix with genes from the human flu and create a new strain.
Intermediate host (pig)
2 A person passes a human strain of influenza A to the same intermediate host.
Human host
Human strain
4 The new strain can spread from the intermediate host to humans.
New strain
Scenario B
Host
H5N1 infects an intermediate host. There, it undergoes small genetic changes that make it more efficient at infecting mammals. This strain then infects humans.
Scenario C
Host
Without undergoing genetic change, H5N1 directly infects humans. Small mutations accumulate that let it spread quickly from human to human.
HOW H5N1 KILLS
How the virus kills people is not completely understood, but lack of exposure to H5N1 means that most people have no antibodies to fight it. Unchecked, it could spread with devastating effects on the body.
Encephalitis
Brain swells, possibly inducing coma and death (1 known case)
Typical symptoms
• high fevers
• severe muscle and joint pain
• respiratory infections
Immune system
The body mounts a strong reaction to H5N1 and overreleases cytokine, or chemical messengers, which tell immune cells to go to the lungs to fight the infection. When too many immune cells clog lung tissue, this "cytokine storm" damages the lungs, and the person suffocates.
Pneumonia
Infection or inflammation causes fluid buildup and impairs lung function. Infection spreading through the bloodstream can lead to death.
TRACKING THE VIRUS
So far, all known cases of H5N1 have been diagnosed in Asia. In the past year, there have been 69 confirmed cases of the H5N1 virus; 46 of those infected, or 70 percent, died. Scientists are keeping a close watch on its spread, hoping to detect the first signs of a pandemic, or global flu outbreak.
China
Japan
South Korea
Hong Kong
Laos
Thailand
Cambodia
Vietnam
Malaysia
Indonesia
All past and present H5N1 outbreaks in poultry
H5N1 detected in humans and poultry
Human carriers?
Two known cases were diagnosed with no symptoms, suggesting that humans could become carriers of H5N1.
SCENARIO D: PANDEMIC
Scientists fear H5N1 will morph into a new virus with the deadliness of avian flu and the transmissibility of a human strain, allowing the new virus to spread quickly among people. How it happens: In a person simultaneously infected with H5N1 and a human flu strain, the two viruses can mix their genes, or "reassort," producing a new strain with the most dangerous traits of both.
H5N1
Human strain
New superstrain
DEVELOPING A VACCINE
H5N1's surface bristles with two types of protein spikes. One type, hemagglutinin (HA), helps the virus stick to a cell to cause infection. The other, neuraminidase (NA), enables newly formed viruses to leave a host cell.
H5N1
HA protein spike
NA protein spike
A successful vaccine will cause the body to make antibodies against these two types of protein spikes on the surface of the virus.
Antibody
Then the antibodies attach to the protein spikes of the invading H5N1 virus, disabling its ability to infect.
HA protein spike
Antibodies created by a person's exposure to other flu strains will not protect against H5N1.
Antibody

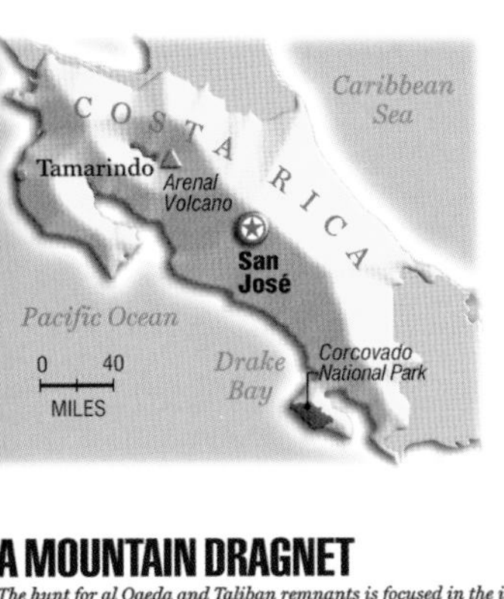

COSTA RICA
Caribbean Sea
Tamarindo
Arenal Volcano
San José
Pacific Ocean
Drake Bay
Corcovado National Park
0 40
MILES

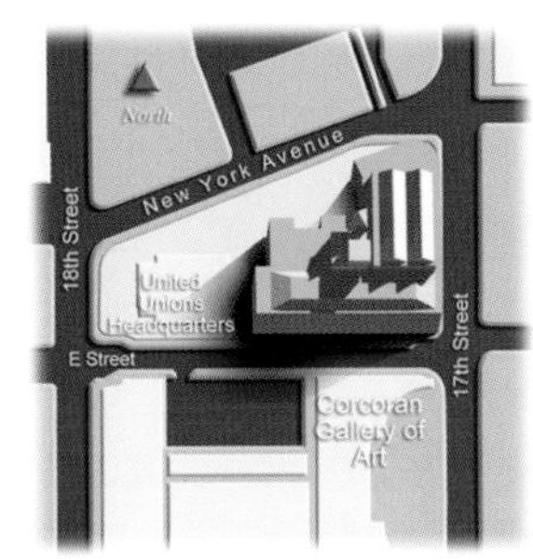

North
New York Avenue
18th Street
17th Street
E Street
United Unions Headquarters
Corcoran Gallery of Art

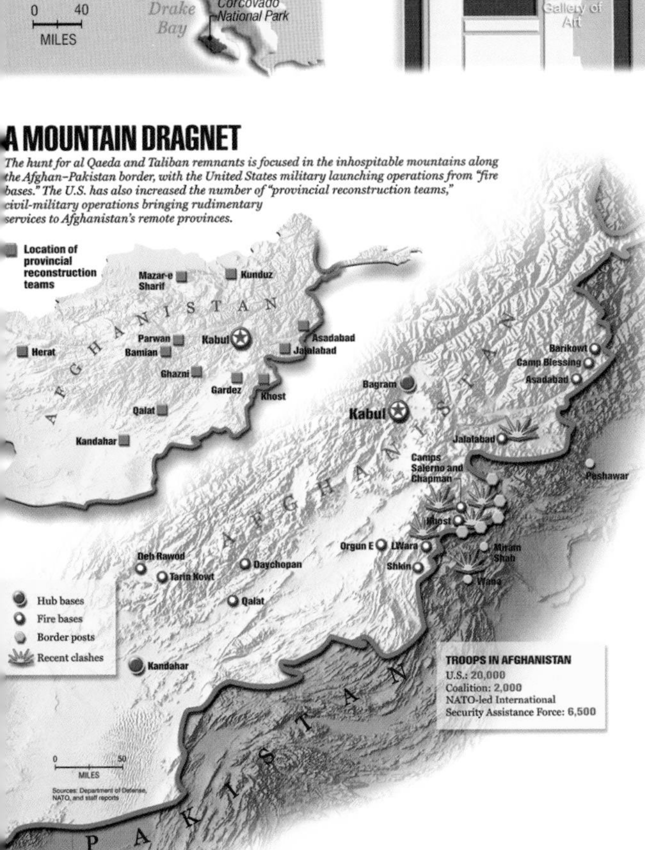

A MOUNTAIN DRAGNET
The hunt for al Qaeda and Taliban remnants is focused in the inhospitable mountains along the Afghan-Pakistan border, with the United States military launching operations from "fire bases." The U.S. has also increased the number of "provincial reconstruction teams," civil-military operations bringing rudimentary services to Afghanistan's remote provinces.
Location of provincial reconstruction teams
AFGHANISTAN
Mazar-e Sharif
Kunduz
Herat
Parwan
Bamian
Kabul
Asadabad
Jalalabad
Ghazni
Gardez
Khost
Qalat
Kandahar
Barikowt
Camp Blessing
Asadabad
Bagram
Kabul
Jalalabad
Camps Salerno and Chapman
Peshawar
Khost
Orgun E
Wara
Shkin
Miram Shah
Wana
Deh Rawod
Tarin Kowt
Daychopan
Qalat
Kandahar
Hub bases
Fire bases
Border posts
Recent clashes
TROOPS IN AFGHANISTAN
U.S.: 20,000
Coalition: 2,000
NATO-led International Security Assistance Force: 6,500
0 50
MILES
PAKISTAN

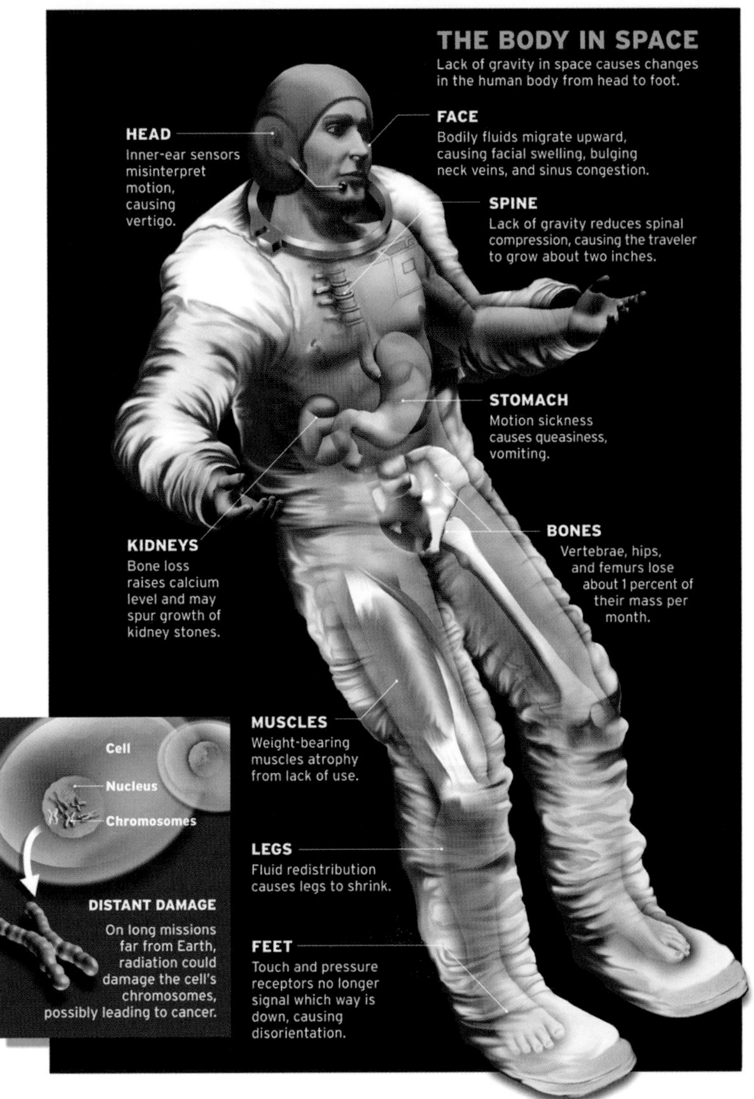

THE BODY IN SPACE
Lack of gravity in space causes changes in the human body from head to foot.
HEAD
Inner-ear sensors misinterpret motion, causing vertigo.
FACE
Bodily fluids migrate upward, causing facial swelling, bulging neck veins, and sinus congestion.
SPINE
Lack of gravity reduces spinal compression, causing the traveler to grow about two inches.
STOMACH
Motion sickness causes queasiness, vomiting.
KIDNEYS
Bone loss raises calcium level and may spur growth of kidney stones.
BONES
Vertebrae, hips, and femurs lose about 1 percent of their mass per month.
MUSCLES
Weight-bearing muscles atrophy from lack of use.
Cell
Nucleus
Chromosomes
DISTANT DAMAGE
On long missions far from Earth, radiation could damage the cell's chromosomes, possibly leading to cancer.
LEGS
Fluid redistribution causes legs to shrink.
FEET
Touch and pressure receptors no longer signal which way is down, causing disorientation.

E-MAIL: rod@informationillustration.com • COMPLETE PORTFOLIO AVAILABLE@WEBSITE: www.informationillustration.com

戴茜

marty braun 207-766-9726 hoganbraun.com

DGRANT

D. GRANT

www.dangrant.com
dgrant@dangrant.com
805·705·0544

Pete Paspalovski

www.prespastudios.com

Prespa Studios, Inc ppaspal@prespastudios.com 330-342-1611

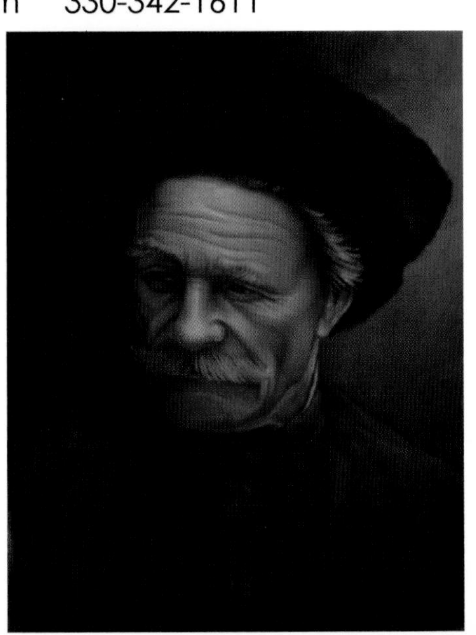

sheila golden

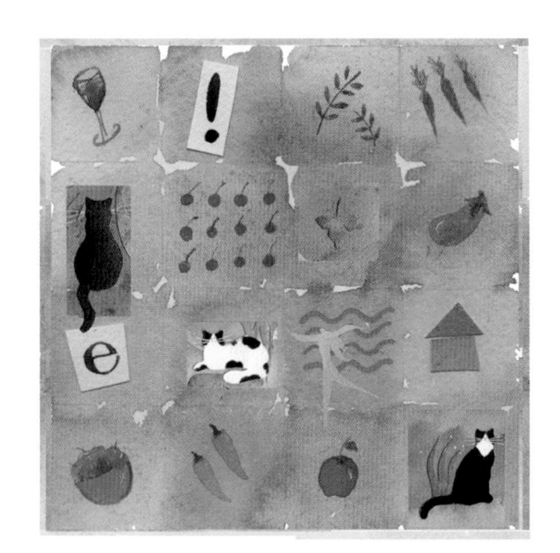

balancing the books

fashion

www.sheilagolden.com
866. 261. 4877

JODY WHEELER
375 South End Ave., Suite 12T
New York, NY 10280
TEL/FAX: (212) 775-1484
e-mail: wheelart50@aol.com

Online portfolios:
www.directoryofillustration.com
www.theispot.com
www.lebook.com
www.childrensillustrators.com
See also *Directory of Illustration* #9, 11, 12, and 14-17

Clients include:
Penguin USA
Random House Inc.
The Paper Magic Group
Kimberly Clark
UNICEF
Scholastic, Inc.
Marian Heath Greeting Cards

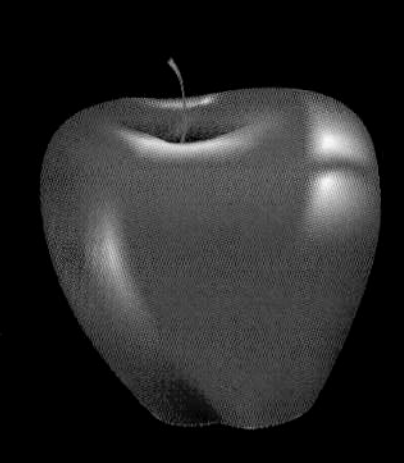

Brian Jensen

brianjensen.com

phone 952-442-7511

email brian@studio-arts.com

LORRAINE DAUPHIN
Potter•Dauphin Studios
3017 Corn Pickers Lane
Myrtle Beach, SC 29579
TEL: (843) 236-0407
www.potterdauphin.com

Client list includes:
Brooks Pharmacy, Special Olympics CT, McQuade Children's Services, High-Lites, Trans-Lux Corporation

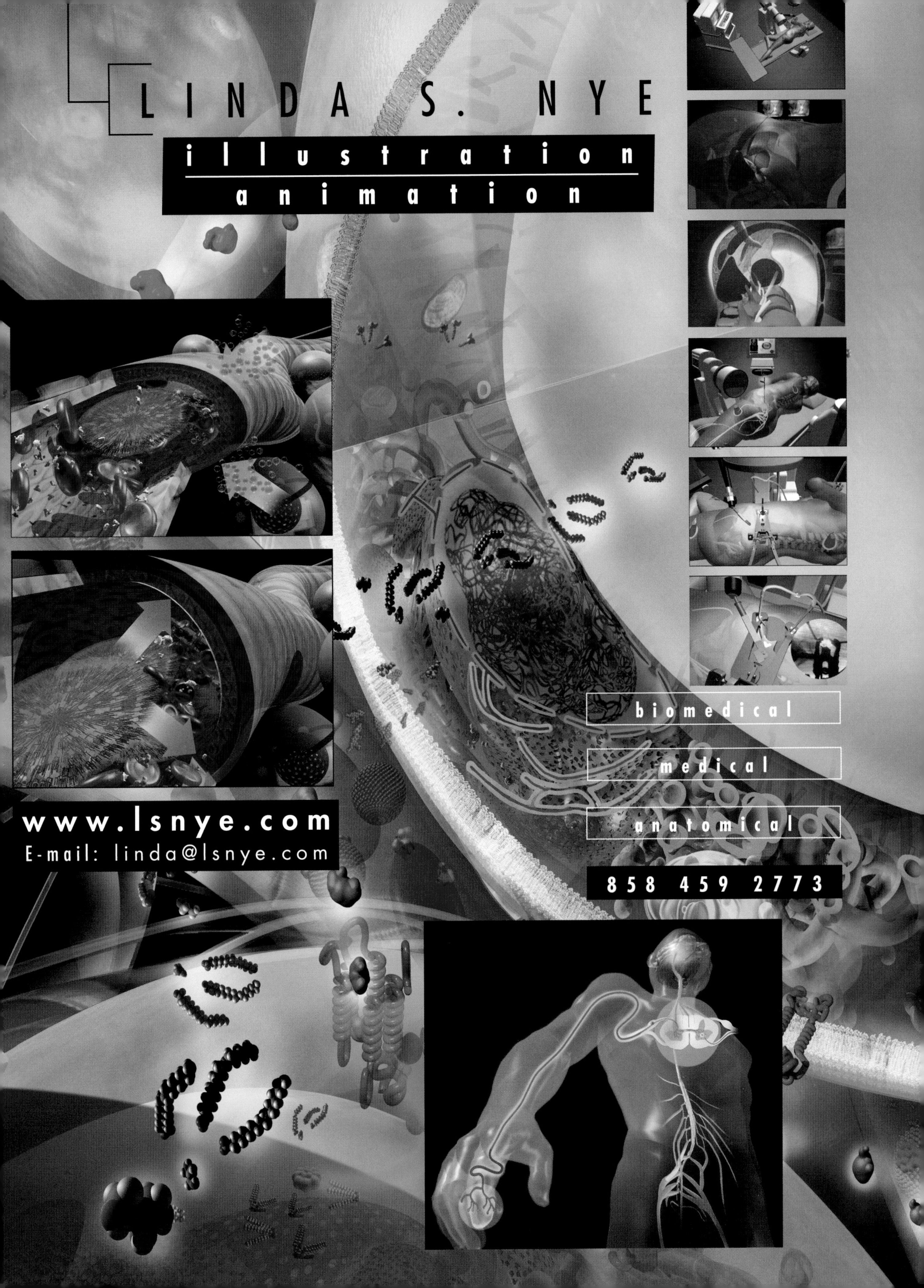

LINDA S. NYE
illustration
animation
www.lsnye.com
E-mail: linda@lsnye.com
biomedical
medical
anatomical
858 459 2773

Kathy
Rusynyk
NATURE ILLUSTRATOR

2309 Twp Rd 257 ~ Jeromesville, Ohio 4484
419.368.3664 ~ cell 419.606.118
www.kathyrusynyk.con

Preslicka Studio
Illustration
and
Type
DESIGN
PH
952-447-8433
fax
952-447-8436
greg@preslickastudio.com
www.preslickastudio.com
MooLatté
FROZEN BLENDED COFFE

BANNER ILLUSTRATION
518.583.7982
banner@capital.net
www.shawnbanner.com

MARK STUTZMAN

Eloqui
com
Inc.
®

a studio devoted exclusively to illustration

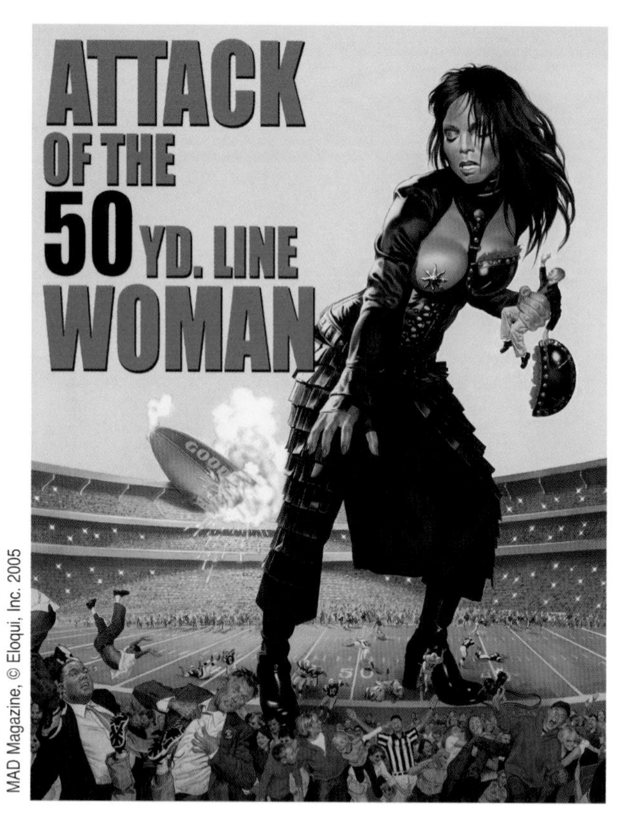
ATTACK
OF THE
50 YD. LINE
WOMAN

MAD Magazine, © Eloqui, Inc. 2005

NWA

NWA For Rolling Stone, © Eloqui, Inc. 2005

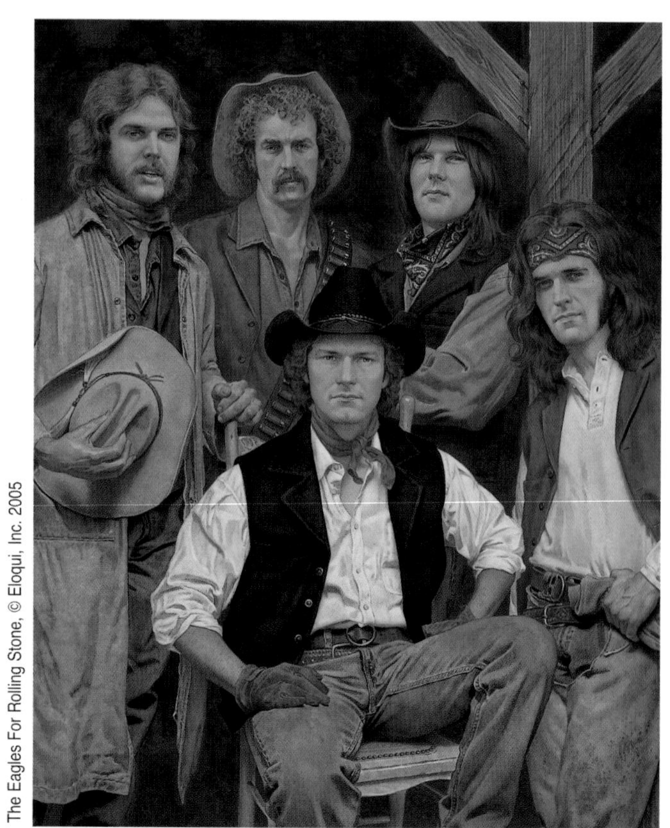

The Eagles For Rolling Stone, © Eloqui, Inc. 2005

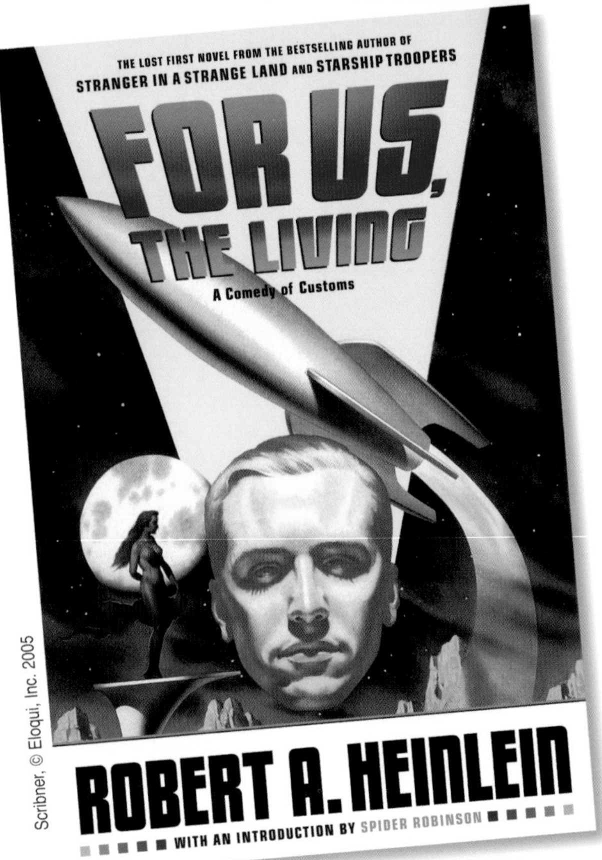
THE LOST FIRST NOVEL FROM THE BESTSELLING AUTHOR OF
STRANGER IN A STRANGE LAND AND STARSHIP TROOPERS
FOR US, THE LIVING
A Comedy of Customs
ROBERT A. HEINLEIN
WITH AN INTRODUCTION BY SPIDER ROBINSON

Scribner, © Eloqui, Inc. 2005

ELOQUI • 100 G STREET • MTN. LAKE PARK • MD 21550 • 301 334 4086 • WWW.ELOQUI.COM

LAURA STUTZMAN

Eloqui.com
Inc.

a studio devoted exclusively to illustration

AMY LYNN

ELOQUI • 100 G STREET • MTN. LAKE PARK • MD 21550 • 301 334 4086 • WWW.ELOQUI.COM

Increase your growth potential
High
Fiber
Diet
Fat on Bandwidth
ENRICHED SPEEDS
Up to 100 Mbps

Richmond Homes

Interlock Construction

Hanley Wood Magazine

CRN

Tuff Shed

RICHMOND
auto mall

Richmond Auto Mall

JAMES YAMASAKI
2698 Emerson Street
Palo Alto, CA 94306
TEL/FAX: (650) 327-2377
e-mail: jimmyy@pacbell.net
www.scientificdog.com/yamasaki

Clients include: Nickelodeon Magazine, National Geographic for Kids, Entrepreneur Magazine, Holiday House

1+2=2

ASTRO DINER
100%
ENJOY!
TIMES
TIGER ESCAPES FROM ZOO

CHANA COTTER
Papercuts, Paintings and Prints by Chana
25 Sherwood Avenue
Rensselaer, NY 12144
TEL: (800) 480-3373
e-mail: info@papercutsbychana.com
www.papercutsbychana.com

ישיבה קרלין סטולין
1818

Chana 2004

Nothing on this page will make you hire me.

go to www.petervanryzin.com

STEVE ROSS

www.SteveRossIllustration.com
email: Steve@SteveRossIllustration.com
1-917-660-7881

Thou shalt not kill.
Thou shalt not steal.
thy neighbor.
Thou shalt not covet.
EXODUS 20:1-7

JANET PIETROBONO ILLUSTRATION
914-666-4730 • janet.pietrobono@verizon.net • www.janshomestudio.com

MELANIE MARDER PARKS
Broadview Lane
Red Hook, NY 12571
TEL/FAX: (845) 758-0656
email: melaniemarderparks@msn.com
www.melaniemarderparks.com

First Place: The New York Book Show 2005 - Cover/Jacket series - Children's Trade Paperback for Padraic Colum's mythology books. 2005 Communication Arts Illustration Annual (Padraic Colum series).

Clients include: Simon and Schuster, Random House, Time Warner Book Group, Time Custom Publishing, Hyperion, HarperCollins, Louise Fili, Ltd., Martha Stewart, Farrar Straus Giroux, McGraw-Hill/Contemporary, Meredith Corporation, Penguin USA, Klutz, Steerforth Press, El Paso Chile Company, Dufour Pastry Kitchens.

ELM CREEK
ALBUM

SLEEP
ON
IT
Prepare Delicious Meals
the Night Before
That You Can Pop in the Oven
the Next Day!
CAROL GORDON
Innkeeper of Nantucket House

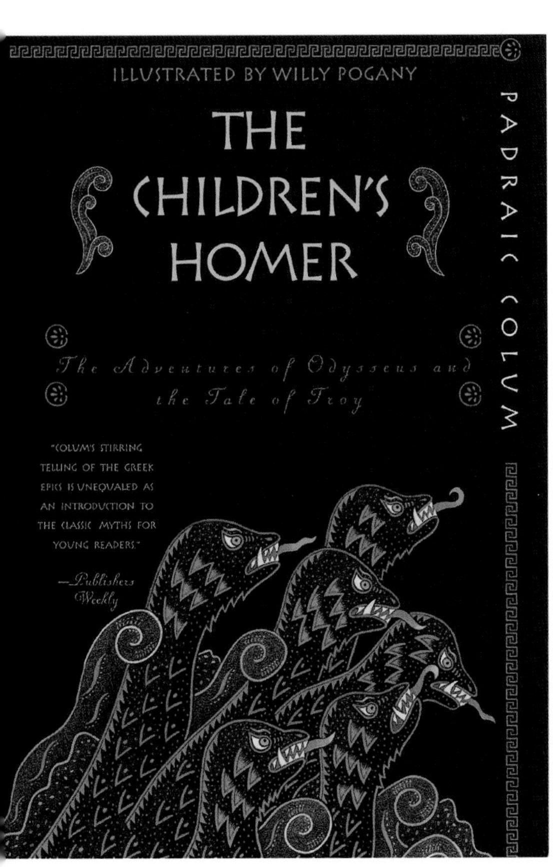
ILLUSTRATED BY WILLY POGANY
THE
CHILDREN'S
HOMER
PADRAIC COLUM
The Adventures of Odysseus and
the Tale of Troy
"COLUM'S STIRRING
TELLING OF THE GREEK
EPICS IS UNEQUALED AS
AN INTRODUCTION TO
THE CLASSIC MYTHS FOR
YOUNG READERS."
—Publishers
Weekly

DAVID MURPHY
David Murphy Illustration
105 South Vega Street
Alhambra, CA 91801
TEL: (626) 282-1749
e-mail: happyjam@mac.com
www.happyjam.biz

Clients include: Turtle Books, The Brown Publishing Network, Houghton Mifflin, The McGraw-Hill Book Company, and Scholastic.

APPY
JAm
APPY
JAm
APPY
JAm

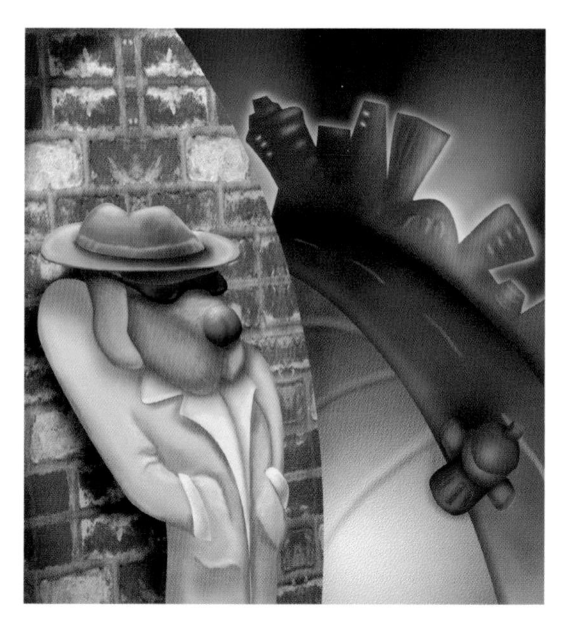

You Are Invited...

Jigsaw

QUACK
KONG

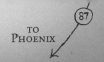

Patty Briles

Phone: 310.823.5594 Fax: 310.827.5501
patty@storymasterpictures.com
http://www.pattybriles.com

#1

BENJAMIN JACOBS
24939 Sunset Vista Avenue
Menifee, CA 92584
TEL: (951) 679-8210
e-mail: benjamin@jollylamas.com
www.jollylamas.com/portfolio.html

Cover Design
Digital Illustration
Icon Design
Web Design
Interface Design
Book Illustration

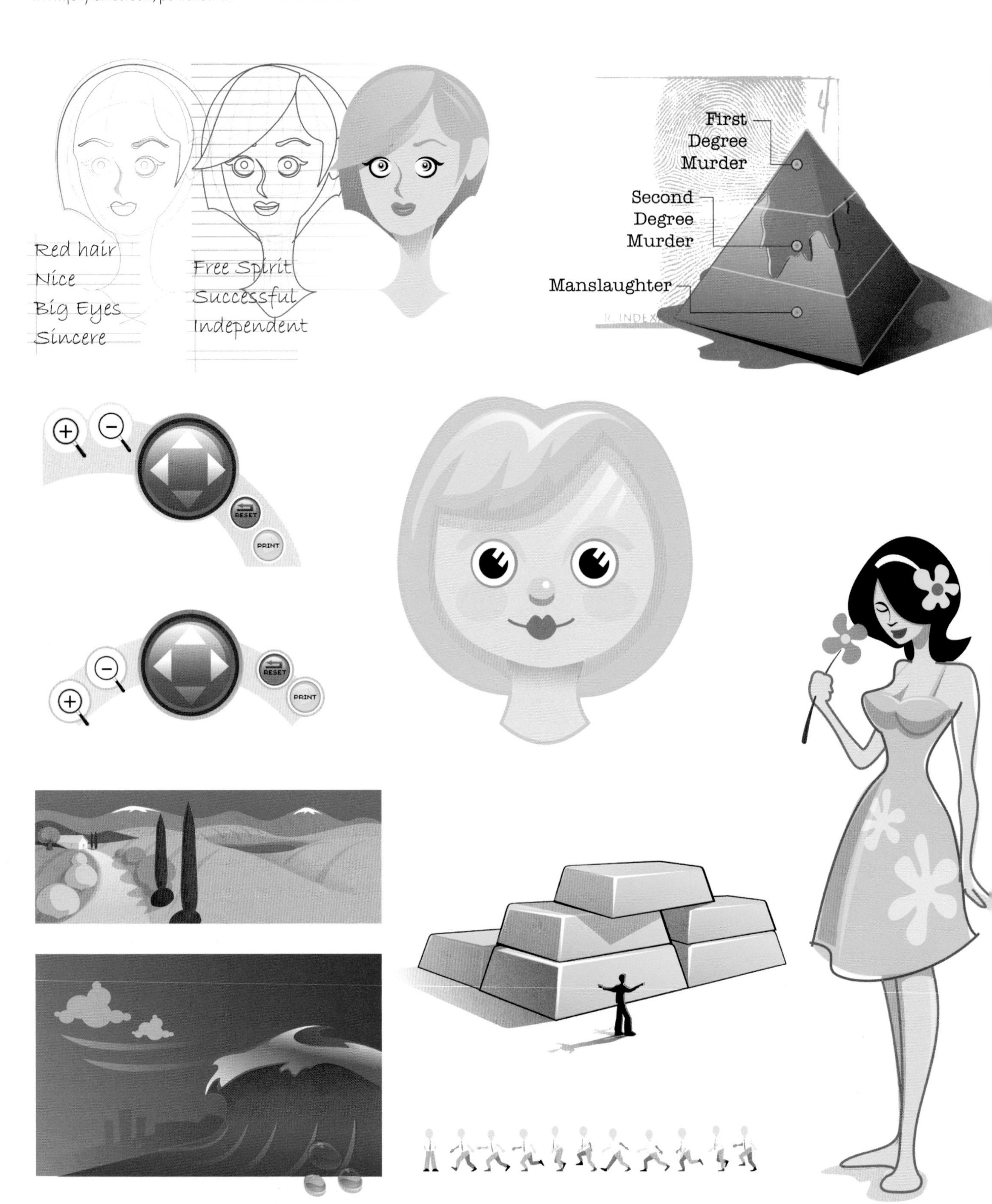
Red hair
Nice
Big Eyes
Sincere
Free Spirit
Successful
Independent
First Degree Murder
Second Degree Murder
Manslaughter
RESET
PRINT
RESET
PRINT

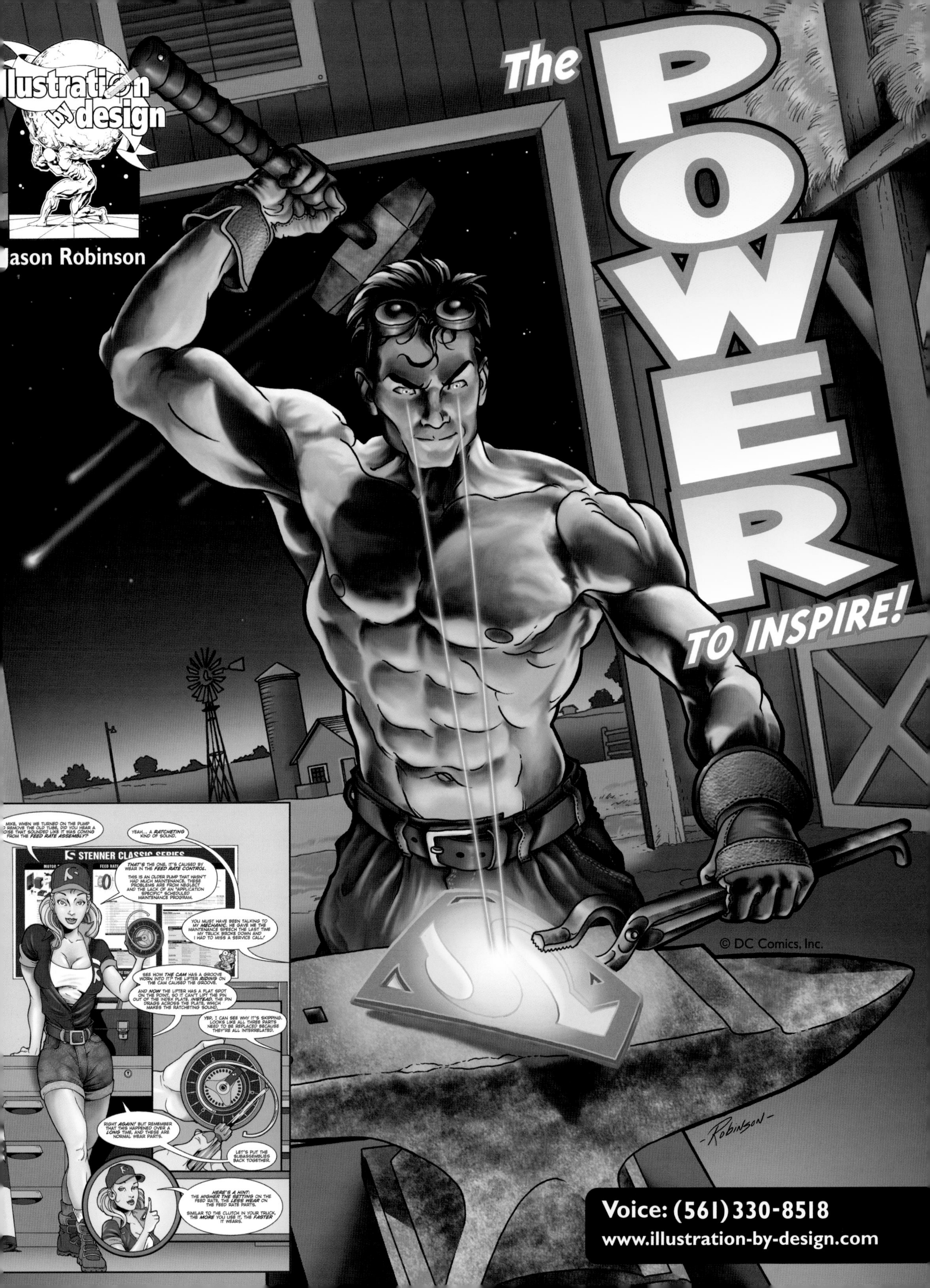
Illustration by design
Jason Robinson
The POWER TO INSPIRE!
MIKE, WHEN WE TURNED ON THE PUMP
REMOVE THE OLD TUBE, DID YOU HEAR A
THAT SOUNDED LIKE IT WAS COMING
FROM THE FEED RATE ASSEMBLY?
YEAH... A RATCHETING KIND OF SOUND.
STENNER CLASSIC SERIES
THAT'S THE ONE. IT'S CAUSED BY WEAR IN THE FEED RATE CONTROL.
THIS IS AN OLDER PUMP THAT HASN'T HAD MUCH MAINTENANCE. THESE PROBLEMS ARE FROM NEGLECT AND THE LACK OF AN "APPLICATION SPECIFIC" SCHEDULED MAINTENANCE PROGRAM.
YOU MUST HAVE BEEN TALKING TO MY MECHANIC. HE GAVE ME THE MAINTENANCE SPEECH THE LAST TIME MY TRUCK BROKE DOWN AND I HAD TO MISS A SERVICE CALL!
SEE HOW THE CAM HAS A GROOVE WORN INTO IT? THE LIFTER RIDING ON THE CAM CAUSED THE GROOVE.
AND NOW THE LIFTER HAS A FLAT SPOT ON THE POINT, SO IT CAN'T LIFT THE PIN OUT OF THE INDEX PLATE. INSTEAD, THE PIN DRAGS ACROSS THE PLATE, WHICH MAKES THE RATCHETING SOUND.
YEP, I CAN SEE WHY IT'S SKIPPING. LOOKS LIKE ALL THREE PARTS NEED TO BE REPLACED BECAUSE THEY'RE ALL INTERRELATED.
RIGHT AGAIN! BUT REMEMBER THAT THIS HAPPENED OVER A LONG TIME, AND THESE ARE NORMAL WEAR PARTS.
LET'S PUT THE SUBASSEMBLIES BACK TOGETHER.
HERE'S A HINT: THE HIGHER THE SETTING ON THE FEED RATE, THE LESS WEAR ON THE FEED RATE PARTS.
SIMILAR TO THE CLUTCH IN YOUR TRUCK, THE MORE YOU USE IT, THE FASTER IT WEARS.
-ROBINSON-
© DC Comics, Inc.
Voice: (561) 330-8518
www.illustration-by-design.com

Lori Klopp Design & Illustration

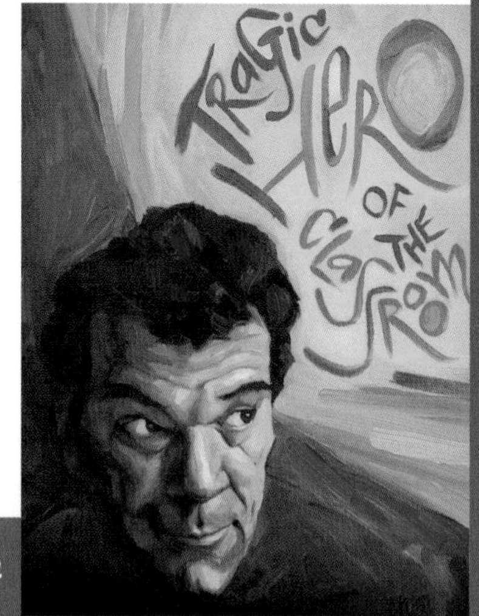
Tragic HERO OF THE Classroom

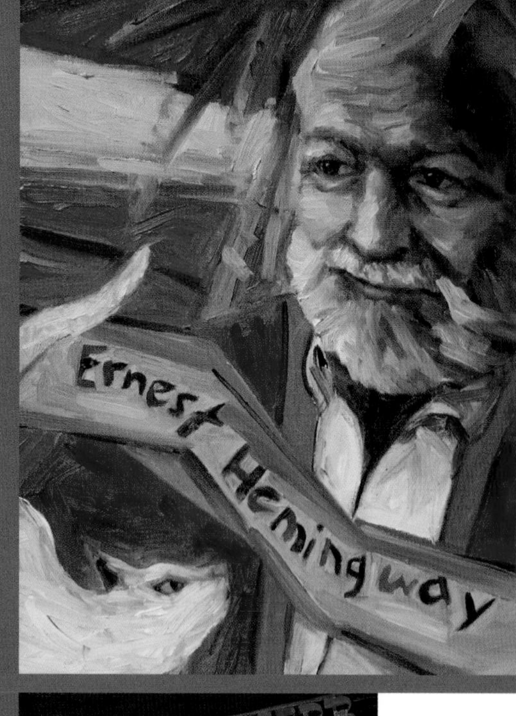
Ernest Hemingway

Branford Marsalis

A TASTE OF HERB
& OTHER DELIGHTS

www.loriklopp.com • lori@loriklopp.com • 404-378-2585

cafe

erin englund
801 557 5193
erin.englund@gmail.com

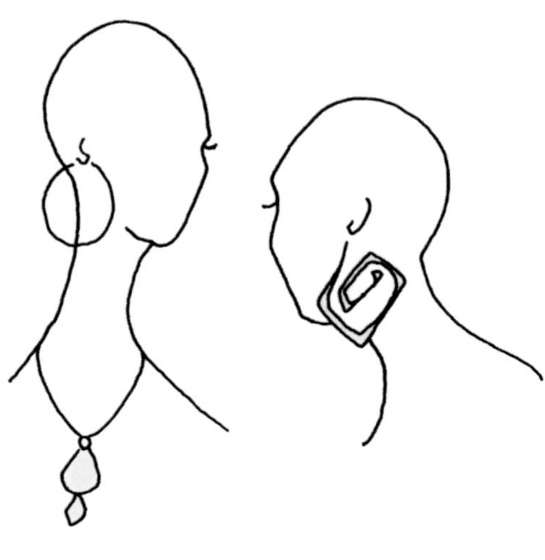

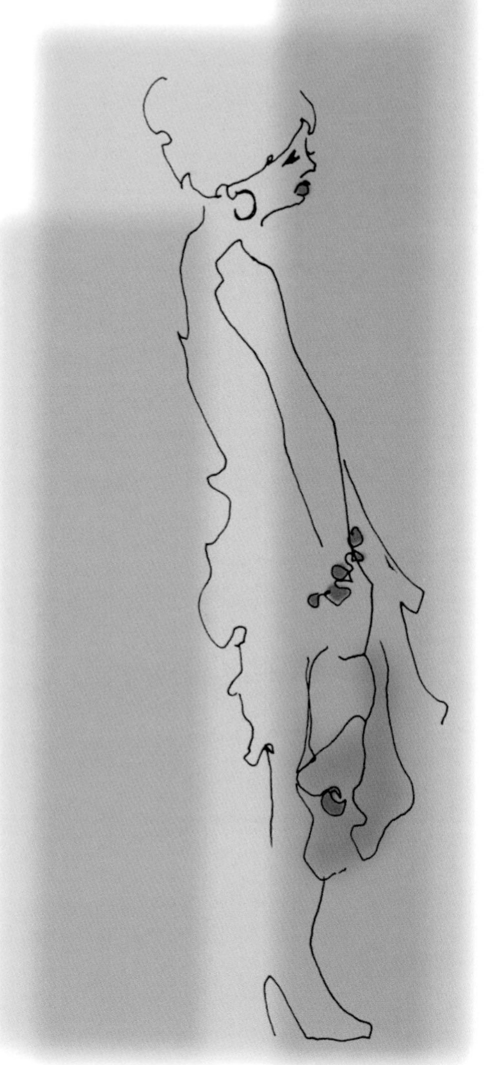

www.erinenglund.com

5275 Westminster
St. Louis MO
6 3 1 0 8

DEANN RUBIN

deannrubin@yahoo.com

314-454-6976

www.djrstudio.com

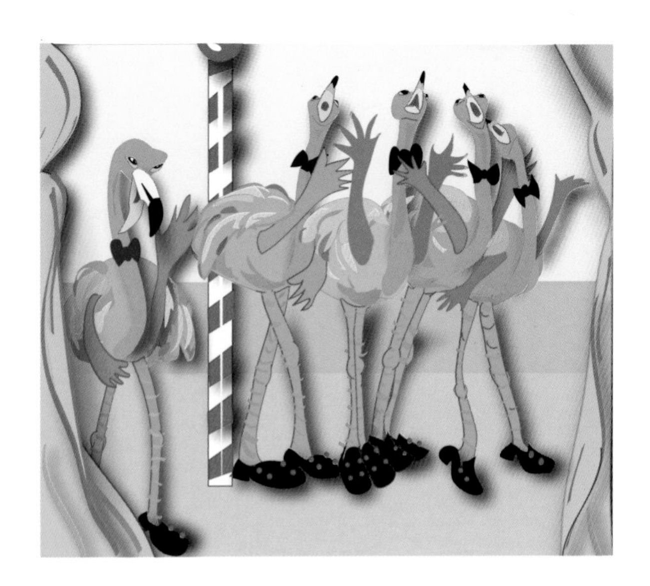

DINO CASTERLINE

DINOCASTERLINE.COM 321-662-8947

"Hey, Chip, how duz this net work?"
HICKVILLE
HUBSTATN
NATE'S
CATTLE CORN
Eat at Jed
Mac Plus
FORD
LOW LIFE

PIZZA on a STIK
TRACT

JAMES
HUNGASKI
illustration

www.hungaskiillustration.com
651-271-1110

Dang! How do I cut this to git half a grain?!
GUN POWDER

VOTE 4 ME
(Por favor...)

SCOTT ALLRED

ARCHITECTURAL ILLUSTRATION

39 MIDDLE GRASSY BRANCH
ASHEVILLE, NC 28805
828-337-0477
WWW.SCOTTALLRED.COM
SCOTT @ SCOTTALLRED.COM

Find what de-stresses you!
Get moving!
Take a walk!
4:34
STAY
Calm!
Keep problems From super-sizing!
I want it now!
no
you are...

isaBelle Dervaux illustration (415) 668-8880 isaBelleDervaux.com

US HEALTHCARE
INSURANCE:
NONE
PROGNOSIS:
DIRE
IAN JONES
7207 park drive parkville maryland 21234
ianx@bizzards.com * www.bizzards.com
Winner of the Graphic Design USA Award
for Excellence in Communication & Design

David Lindroth Inc. *custom cartography*

85 Broadway, West Milford, NJ 07480
973-697-1965 (voice) 973-697-1967 (fax)

Clients include: Fodors, Knopf, Random House, Pentagram, Harper-Collins, Newsweek, NYCVB, Holt-Rinehart, Washingtonian Magazine, and St. Martin's Press

North Sea
Netherlands
Germany
Ostend
Antwerp
Calais
Ghent
Cologne
Ypres
Brussels
Aix-la-Chapelle
Lille
Liège
Belgium
Arras
Cambrai
Amiens
Ardennes
St. Quentin
Sedan
Luxemburg
Argonne
Compiègne
Soissons
Château-Thierry
Reims
Verdun
Lorraine
Paris
Champagne
Châlons sur-Marne
Nancy
France
Alsace
Epinal
Mulhouse
Besançon
Germany 1914
German offensive, 1914
Deepest German penetration, Sept. 1914
Front at beginning of 1915
German offensive, Summer 1918
Allied offensive, Fall 1918
Armistice line, November 1918
Hindenburg line
The Morgue Bar
Sewermen's bath hall
Old Bowery Theater
Maria's Rooming House
The Tombs
Wah Kee's
Five Points
The O'Gamhnas
The Dolans
Billy's Bar
Chambers St.
Cherry St.
the new Noe Brush factory
City Hall
Catharine St.
Brooklyn Bridge
Fulton St.
The Grotto (underground)
Smith-Blacksall Clinic
Old Post Office
Fulton Ferry
Trinity Church
Wall St.
Henley House
Coffee House Slip
Wall St. Ferry
Castle Garden
The Battery
South Ferry
Staten Island Ferry
Atlantic Ave. Ferry
PHILIPPINE ISLANDS
SULU SEA
Mindanao
Union Street
Walnut Street
Eighth Street
Cubine and Brown
Knoxville
Tennessee & Georgia
Chattanooga
Western & Atlantic RR
Resaca
Rome
Kennesaw Mountain
Dallas
July 22, 1864
Atlanta
Georgia RR
Jonesborough
GEORGIA
Kokoretsa River
North Sally Port
Underground Cistern
ACROPOLIS
LOWER TOWN
Hellenistic town wall
Charos River
Chambers St.
Warren St.
Murray St.
Church St.
West Broadway
Civic Center
City Hall Park
Brooklyn Bridge
Spruce St.
Beekman St.
Vesey St.
Barclay St.
Fulton St.
Ann St.
World Financial Center
Dey St.
Cortlandt St.
John St.
Liberty St.
Cedar St.
Pine St.
Wall St.
Exchange Pl.
Nassau St.
William St.
Pearl St.
Water St.
Front St.
Albany St.
Carlisle St.
Rector St.
Rector Park
West Thames St.
3rd Pl.
2nd Pl.
1st Pl.
Battery Pl.
Bowling Green
South Cove
State St.
Battery Park
Downtown Heliport
Brooklyn-Battery
San Isabel National Forest
Mt. Yale
Sawatch Range
Brown's Cabin
Magdalene Gulch
North Texas Creek
South Texas Creek
Continental Divide
Chaffee County
Gunnison County
The Three Apostles
Texas Creek
Gunnison National Forest

avril
Lynne Avril Cravath
www.lynneavril.com
480.893.1482

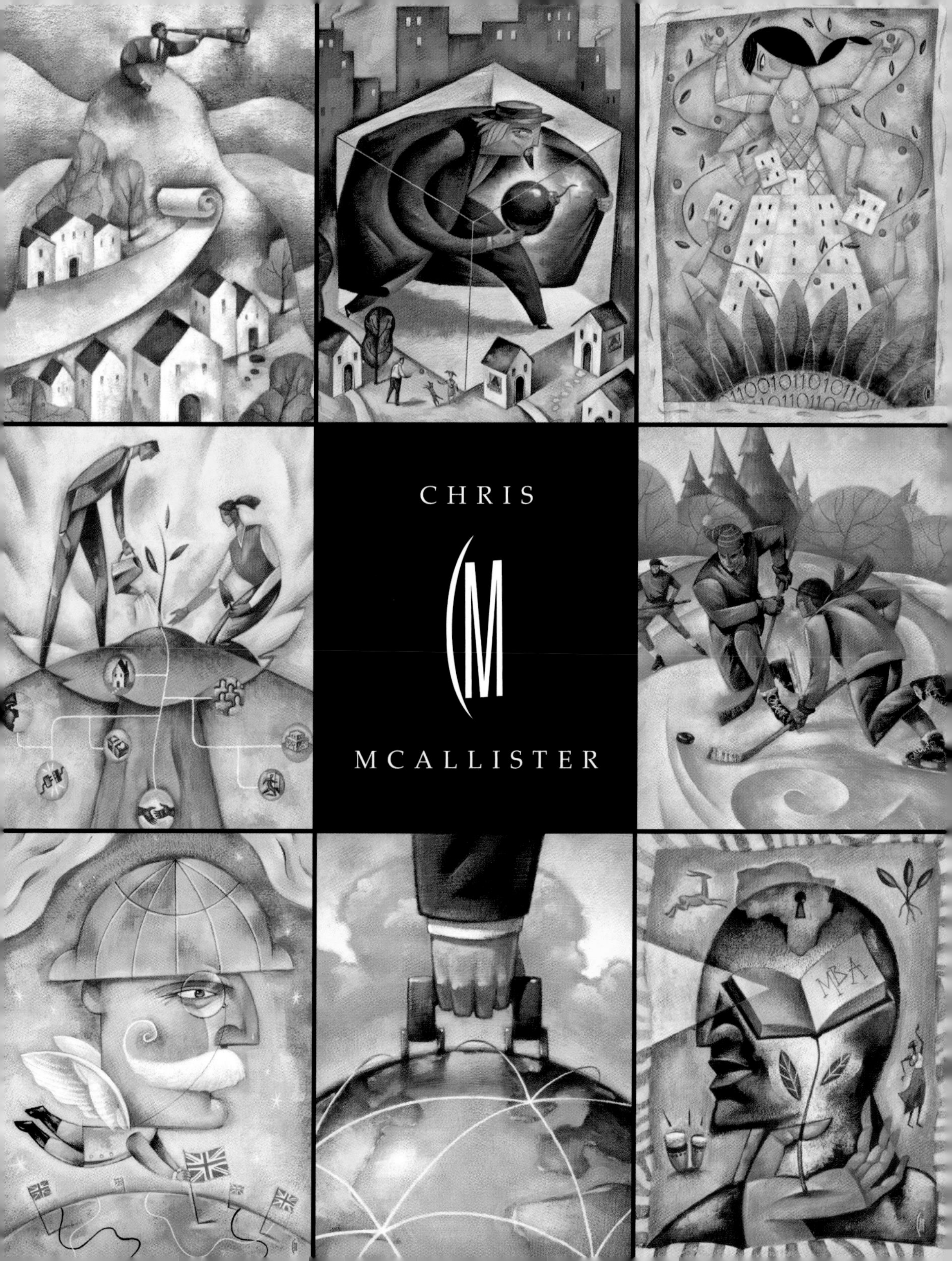

CHRIS
CM
MCALLISTER
MBA

Faster than a spitting toddler,
more powerful than a local bully,
able to leap tall piles of clothes in a single bound, its...

SuperMom
TUES
WED
M
24

michael sprong
www.sprongdesign.com

John Berg

JOHN BERG ILLUSTRATION 110 Cottage St. Buffalo NY 14201 716.884.8003 www.johnbergstudio.com

HOWDY!

Orlandos
SPACE
SALVAGE
"THIS IS ROCKET SCIENCE"

GET
AHEAD

Girly Talk/Gouache

Ice Cream Dream/Gouache

Patti Jennings

508 385 3243
917 593 3973
pattijennings@mac.com
www.pattijennings.com

EDITORIAL

PACKAGING

PUBLISHING

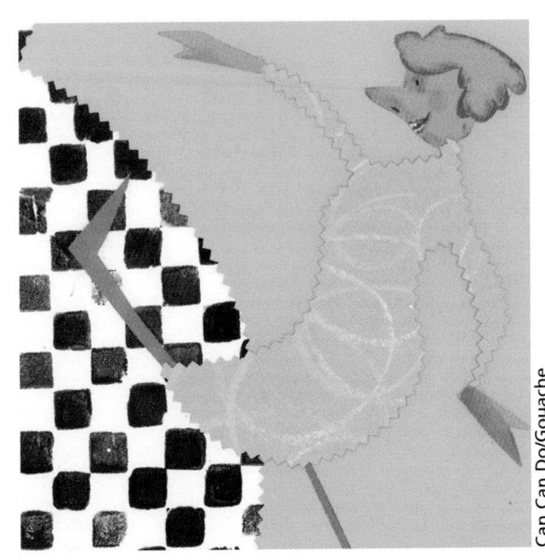

Can Can Do/Gouache

Western Whimsy/Gouache

JEFF HAM
209 California Avenue
Michigan City, IN 46303
TEL/FAX: (219) 873-9459
e-mail: g.hurd@comcast.net
www.jeff-ham.com

Carl's®
"ALWAYS FRESH"

carl mazer 415·552·2188 / fax 2189 create@carlmazer.com www.carlmazer.com

CHARLIE POWELL
1228 Martin Road
Santa Cruz, CA 95060
TEL: (831) 457-9470
FAX: (831) 457-0226
e-mail: cpowell@cruzio.com
www.charliepowell.net

POWELL

CHARLIE POWELL
1228 Martin Road
Santa Cruz, CA 95060
TEL: (831) 457-9470
FAX: (831) 457-0226
e-mail: cpowell@cruzio.com
www.charliepowell.net

POWELL

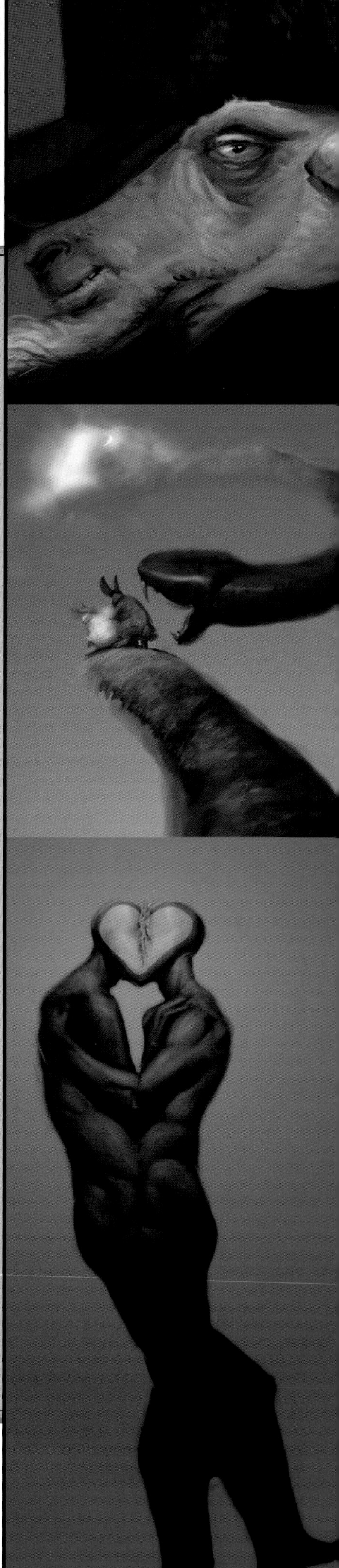

Björkman

Steve Björkman
949-349-0109 FAX 949-349-0124
stevebjorkman.com

MAURA CONDRICK ILLUSTRATION

BBRRRINNNNG!!

maura@condrick.com (212) 966-5595 www.condrick.com

DAN PIEPER
realizing imagination

1803 Judah St. No. 1
San Francisco, CA 94122

tel: 415.517.7489

web: www.pieperillustration.com
mail: dan@pieperillustration.com

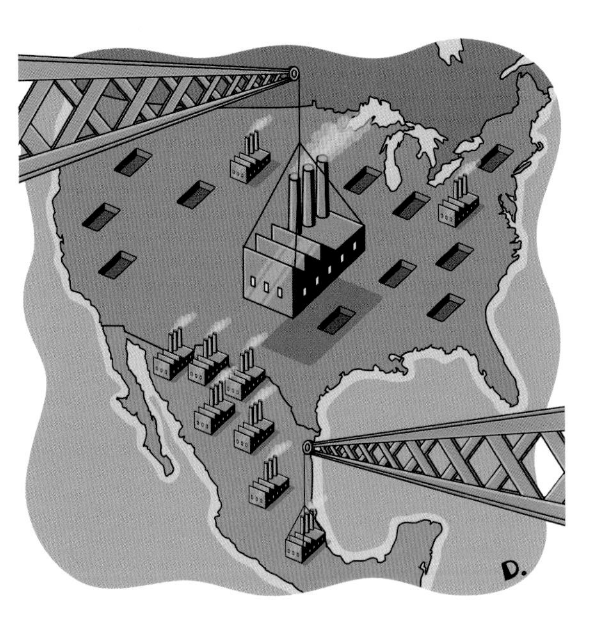

Daryl & Keri **Stevens**

212.741.1610 ■ **www.studio202.com**

illustration ■ animation ■ web design

Brian T. Jones **Illustration and Design**

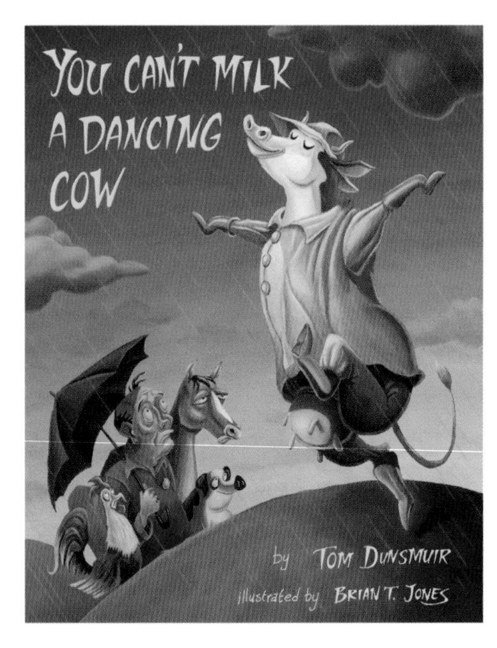
YOU CAN'T MILK
A DANCING
COW
by TOM DUNSMUIR
Illustrated by BRIAN T. JONES

B.B.C.

626 356 0061 h
831 566 3642 c
email: briantjones@sbcglobal.net
briantjones.com

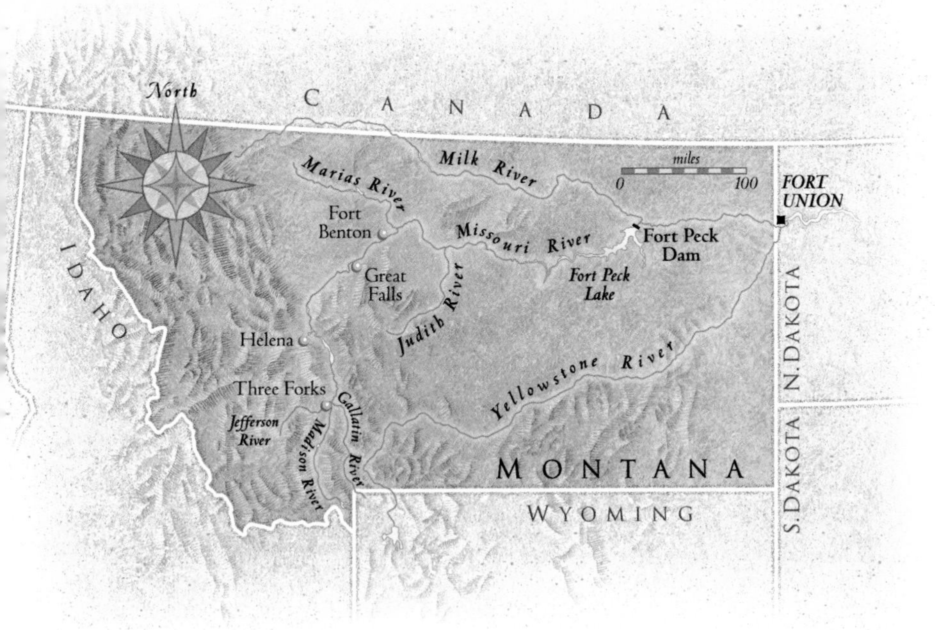
North
CANADA
Milk River
Marias River
miles
0
100
FORT UNION
Fort Benton
Missouri River
Fort Peck Dam
Great Falls
Judith River
Fort Peck Lake
IDAHO
N. DAKOTA
Helena
Yellowstone River
Three Forks
Gallatin River
Jefferson River
Madison River
MONTANA
WYOMING
S. DAKOTA

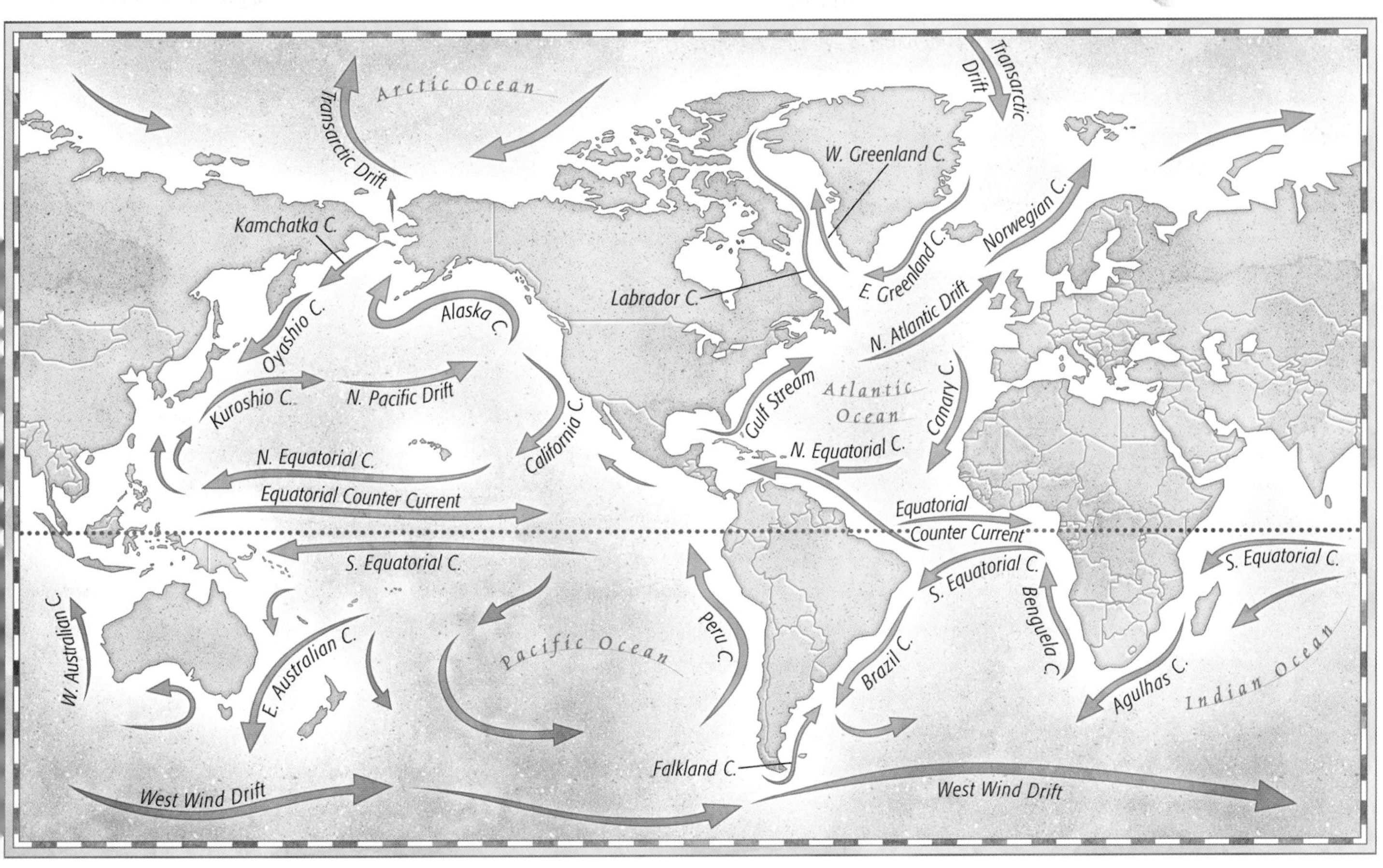
Arctic Ocean
Transarctic Drift
Transarctic Drift
W. Greenland C.
Kamchatka C.
Norwegian C.
E. Greenland C.
Labrador C.
Alaska C.
Oyashio C.
N. Atlantic Drift
Kuroshio C.
N. Pacific Drift
Gulf Stream
Atlantic Ocean
Canary C.
California C.
N. Equatorial C.
N. Equatorial C.
Equatorial Counter Current
Equatorial Counter Current
S. Equatorial C.
S. Equatorial C.
S. Equatorial C.
W. Australian C.
E. Australian C.
Pacific Ocean
Peru C.
Brazil C.
Benguela C.
Agulhas C.
Indian Ocean
Falkland C.
West Wind Drift
West Wind Drift

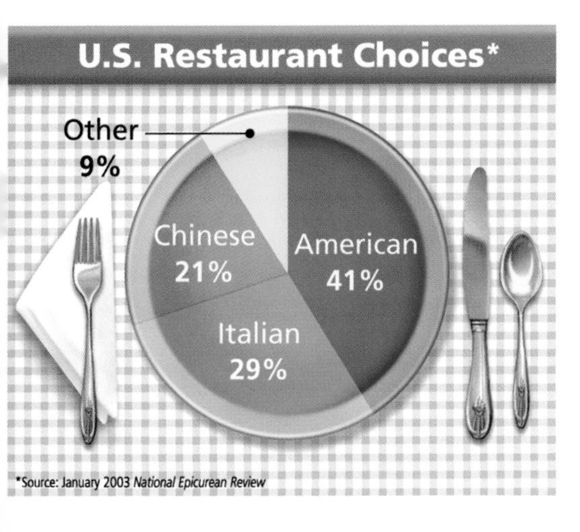
U.S. Restaurant Choices*
Other 9%
Chinese 21%
American 41%
Italian 29%
*Source: January 2003 National Epicurean Review

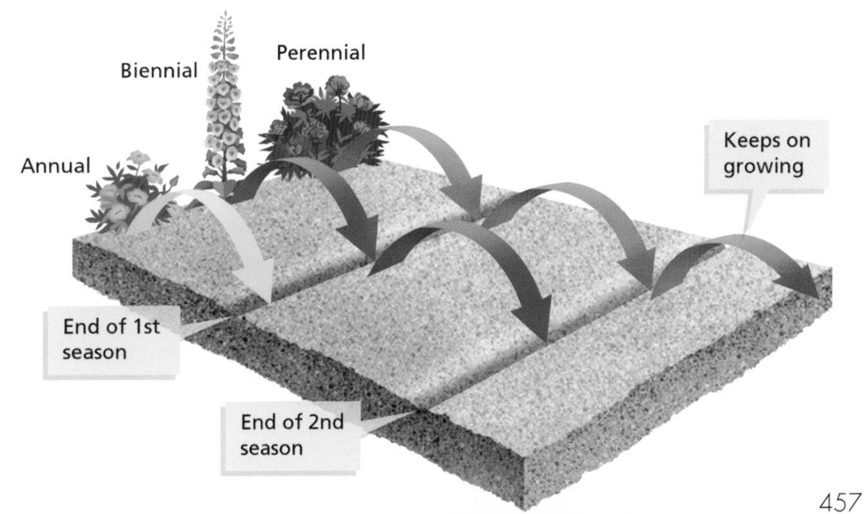
Biennial
Perennial
Annual
Keeps on growing
End of 1st season
End of 2nd season

ANNMARIE SICILIANO
5301 East Daggett Street
Long Beach, CA 90815
TEL: (562) 225-2978
FAX: (562) 986-5708
e-mail: amsiciliano@yahoo.com
www.amsiciliano.com

Over 10 years experience in illustration/design

Awards:
Art Directors Club of Houston 1994, Print 2001, Logo 2004, International Brand Packaging 2004

Frida
Ahlo

KYY
ODKA

Call me
520-8420

MAPS ▸ CHARTS ▸ INFORMATIONAL GRAPHICS

▼ 284 county and state maps for *Texas Almanac*

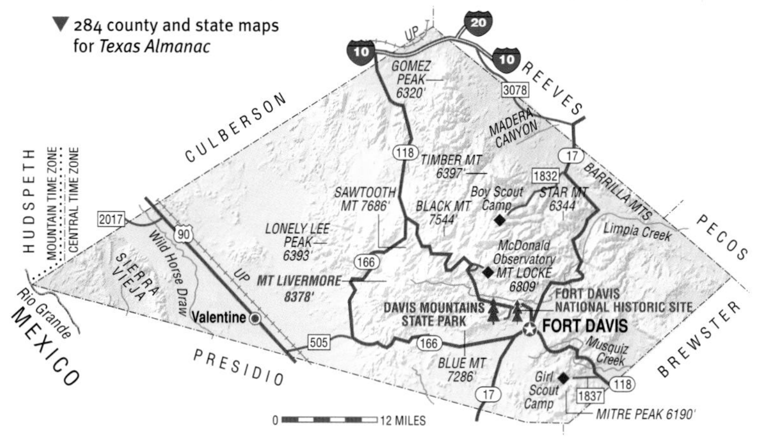

CULBERSON
REEVES
PECOS
BREWSTER
PRESIDIO
HUDSPETH
MOUNTAIN TIME ZONE
CENTRAL TIME ZONE
MEXICO
Rio Grande
GOMEZ PEAK 6320'
TIMBER MT 6397'
MADERA CANYON
SAWTOOTH MT 7686'
BLACK MT 7544'
Boy Scout Camp
STAR MT 6344'
BARRILLA MTS
Limpia Creek
LONELY LEE PEAK 6393'
SIERRA VIEJA
Wild Horse Draw
McDonald Observatory
MT LOCKE 6809'
MT LIVERMORE 8378'
DAVIS MOUNTAINS STATE PARK
FORT DAVIS NATIONAL HISTORIC SITE
FORT DAVIS
Valentine
BLUE MT 7286'
Musquiz Creek
Girl Scout Camp
MITRE PEAK 6190'
0 12 MILES

ZM
CHARTS
INFOGRAPHICS
& MAPS

CAROL ZUBER-MALLISON

214-906-4162
2340 Edwin St.
Fort Worth, Texas 76110-6634
carol@zmgraphics.com
fax: 817-924-7784

◀ Two-page spread for *Diversity Inc.* magazine

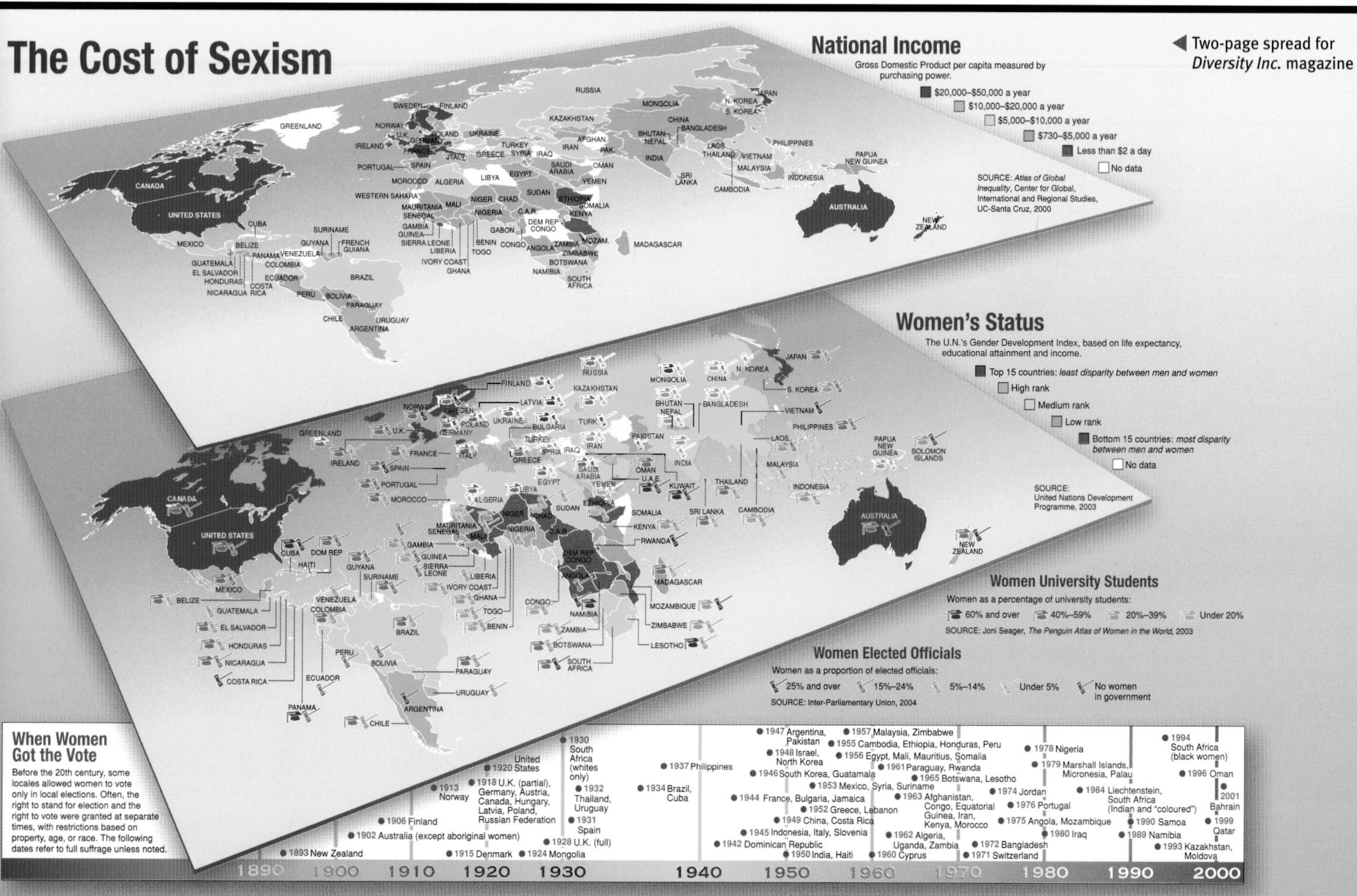

The Cost of Sexism
National Income
Gross Domestic Product per capita measured by purchasing power.
$20,000–$50,000 a year
$10,000–$20,000 a year
$5,000–$10,000 a year
$730–$5,000 a year
Less than $2 a day
No data
SOURCE: Atlas of Global Inequality, Center for Global, International and Regional Studies, UC-Santa Cruz, 2000
Women's Status
The U.N.'s Gender Development Index, based on life expectancy, educational attainment and income.
Top 15 countries: least disparity between men and women
High rank
Medium rank
Low rank
Bottom 15 countries: most disparity between men and women
No data
SOURCE: United Nations Development Programme, 2003
Women University Students
Women as a percentage of university students:
60% and over
40%–59%
20%–39%
Under 20%
SOURCE: Joni Seager, The Penguin Atlas of Women in the World, 2003
Women Elected Officials
Women as a proportion of elected officials:
25% and over
15%–24%
5%–14%
Under 5%
No women in government
SOURCE: Inter-Parliamentary Union, 2004
When Women Got the Vote
Before the 20th century, some locales allowed women to vote only in local elections. Often, the right to stand for election and the right to vote were granted at separate times, with restrictions based on property, age, or race. The following dates refer to full suffrage unless noted.
1893 New Zealand
1902 Australia (except aboriginal women)
1906 Finland
1913 Norway
1915 Denmark
1918 U.K. (partial), Germany, Austria, Canada, Hungary, Latvia, Poland, Russian Federation
1920 United States
1924 Mongolia
1928 U.K. (full)
1930 South Africa (whites only)
1931 Spain
1932 Thailand, Uruguay
1934 Brazil, Cuba
1937 Philippines
1942 Dominican Republic
1944 France, Bulgaria, Jamaica
1945 Indonesia, Italy, Slovenia
1946 South Korea, Guatemala
1947 Argentina, Pakistan
1948 Israel, North Korea
1949 China, Costa Rica
1950 India, Haiti
1952 Greece, Lebanon
1953 Mexico, Syria, Suriname
1955 Cambodia, Ethiopia, Honduras, Peru
1956 Egypt, Mali, Mauritius, Somalia
1957 Malaysia, Zimbabwe
1960 Cyprus
1961 Paraguay, Rwanda
1962 Algeria, Uganda, Zambia
1963 Afghanistan, Congo, Equatorial Guinea, Iran, Kenya, Morocco
1965 Botswana, Lesotho
1971 Switzerland
1972 Bangladesh
1974 Jordan
1975 Angola, Mozambique
1976 Portugal
1978 Nigeria
1979 Marshall Islands, Micronesia, Palau
1980 Iraq
1984 Liechtenstein, South Africa (Indian and "coloured")
1989 Namibia
1990 Samoa
1993 Kazakhstan, Moldova
1994 South Africa (black women)
1996 Oman
1999 Qatar
2001 Bahrain
1890 1900 1910 1920 1930 1940 1950 1960 1970 1980 1990 2000

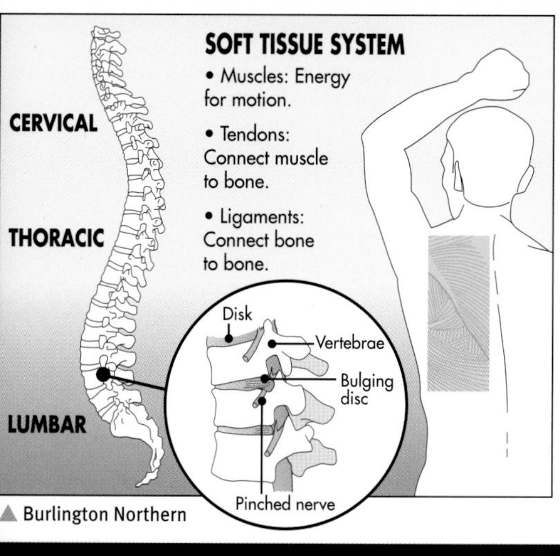

SOFT TISSUE SYSTEM
• Muscles: Energy for motion.
• Tendons: Connect muscle to bone.
• Ligaments: Connect bone to bone.
CERVICAL
THORACIC
LUMBAR
Disk
Vertebrae
Bulging disc
Pinched nerve

▲ Burlington Northern

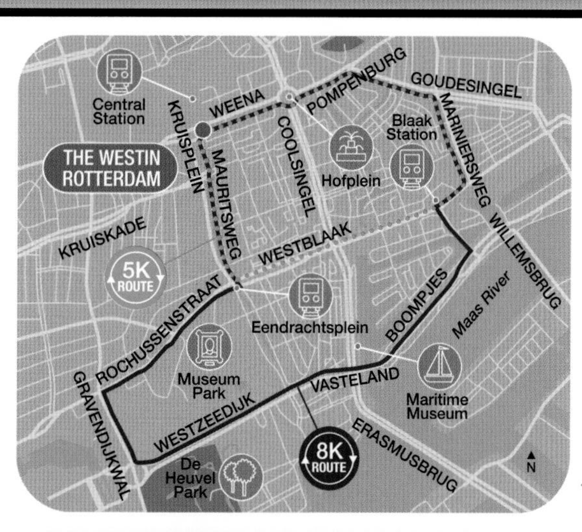

Central Station
WEENA
POMPENBURG
GOUDESINGEL
KRUISPLEIN
MAURITSWEG
COOLSINGEL
Blaak Station
MARINIERSWEG
THE WESTIN ROTTERDAM
Hofplein
KRUISKADE
WESTBLAAK
WILLEMSBRUG
5K ROUTE
ROCHUSSENSTRAAT
Eendrachtsplein
BOOMPJES
Maas River
GRAVENDIJKWAL
Museum Park
VASTELAND
Maritime Museum
WESTZEEDIJK
De Heuvel Park
8K ROUTE
ERASMUSBRUG
N

◀ 115-map project for *Runners' World* magazine and Westin hotels

▼ Pharmaceutical company's internal report

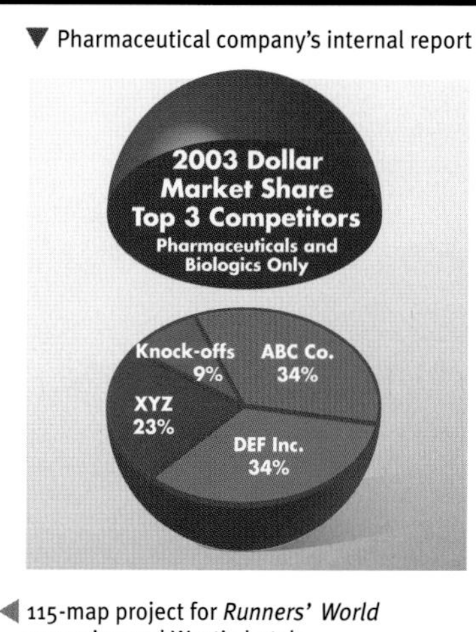

2003 Dollar Market Share Top 3 Competitors
Pharmaceuticals and Biologics Only
Knock-offs 9%
ABC Co. 34%
XYZ 23%
DEF Inc. 34%

Sean O'Connor
ST. LOUIS
LOCAL 268
Rosie's DINER
35
SO'CONNOR
naesronnoco@hotmail.com
(636) 262-8443
3321 Steeple Hill. St.Charles MO, 63301

OOGA BOOGA!
INC.
for ages 13-113
travel Mania
tM
Your Passport To A World Of Fun!
WWW.PLAYTRAVELMANIA.COM

Jim Paillot 480-633-2485 Fax: 480-633-2486 e-mail:jim@jimpaillot.com web:www.jimpaillot.com

2625
5024
1672
10021
3205
7702
2810
11952
5240

Laurie Wigham | Information Graphics

209 Mississippi Street, San Francisco, CA 94107

(415) 863-6113

www.lauriewigham.com

Clients include:
- AAA
- Aetna
- Addison-Wesley
- Agfa
- Apple Computer
- Autodesk
- California Federation of Teachers
- IDG Publications
- Netscape
- Pacific Bell
- Peachpit Press
- PG&E
- Public Media Center
- UC, UCSF, UCSB
- Virologic

information
hands-on exhibits
transit
passes & schedules
matchlists

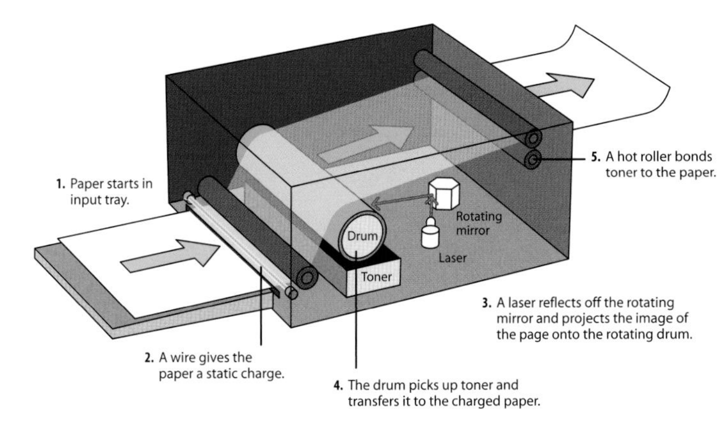
1. Paper starts in input tray.
2. A wire gives the paper a static charge.
3. A laser reflects off the rotating mirror and projects the image of the page onto the rotating drum.
4. The drum picks up toner and transfers it to the charged paper.
5. A hot roller bonds toner to the paper.
Drum
Toner
Rotating mirror
Laser

How a laser printer works, from *Danny Goodman's Computer Concepts*

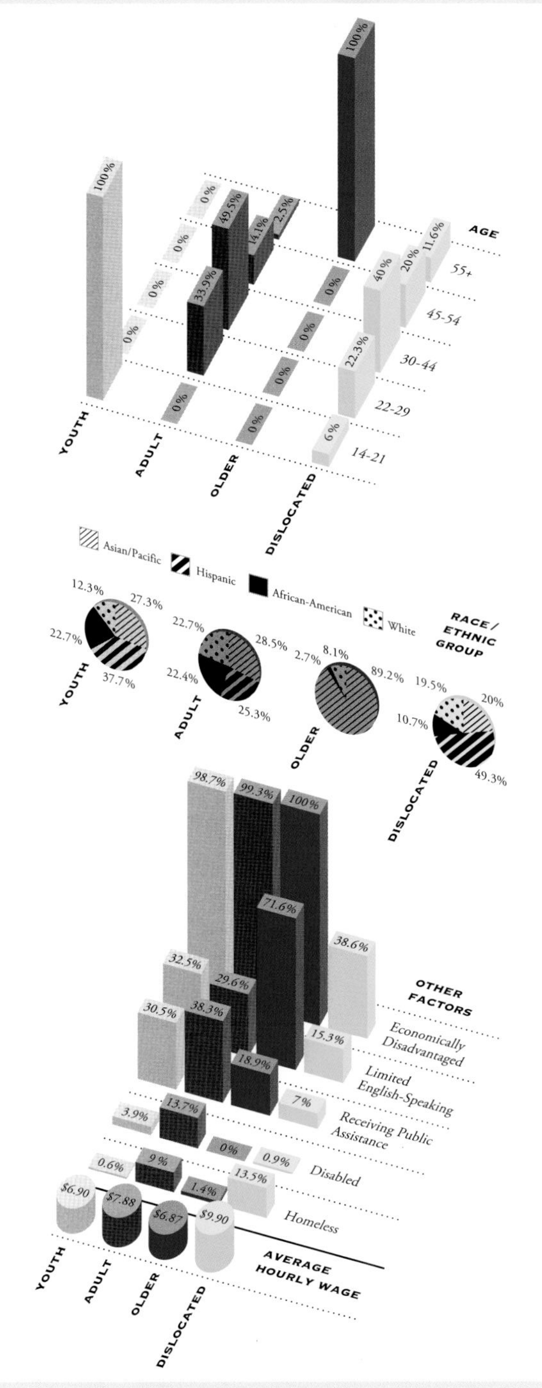
AGE
55+
45-54
30-44
22-29
14-21
YOUTH
ADULT
OLDER
DISLOCATED
100%
0%
49.5%
33.9%
14.1%
2.5%
100%
22.3%
40%
20%
11.6%
6%
Asian/Pacific
Hispanic
African-American
White
RACE / ETHNIC GROUP
12.3%
27.3%
22.7%
37.7%
28.5%
22.4%
25.3%
2.7%
8.1%
89.2%
19.5%
20%
10.7%
49.3%
98.7%
99.3%
100%
71.6%
38.6%
32.5%
29.6%
30.5%
38.3%
15.3%
18.9%
7%
3.9%
13.7%
0%
0.9%
0.6%
9%
1.4%
13.5%
OTHER FACTORS
Economically Disadvantaged
Limited English-Speaking
Receiving Public Assistance
Disabled
Homeless
$6.90
$7.88
$6.87
$9.90
AVERAGE HOURLY WAGE

Private Industry Council: *Annual Report*

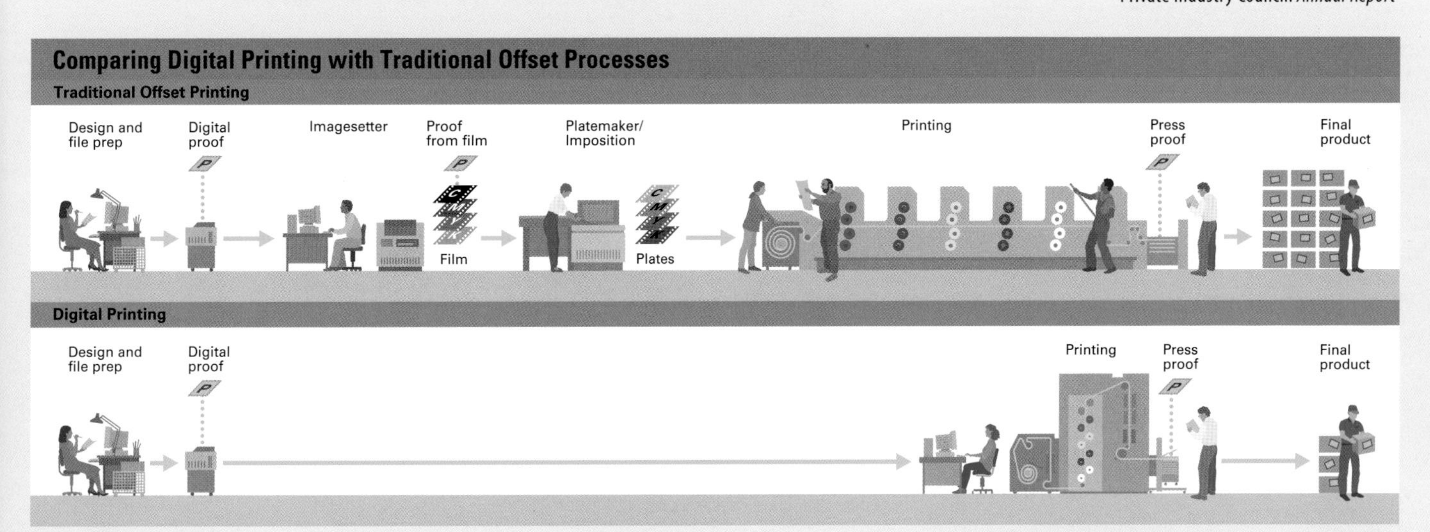
Comparing Digital Printing with Traditional Offset Processes
Traditional Offset Printing
Design and file prep
Digital proof
Imagesetter
Proof from film
Platemaker/ Imposition
Printing
Press proof
Final product
Film
Plates
P
C
M
Y
K
Digital Printing
Design and file prep
Digital proof
Printing
Press proof
Final product

Agfa: *Introduction to Digital Color Printing*

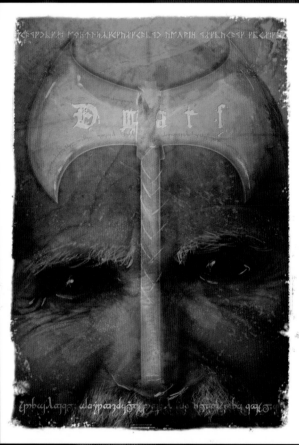

Budweiser

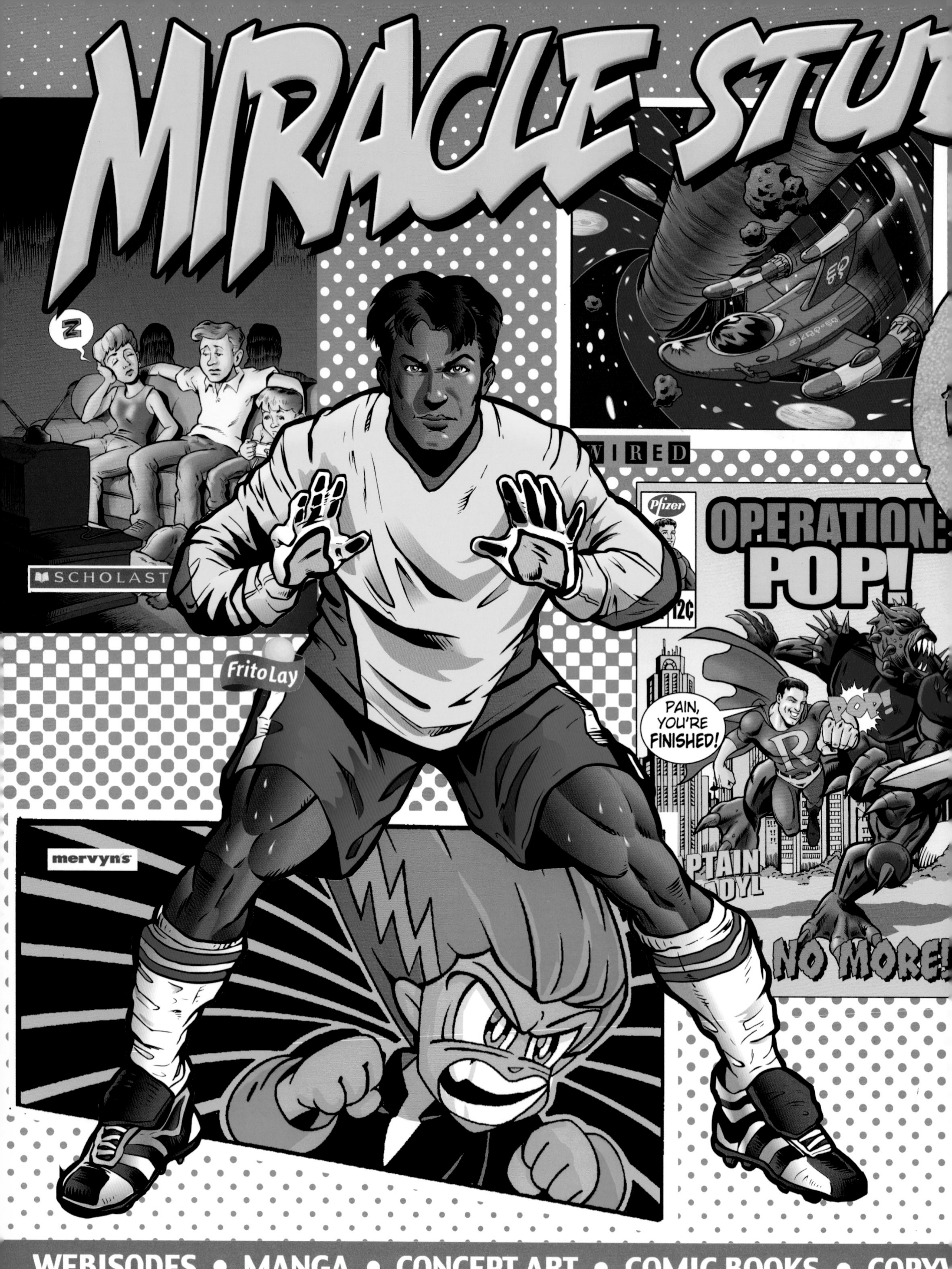
MIRACLE STU
Z
SCHOLAST
WIRED
Pfizer
OPERATION:
POP!
12¢
PAIN, YOU'RE FINISHED!
POP!
NO MORE!
FritoLay
mervyns
WEBISODES • MANGA • CONCEPT ART • COMIC BOOKS • COPYW

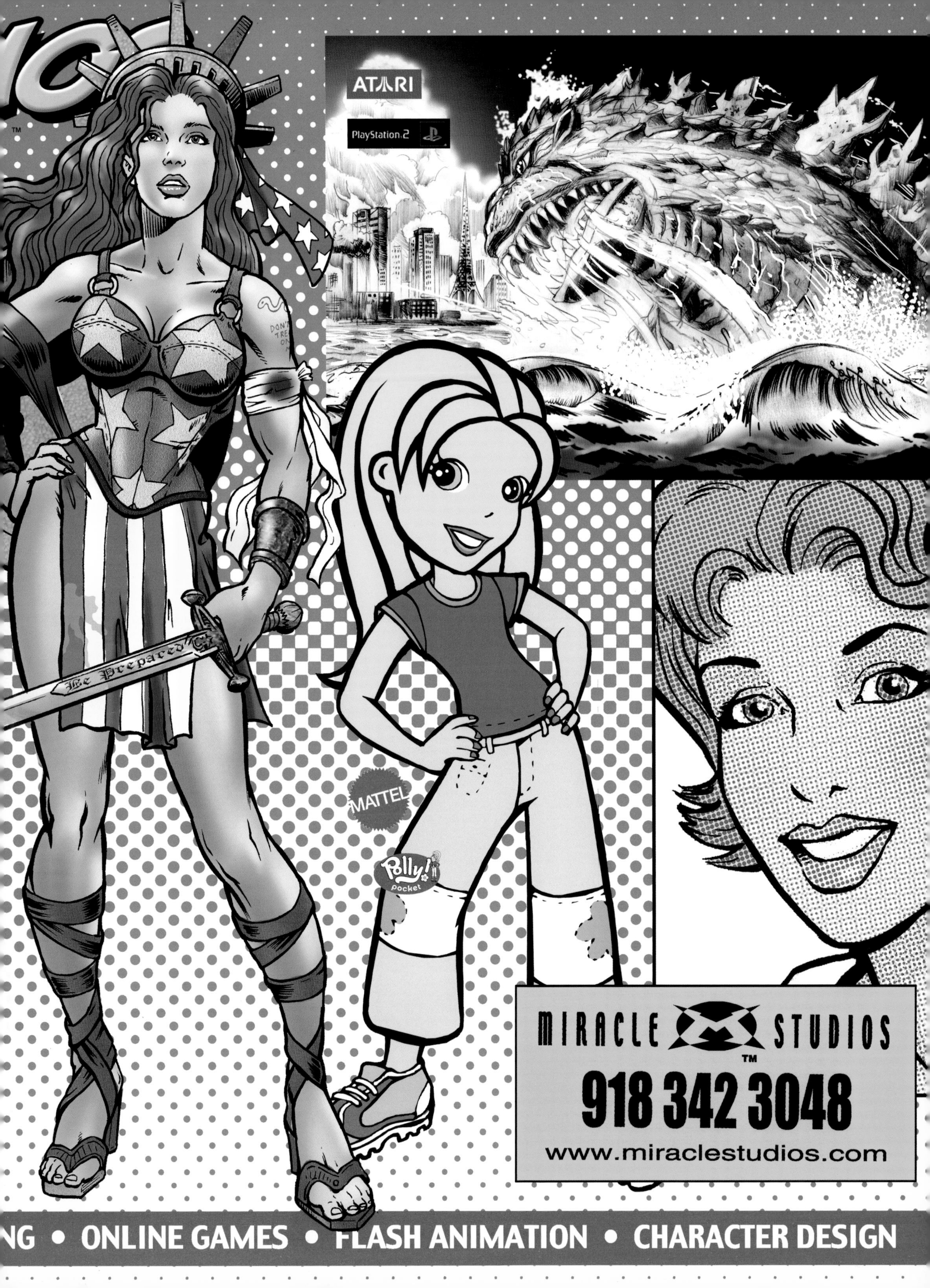
ATARI
PlayStation 2
Be Prepared
MATTEL
Polly! pocket
MIRACLE STUDIOS
TM
918 342 3048
www.miraclestudios.com
NG • ONLINE GAMES • FLASH ANIMATION • CHARACTER DESIGN

SANDY YOUNG

photo-illustration

707.939.1131

General Learning Communications

Guideposts for Teens

Society for Organizational Learning

SANDY YOUNG / STUDIO Y

portfolio: www.studio-y.com

e: illustration@studio-y.com

707.939.1131

San Francisco Chronicle Magazine

TIME Magazine

HEATHER PRICE
ILLUSTRATIONS
art & design

APOLLO: GOD OF THE LIGHT
SON OF ZEUS AND LETO. A GOD
OF PROPHECY
AND
BROTHER OF
ARTEMIS. OR
A SUN-GOD.

www.heatherprice.com
604. 877. 0446

CALL FOR...
COMIX
THE OLD FASHION WAY!
FRIEND OF THE FRIENDLESS...PROMOTER OF THE SHY!
GIVE OL' DADDY SOME WORK!
YOU HAVE THE PEARLS, WE HAVE THE SWINE!
WE DO MOST STUFF, FROM THE GOOEY SWEET TO DRAWINGS OF THE DAMNED. DON'T BE BE AFRAID TO ASK ANYTHING.
TOOMER
TOOMER
MIXED INFECTION. SOME YEAST CELLS. IT'S FULL-BLOWN OTITIS!
WE'LL NEED ENROFLOXACIN AND SILVER SULFADIAZINE.
GRAM +, GRAM -
MEANWHILE...
HOPE THIS ISN'T SERIOUS, OLD PAL.
THE CYTOLOGY SHOWS A MIXED INFECTION. FLASH NEEDS A BROAD SPECTRUM TREATMENT.
ZEN AXIOM NO. 27B
YOU CAN GET US FAST... YOU CAN GET US CHEAP. BUT YOU CAN'T GET US FAST & CHEAP.
GEORGE TOOMER
3923 COLE AVENUE / DALLAS, TX 75204 / 214 522-1171
FAX: 214 528-3588 / EMAIL: GToomer@aol.com
WEB SITE: WWW. georgetoomer.com

HE RUNS WITH SCISSORS!
PEOPLE WHO CAN DRAW GOOD ARE A DIME-A-DOZEN
DSVC PRESENTS...
ANNUAL
CRAWFISH
MADNESS
DAMAGED DAMES A SPECIALTY.
BEHOLD THE HORROR!
SATURDAY, MAY 21 / 12
OLD TIME COMIC STYLES BY AN OLD GUY!
BUY SOMETHING BEFORE I GO BLIND!
OUR CEO, LEROY.
WE CAN TURN ANY EXECUTIVE INTO A BLUES GUY.
Max Brewski
WORLD TOUR
of BEERS
IF YOU CAN'T USE US, BUT LIKE
THIS CRAP.. SAY "HOWDY!"
GToomer@aol,com

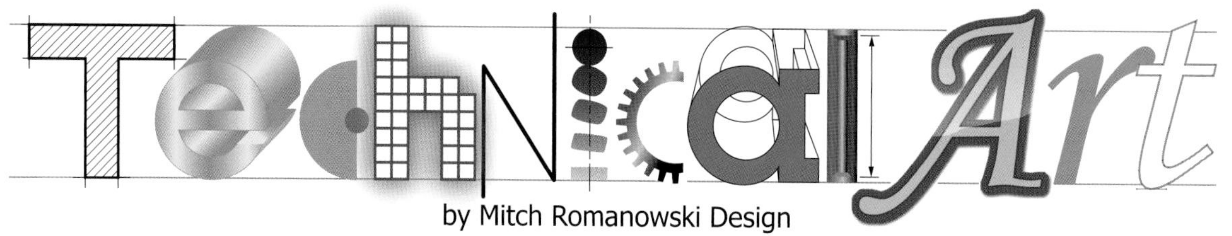
Technical Art
by Mitch Romanowski Design

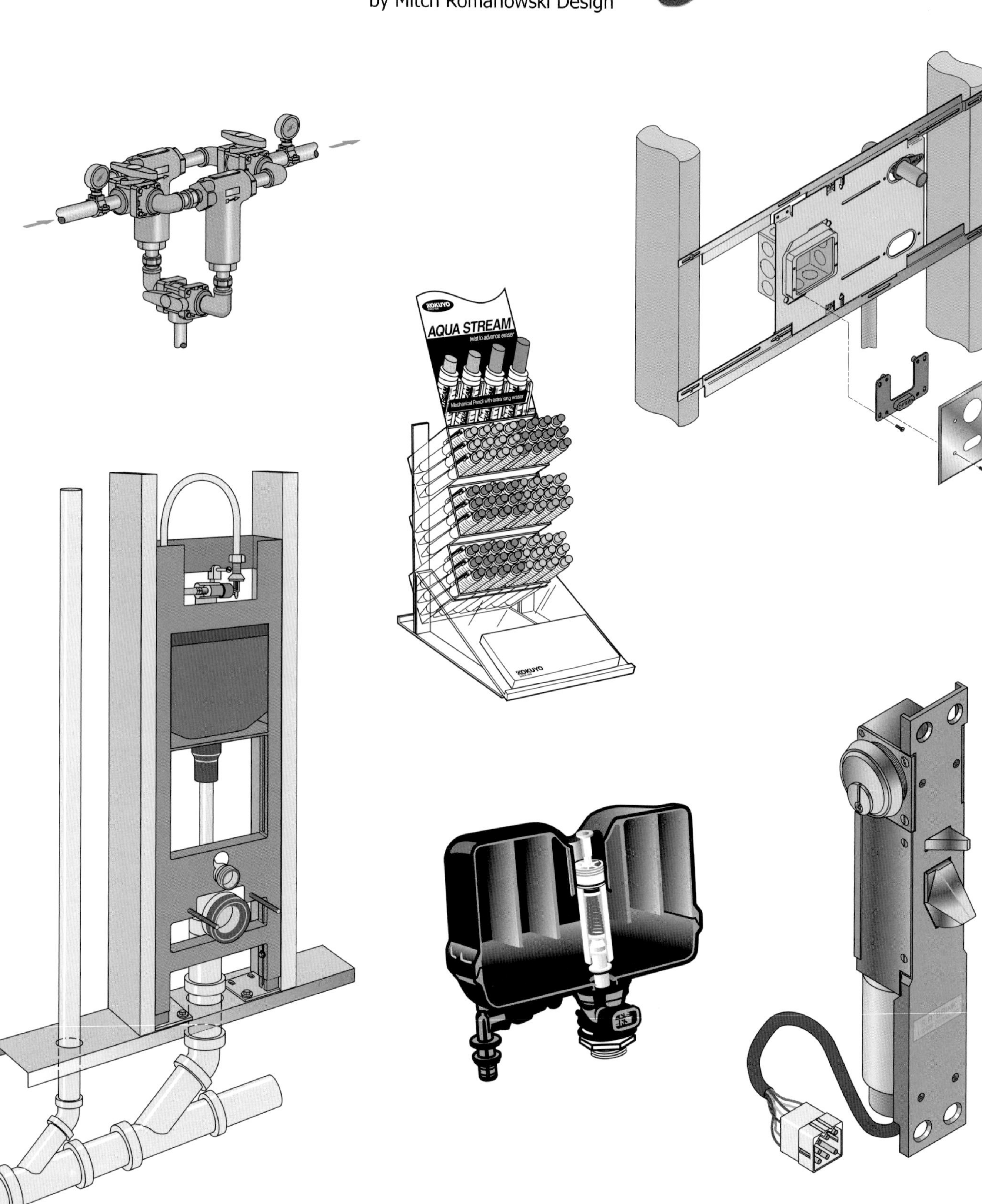
AQUA STREAM
twist to advance eraser
Mechanical Pencil with extra long eraser

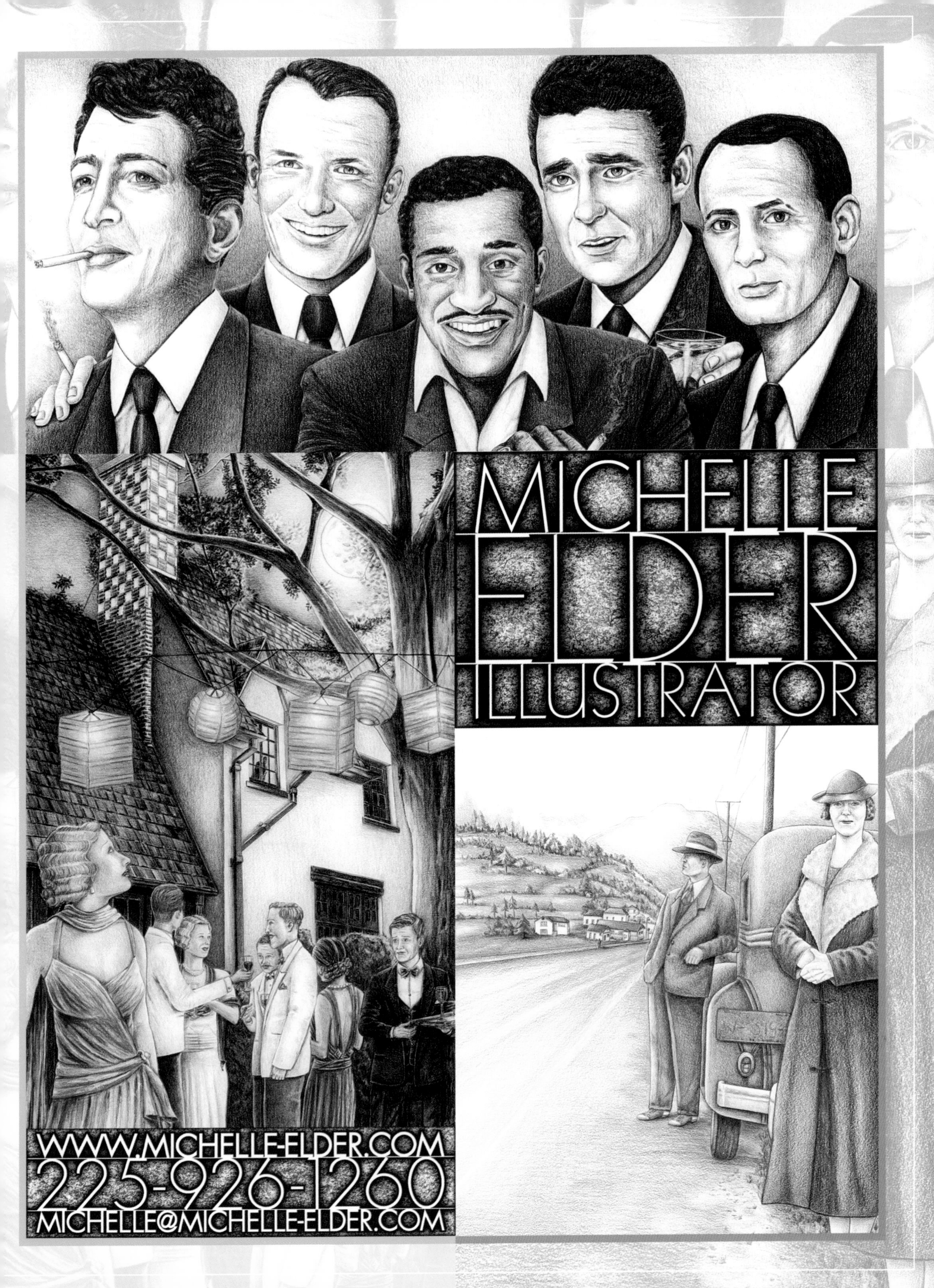
MICHELLE
ELDER
ILLUSTRATOR
WWW.MICHELLE-ELDER.COM
225-926-1260
MICHELLE@MICHELLE-ELDER.COM

Product Renderings

Technical Line Art

Cutaways

Exploded Views

Infographics

Diagrams

Charts/Maps

Instructional/How-To's

3D Modeling

AARONASHLEY
ILLUSTRATION

Clients include:

Argonne National Laboratory

Golf Magazine

WM. Wrigley Jr. Co.

Omron Electronics, LLC.

Alexander Isley, Inc.

Riverside Publishing

Merck

Shering-Plough

Middleton Pest Control

Wellmark International

bp

see also:

DI #19 & #20

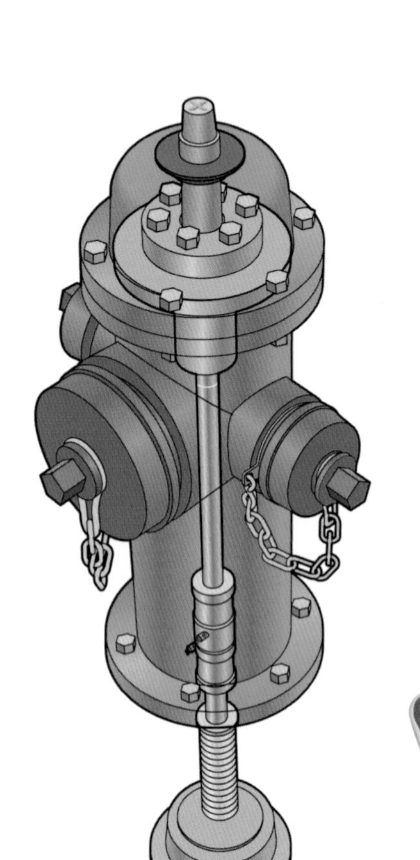

AARONASHLEY
ILLUSTRATION

TEL/FAX: 847.289.9505 • E: apash@ashleyillustration.com
www.ashleyillustration.com

ockmacrae•com
jmacrae8@sympatico•ca
JOCK MACRAE 416•690•0401

Pale Winter
arose, from
her Sleepy
couch of snows.
Shivery
Flakes...
Silver wind
blows.
KAT THACKER EMBELLISHMENTS WWW.KATTHACKER.COM 248.545.0396

CAMP
Silver Lake

Minute Maid
PINK LEMONADE
MADE WITH REAL LEMONS
Minute Maid
LIMEADE·LIMONADA
MADE WITH REAL LIMES

www.HowDoYouHangOut.com
Hi-C
Sour
Blast
wild cherry

PURINA
secondnature
HOUSETRAINING PADS
Peace of mind for you and your dog.
4 ultra-absorbent layers help fight tough odors
Unique, attractive scent for dogs
Non-slip backing
Blue layer helps mask urine stains
for PUPPIES

PURINA
TIDY CATS
SCOOP
Small Spaces
Power Pieces
MULTIPLE CATS

CULINARY CAFE
YAKISOBA CHICKEN STIR FRY

phone: 314.968.5076
email: jean@jeanprobert.com
web site: www.jeanprobert.com

DAWUD ANYABWILE

2020 Howell Mill Road NW, Suite C-228 • Atlanta, GA 30318-1732
404.213.9689 - Studio • 270.518.9291 - Fax

The FAR OUT TROOPERS®
RUN-DMC
and Jam Master Jay

www.ARTBYDAWUD.com

DMA

Productions

DANIEL AYCOCK • (917)-586-8146
daniel@dmaproductions.com

DMA

dmaproductions.com

Monte Michael Moore
Maverick Illustration
Client List: Lucasfilm Ltd, Playboy
Coors, Microsoft, Playstation2, DC
Comics, Marvel Comics, StarTrek.
5360 N. Franklin St.
Denver, CO 80216
303-294-0146
mavmktg@Qadas.com
www.mavarts.com
www.myndzei.com
© 2005 Lucasfilm Ltd. & ™. All rights reserved. Used under authorization.
Realistic
Whimsical
Black & White
Packaging Art
Dynamic
Sexy
Bold
PlayStation 2
X-TREME QUADS
3+

Annual report

Consultants' professional association

Ad campaign for semiconductors

High-tech product capability brochure

Conservation campaign

Exotic bird rescue group

Karen Olsen Design & illustration

T: 650-851-8584
C: 650-575-9411
karenofpv@aol.com
www.karenolsendesign.com

KR

ph 818.468.1737 • KeriR@earthlink.net • www.KeriRosebraugh.com

Keri Rosebraugh
Illustration & Design

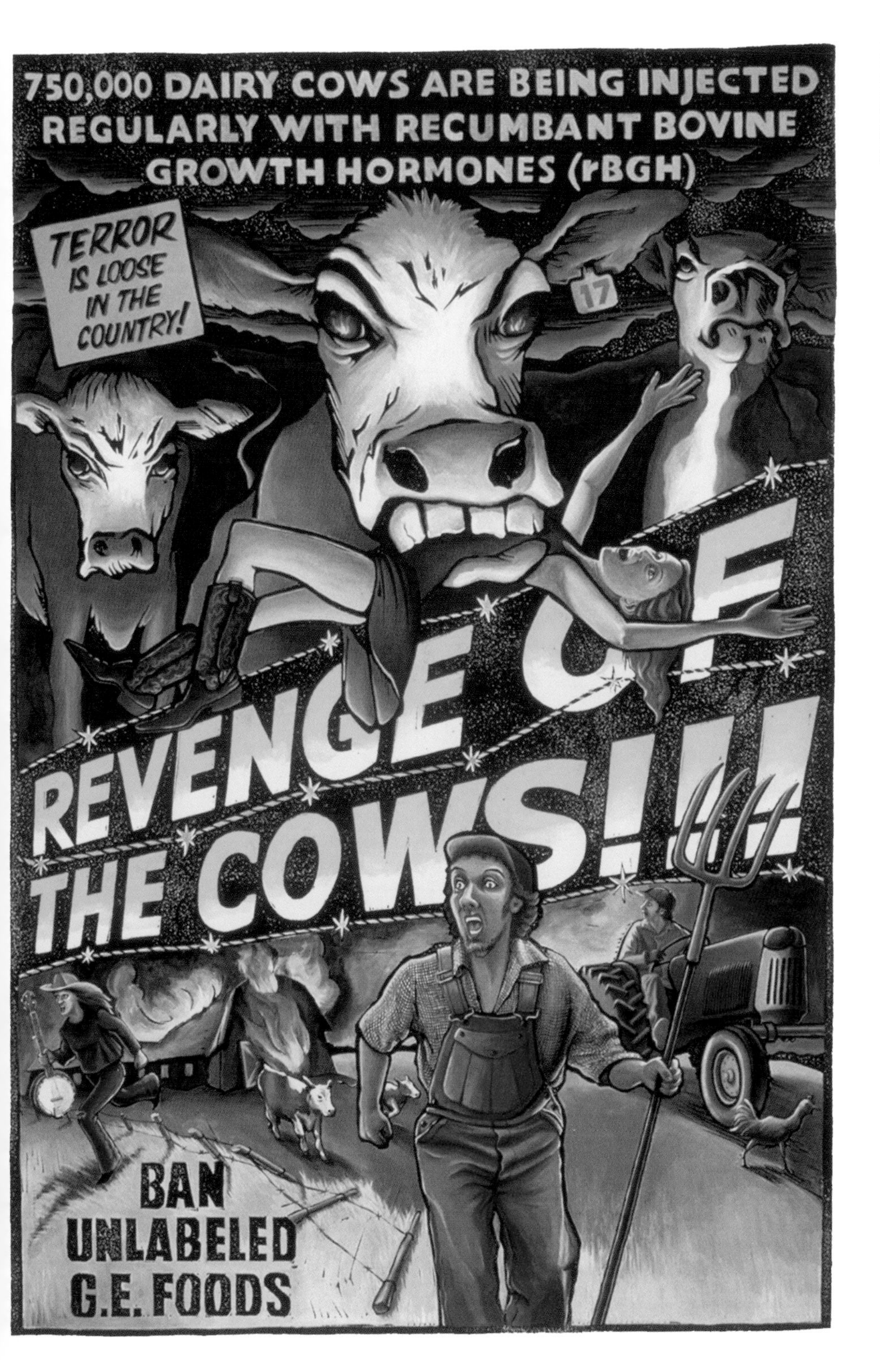
750,000 DAIRY COWS ARE BEING INJECTED REGULARLY WITH RECUMBANT BOVINE GROWTH HORMONES (rBGH)
TERROR IS LOOSE IN THE COUNTRY!
17
REVENGE OF THE COWS!!!
BAN UNLABELED G.E. FOODS

"WE MUST RE-MEMBER OUR PROPER ROLES
Wife and Mother COME FIRST..."
—MISS OREGON
PRO CHOICE
K.F.

Holly Peters
(studio) 650.965.8509
(mobile) 650.678.0004
holly@petersillustration.com
P.O. Box 1492
Mountain View, CA 94042
WWW.PETERSILLUSTRATION.COM

MARTIN CÔTÉ
4271 Boyer
Montreal, QC H2J-3C8 CANADA
TEL: (514) 521-1253
e-mail: martinco@videotron.ca
www.lisemadore.com

Represented by:
Lise Madore
TEL: (888) 440-8663
e-mail: madore@videotron.ca

Personal work "Window", oil

KEITH SKEEN

TEL: 608 423 3020
kskeen@smallbytes.net

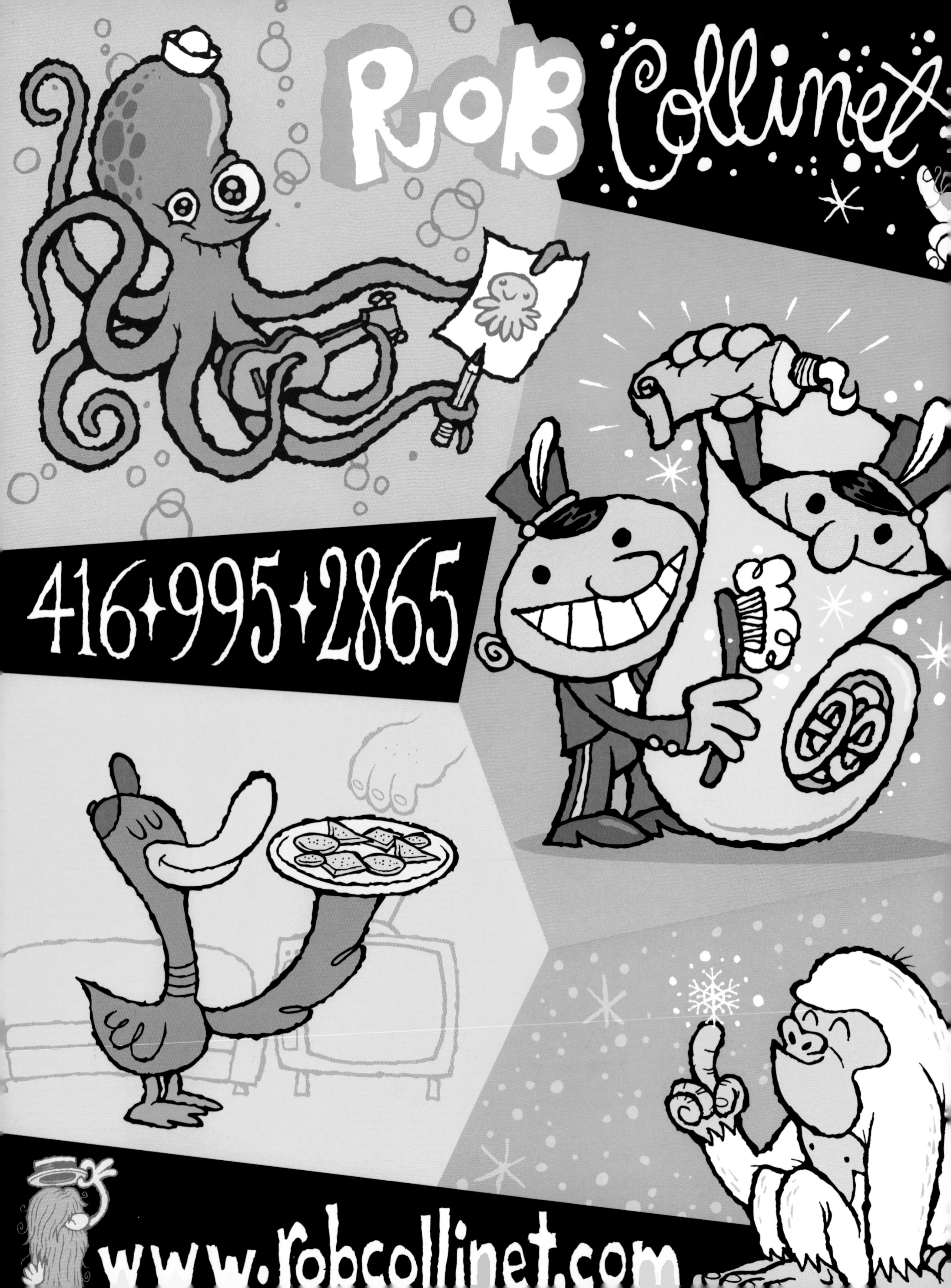

ROB Collinet
416•995•2865
www.robcollinet.com

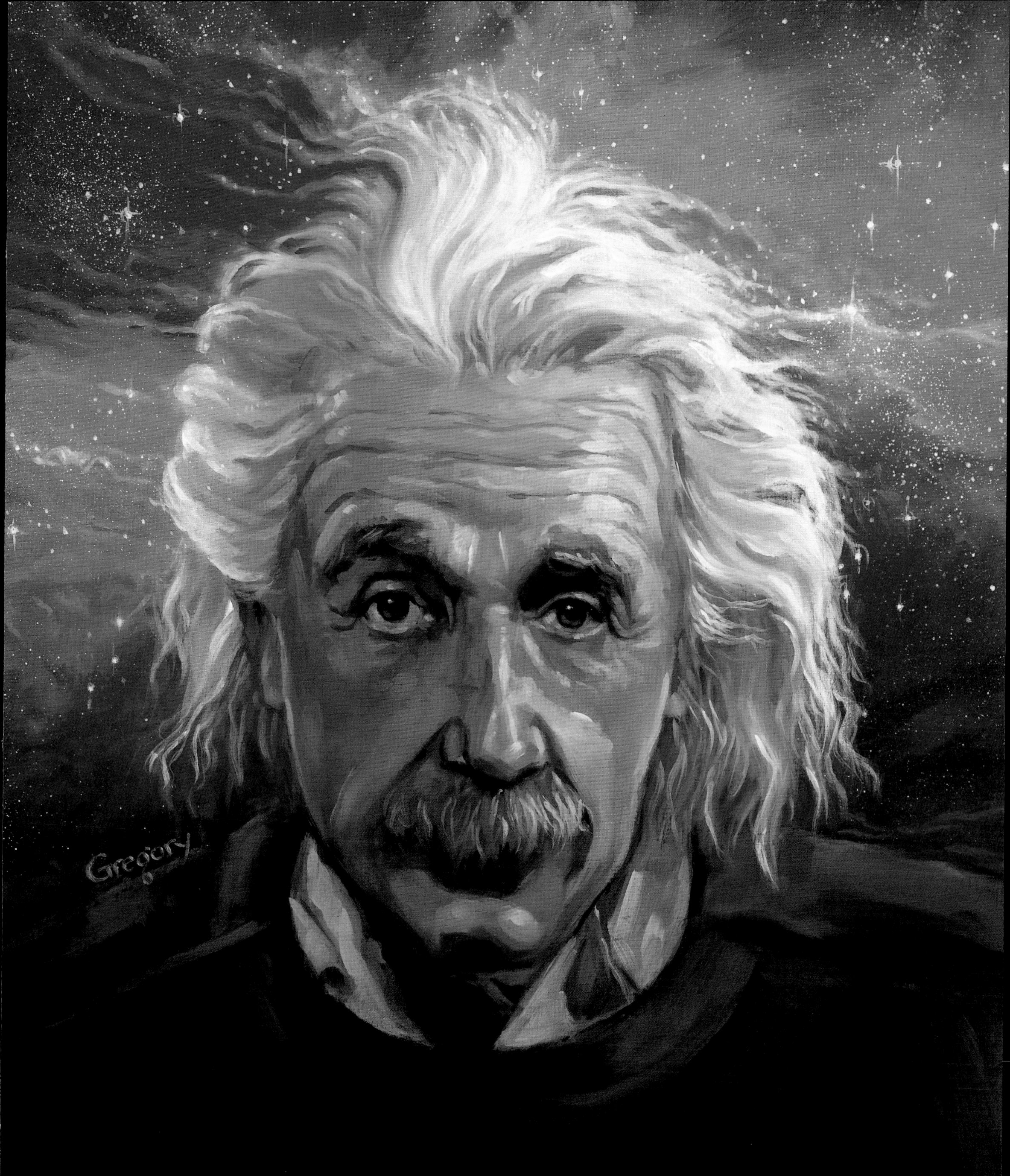
Gregory

Lizard graphix
ILLUSTRATION WITH IMAGINATION
Liz Kassler 201-384-9784 www.LizKassler.com
Happy Birthday
REPRESENTED BY CUTLASS COMMUNICATIONS 973-452-4547
© LIZ KASSLER 2005

ALECE BIRNBACH www.alecebirnbach.com 310.729.1261

npr

CLAUDE MARTINOT

DARWIN
ON THE
ORIGIN
OF
SPECIES

Todd Leonardo

510 · 728 · 1076

e-mail: tleoi @aol.com

www.toddleonardo.com

CHRISTIAN MUSSELMAN | ILLUSTRATION

DON PETERSEN
7004 Via Quito
Pleasanton, CA 94566
TEL/FAX: (925) 484-0342
e-mail: dppencil@sbcglobal.net
www.donpetersenart.com

Clients include: Addison-Wesley, Advanced Micro Devices, Apple Computer, ASPCA, Harcourt, KGO-TV (ABC), KQED (PBS), McGraw-Hill, Memorex, National Wildlife Federation, *Oxford American*, Pearson Learning, Pentagram Design, Port of Oakland, Safeway Stores, *TIME for Kids*, United States Postal Service

For additional work see: *Directory of Illustration #13-17, 20 & 21* or my website

DP

DP

DP

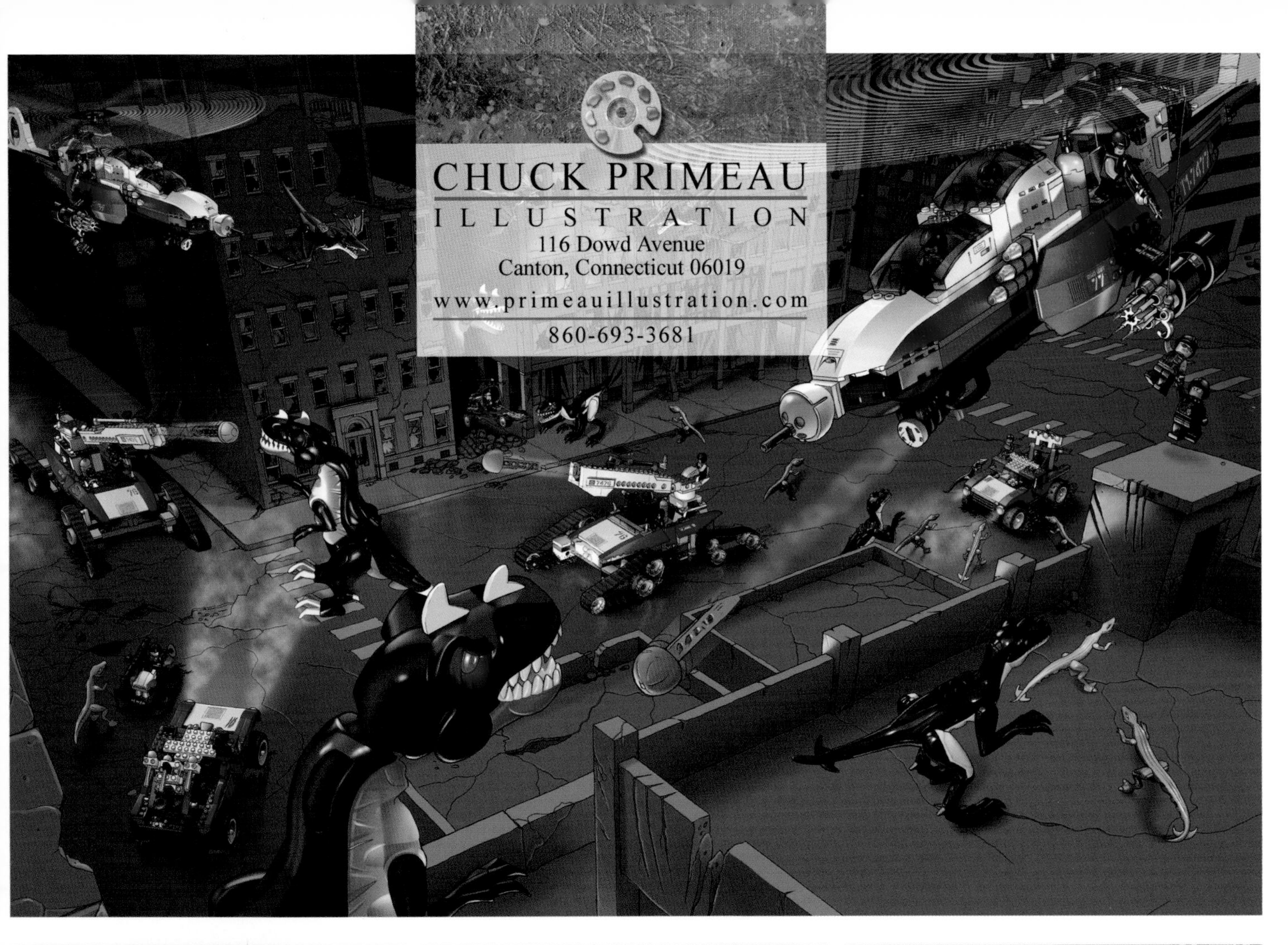
CHUCK PRIMEAU
ILLUSTRATION
116 Dowd Avenue
Canton, Connecticut 06019
www.primeauillustration.com
860-693-3681

SHREK 2
TWISTED FAIRY TALE GAME

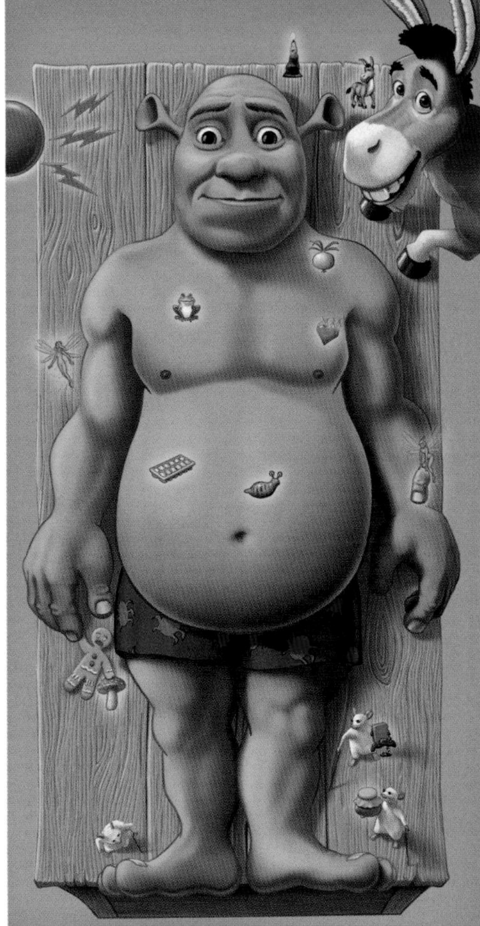

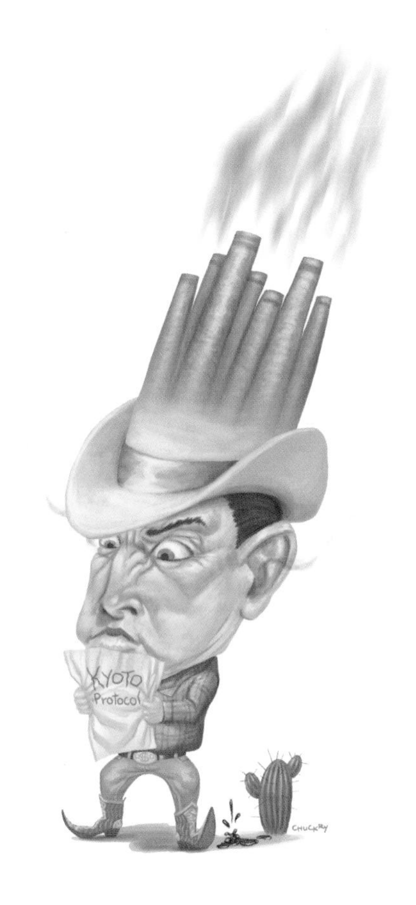
KYOTO
Protocol

Christopher Chuckry
tel - 204-942-0250
fax - 204-480-3011
www.chuckry.com
chris@chuckry.com

10
Debt
Equity
bradwalker@centurytel.net

CAMPAIGN
2004
INDECISION
2004
Fair &
Balanced

Julia Woolf Illustration
2463 Meadow Valley Terrace
Los Angeles CA 90039
323 664 8093
juliawoolf@earthlink.net

Client List includes:
Dreamworks Animation,
Universal Studios,
Playhouse Publishing,
Highlights for Children,
Scholastic, Pearson,
Clubhouse Jr,
and Paramount Cards.

SCBWI Member
www.directoryofillustration.com/juliawoolf

RON CLOWNEY DESIGN ILLUSTRATION
5513 Adobe Falls Rd. #10
San Diego, CA 92120
TEL: (619) 501-5740
CELL: (619) 459-8805
e-mail: ron@rclowney.com
www.rclowney.com

I specialize in the area of realism and in the examples below I used ink or pencil as the medium to create these images. I can provide realistic representations of any subject matter in black & white and color although no color work is shown here.

More examples of my work can be seen at:
www.directoryofillustration/RonClowney
www.rclowney.com

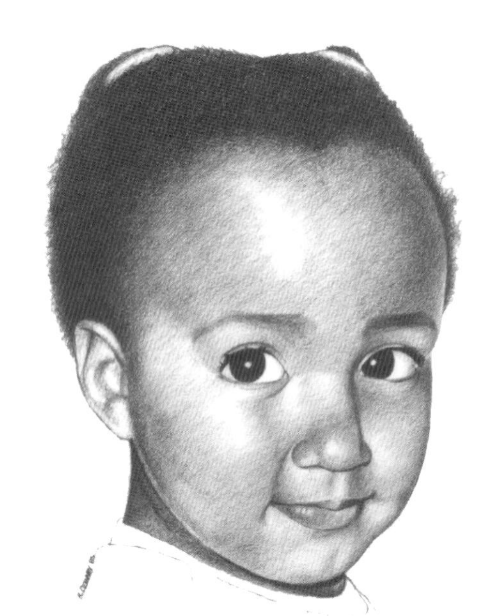

Alexis Age 4

My Grandmother

Geisel Library

Hepner Hall

Rucker The Wonder Dog

SHELLY MARTIN

ANIMATION.ILLUSTRATION.CONCEPT

WATER RULZ
The Great Water Odyssey SM
© 2004, 2005 St. Johns River Water Management District. used with permission of SJRWMD.

TM
Fizz
NYC LOTTO

431 E. CENTRAL BLVD. #603 ORLANDO, FL 32801
407.617.4488 SPARKYSDOODLE.COM

miketartworks

mikethompson
urban illustration for the masses

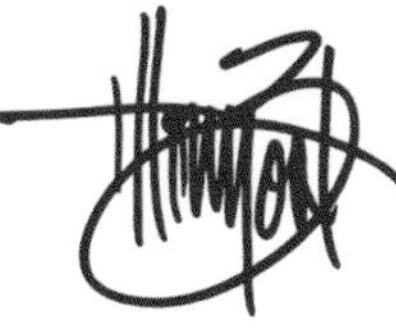

www.**miket**artworks.com
mike@miketartworks.com
studio 301**793**6569

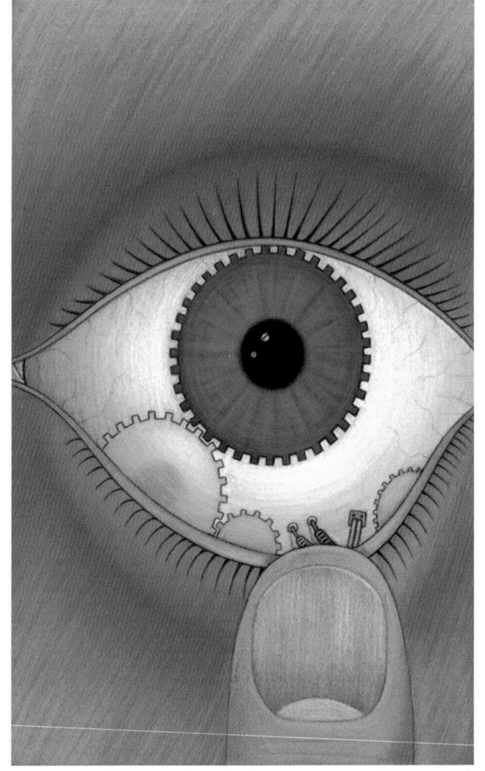

DEATH

DAN BERLIN - ILLUSTRATOR

Danberlin.com - berlinil@yahoo.com - 941-735-0345

Magic
Bubbles

Deborah Collins, Illustration

Ph: (949) 721-1149

Fax: (949) 721-1135

www.debzart.biz

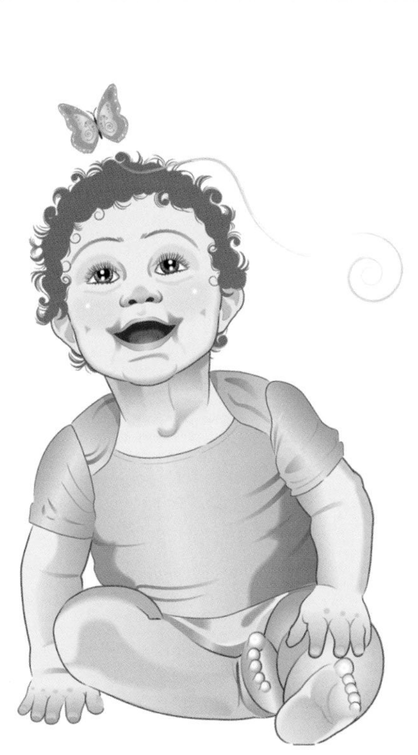

ROB CABRERA
2771 NE 15th Street, Studio 7
Fort Lauderdale, FL 33304
TEL/FAX: (954) 565-4977
e-mail: silorob@aol.com
www.robtoons.com
www.siloroberts.com

W
P
MIAMI
Sugar Juice
Rob. '05

9
9
ERIC

MATTHEW HOLMES
ARTIST
I ♡ Mom
Dentyne
ice

Matthew Holmes • Artist
5014 Primrose Drive
Fair Oaks, CA 95628

916 965-8683
916 965-8734 Fax
mhartist@pacbell.net

MATTHEW HOLMES • ARTIST •
JavaMint
Chocolate Chip
SHAKE
QUITE POSSIBLY THE WORLD'S MOST REFRESHING MILKSHAKE.
Corona
Extra
LA CERVEZA MAS FINA
BEER
12FL.OZ
Brewed and bottled by
CERVECERIA MODELO, S.A. DE C.V.
MEXICO, D.F.
BEN&JERRY'S
76

Matthew Holmes • Artist
5014 Primrose Drive
Fair Oaks, CA 95628

916 965-8683
916 965-8734 Fax
mhartist@pacbell.net

Illustration
Control Art for Sculpture
Game Assets
LCD Art
Content Development
WINTER 2005
Atomic Orange Productions
-all
snowflake
down
snow
flake
every
under
water
forest
Toby the Totbot

Illustration

atomic orange
PRODUCTIONS

Illustrator - Mary Bakowski
Baltimore, MD
P 443.739.4535
F 413. 828.6588
mary@atomicorangeproductions.com

atomicorangeproductions.com
Transforming ideas into products kids love!

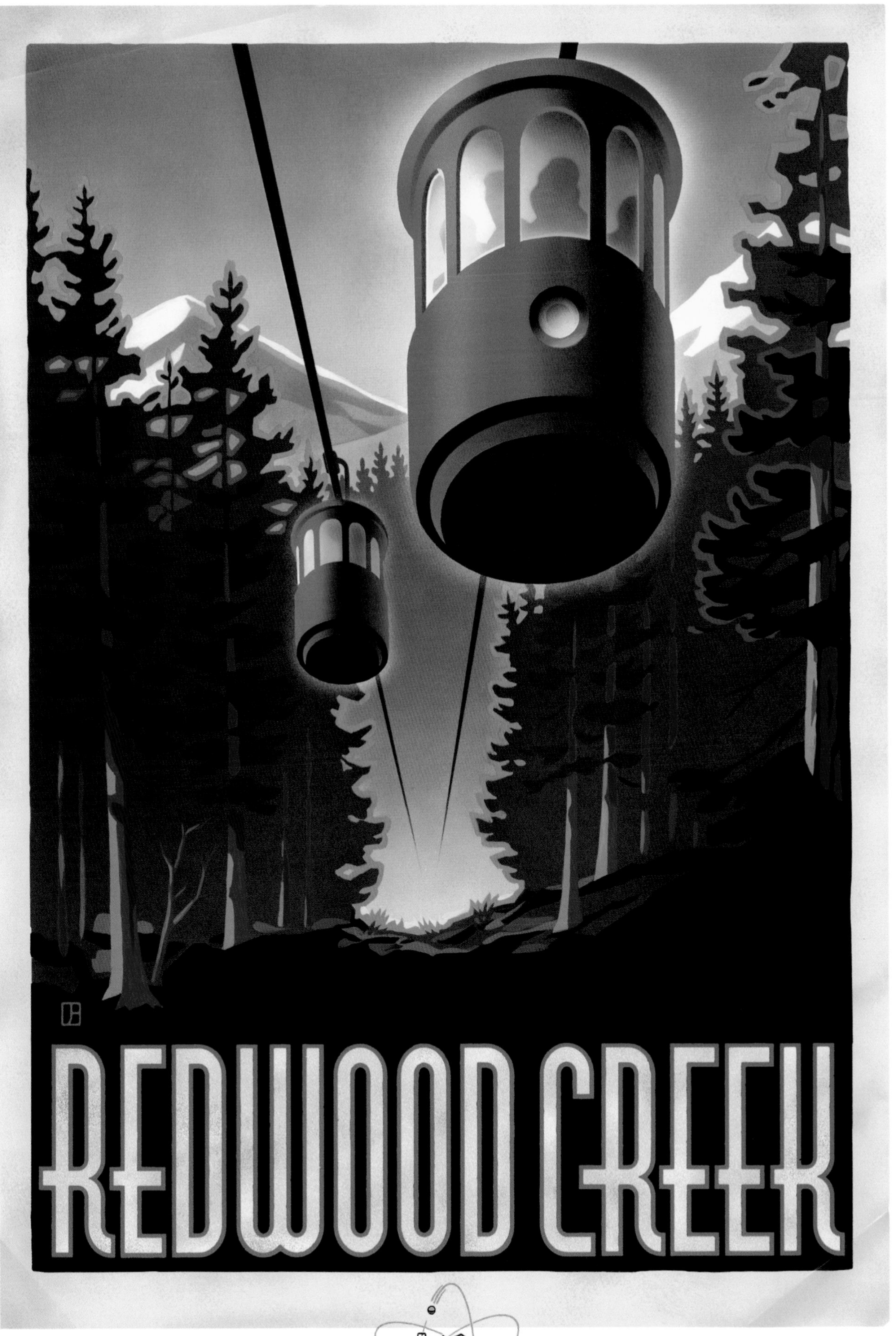
REDWOOD CREEK

JEFF FOSTER.com

www.greg-martin.com

Duck Dodgers
In The 24th and 1/2 Century
WB

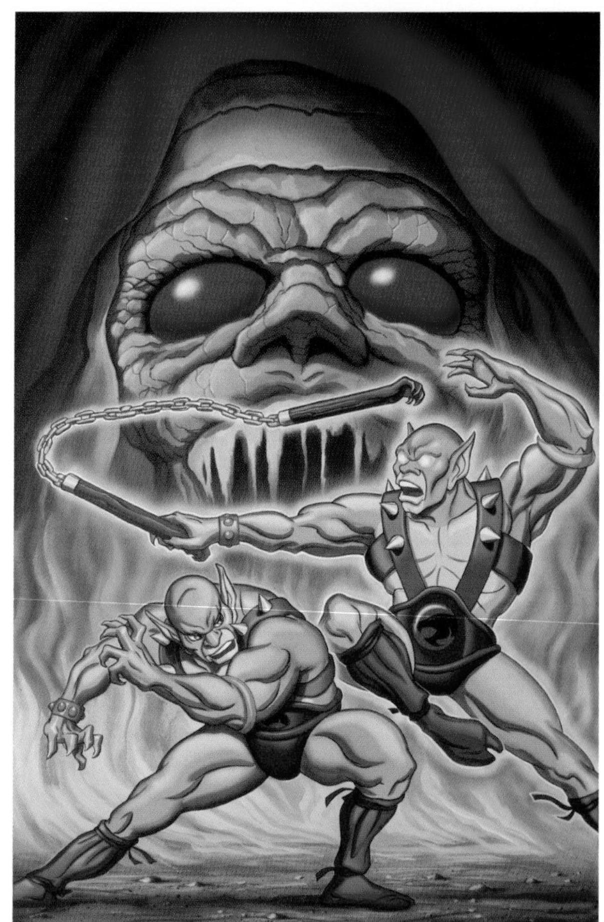

family
ALBUM

Disney's
DuckTales 2

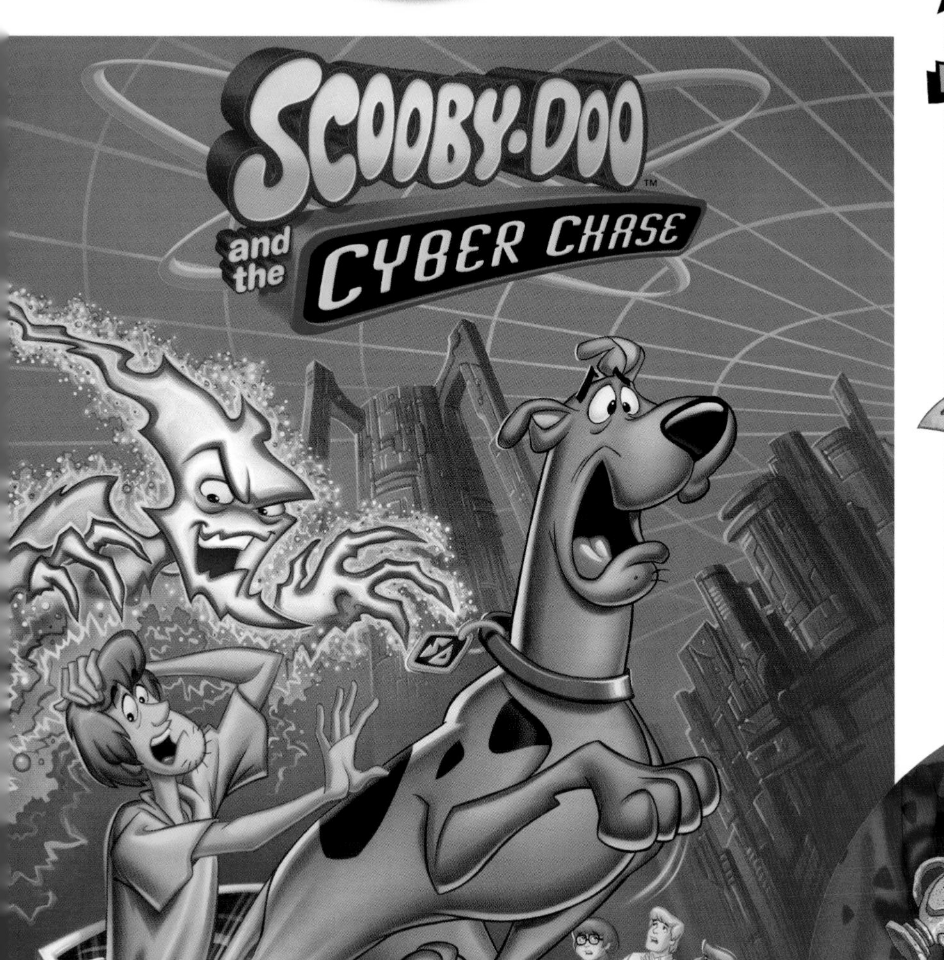
Scooby-Doo™
and the
Cyber Chase

COWABUNGA!
TEENAGE MUTANT NINJA
TURTLES

MEET
GEORGE JETSON 2

(800)406-8987

Catherine Post Illustration

Whimsical Humor Specialist (916) 739-8839 www.catherinepost.com

FLY
HY-brid

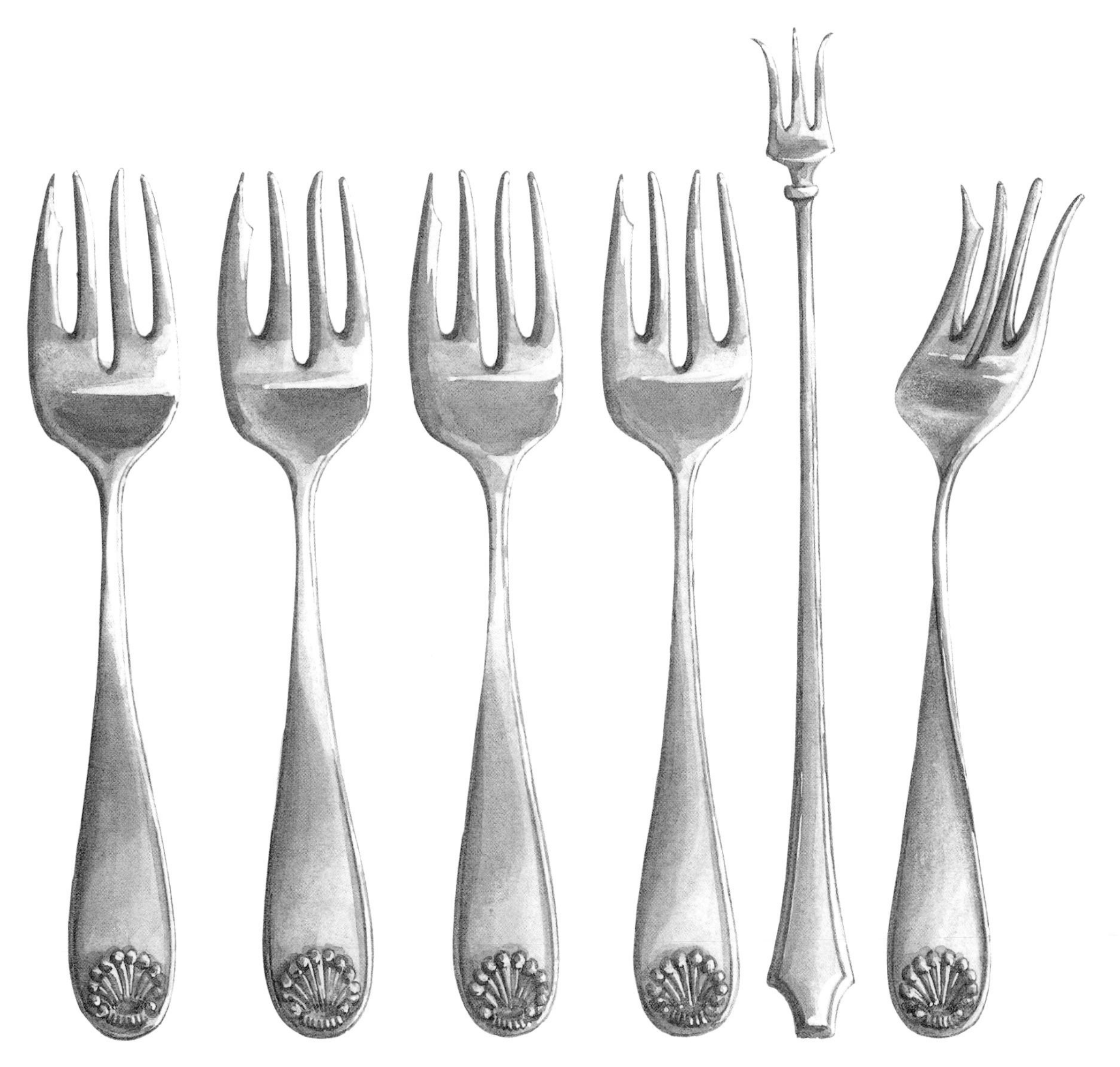

DANGE

X-RAY FILM

Medbery Illustration
Washington, DC

Sensitive, insightful,
powerful images of
people at work and play for
marketing and communication

Clients include:
AARP
Gannett
Washington Post
Pratt & Buehl Advertising
National Endowment
for the Humanities

Sherrell Medbery, 240 381 7981 smguild@verizon.net www.medberyillustration.com

ROBERT HENDRICKSON

6929 Newcastle Ave Reseda, Ca 91335 tel/fax (818) 881-8636
hendricksondesign@earthlink.net http://hendricksondesign.tripod.com

Julianne Snider

VISUAL SCIENCE INC.
4810 Riverbend Road, 3rd Floor
Boulder, Colorado 80301-2643
303.938.9488
jsnider@visualsci.com
www.visualsci.com

KEEP COUPON
ADMIT ONE

She was
a blonde
bombshell.
Twas all I
could do to

USHER
FRAGILE
THIS END UP

14%
That's this year's tuition hike for California's higher ed system. (Stanford rose 4.5%.)

www.DuetStudio.com

john_corbitt@duetstudio.com

407-260-5755

Partial client list: TIME, BusinessWeek, Fortune Vanity Fair, Golf Digest, Disney, Focus On The Family, Reader's Digest, AARP, Erie Insurance, Esquire, Coca-Cola.

amazon.com.
Boss Tweed

PHIL'S
FISH
FOOD
PLEASE
TAKE ME
HOME
Not For Sale

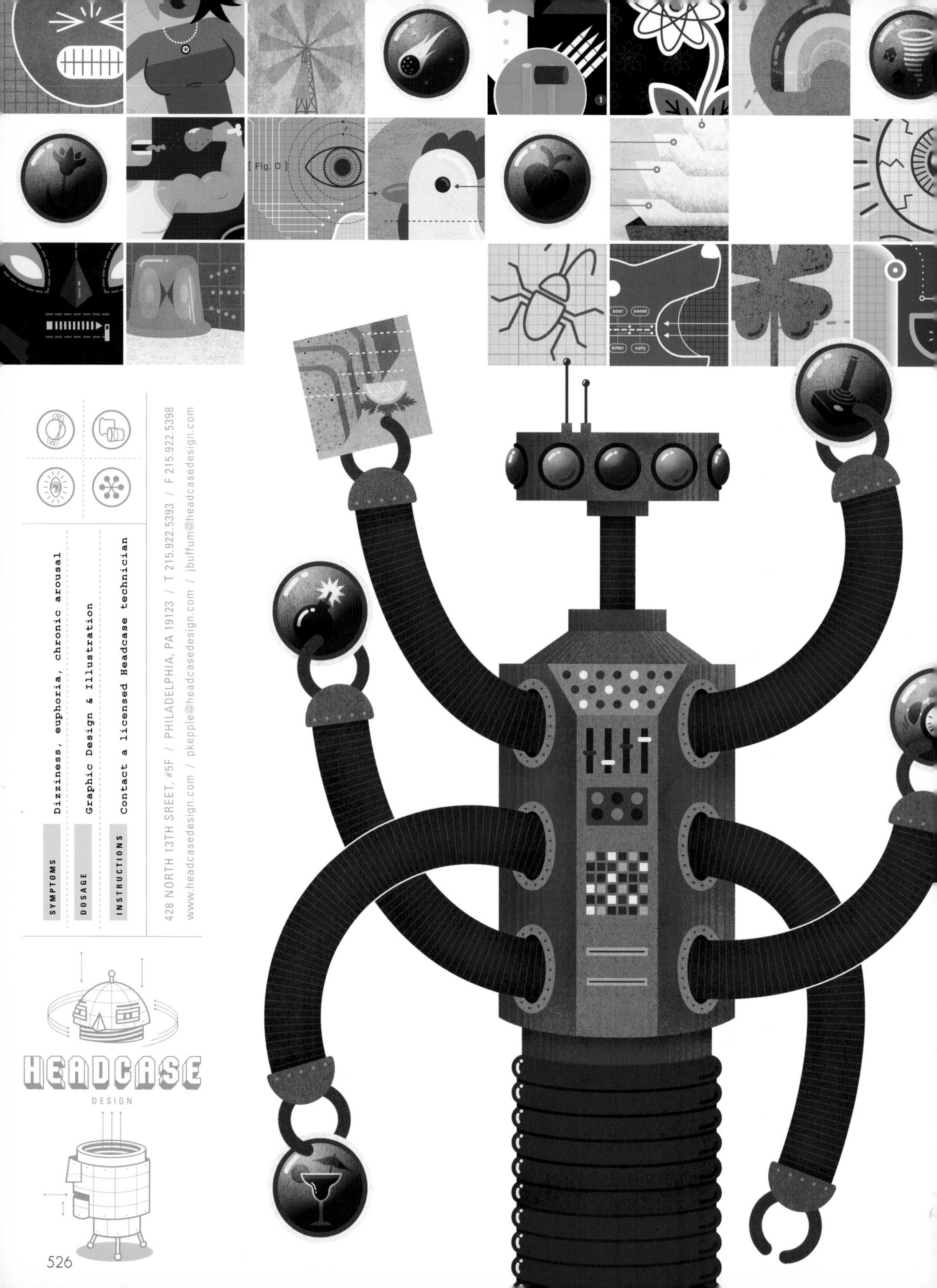
[Fig. O]
sour
sweet
bitter
salty
SYMPTOMS
Dizziness, euphoria, chronic arousal
DOSAGE
Graphic Design & Illustration
INSTRUCTIONS
Contact a licensed Headcase technician
428 NORTH 13TH SREET, #5F / PHILADELPHIA, PA 19123 / T 215.922.5393 / F 215.922.5398
www.headcasedesign.com / pkepple@headcasedesign.com / jbuffum@headcasedesign.com
HEADCASE
DESIGN

www.PIXELGARDEN.com
CLEAN, TIDY, WELL-GROOMED ARTWORK GUARANTEED!
tmi
tyson mangelsdorf illustration
503.579.5997
TYSON@PIXELGARDEN.COM
Stylograph

Good Ferret Greetings/www.goodferret.com

PCT

PEST CONTROL TECHNOLOGY

February 2005 | www.pctonline.com

CUSTOM-TAILORED

>> TERMITE CONTROL

A GROWING NUMBER OF PCOs ARE OFFERING CUSTOMIZED TERMITE CONTROL SERVICES FEATURING A MIX OF TREATMENT OPTIONS.

ALSO IN THIS ISSUE

PCT Magazine/GIE Media

Sundance Publishing

From 'The Jumping Contest'/Sundance Publishing

From 'Meerkat's Safari'/XLibris/www.meerkatsadventures.c

Flamingos

Flamingos are known
for their long skinny legs.

In nests of mud
they lay a single white egg.

Flamingos prefer
salty marshes and seas.

They mingle in groups
called colonies.

S.S. MEERKAT

Low Carb!
Tastes D-LISH BEER
D-LISH BEER LIGHT
LOW CARB
MEGA
LIGHT BEER
HEALTHY DIET
BEERS TAP INTO LOW-CARB FRENZY,BRINGING EXCITEMENT TO THE LIGHT BEER CATEGORY
File this one in the strange but true department: Diets—that's right, diets—are bringing new life to the light beer category. • Riding the wave of the low-carbohydrate frenzy that includes the Atkins and South Beach diets has the potential to fatten up, industry executives and retailers say, thanks to the introduction of low-carb beers. • "I really didn't think it would sustain itself," says Wayne Laing [cq name], owner of Wine Underground, a single-location store in Baltimore, "but it looks like it's here to stay, driven by the low-carb diets."
BY JOHNNY D. BOGGS
LOW CARB
MEGA LOW CARB BEER
Call today!
FRANK
GF
Michelle Barbera
tel: 877.787.9896
www.barberaillustration.com
michelle@barberaillustration.com
CAFE
No Pets
No Earthlings
Market Watch

Sundance Publishing

Good Ferret Greetings

Reed Business

Dinardo Design/Pierson

Boys' Life

"Actors in 2D"
www.alleycat-art.com
V.L. TOTIRE
216-228-4376
alleycatstudio1@sbcglobal.net
© AGC
SPECIALTIES:
humorous illustration
concepting
character design
© AGC
© AGC

RAY GONZALEZ
illustration & design

studio 973 872-0580
mobile 973 202-5014
e mail xraygun @ earthlink.net
website www.xraygun.net

photorealistic illustration

VERA WANG
VERA WANG
FOR MEN

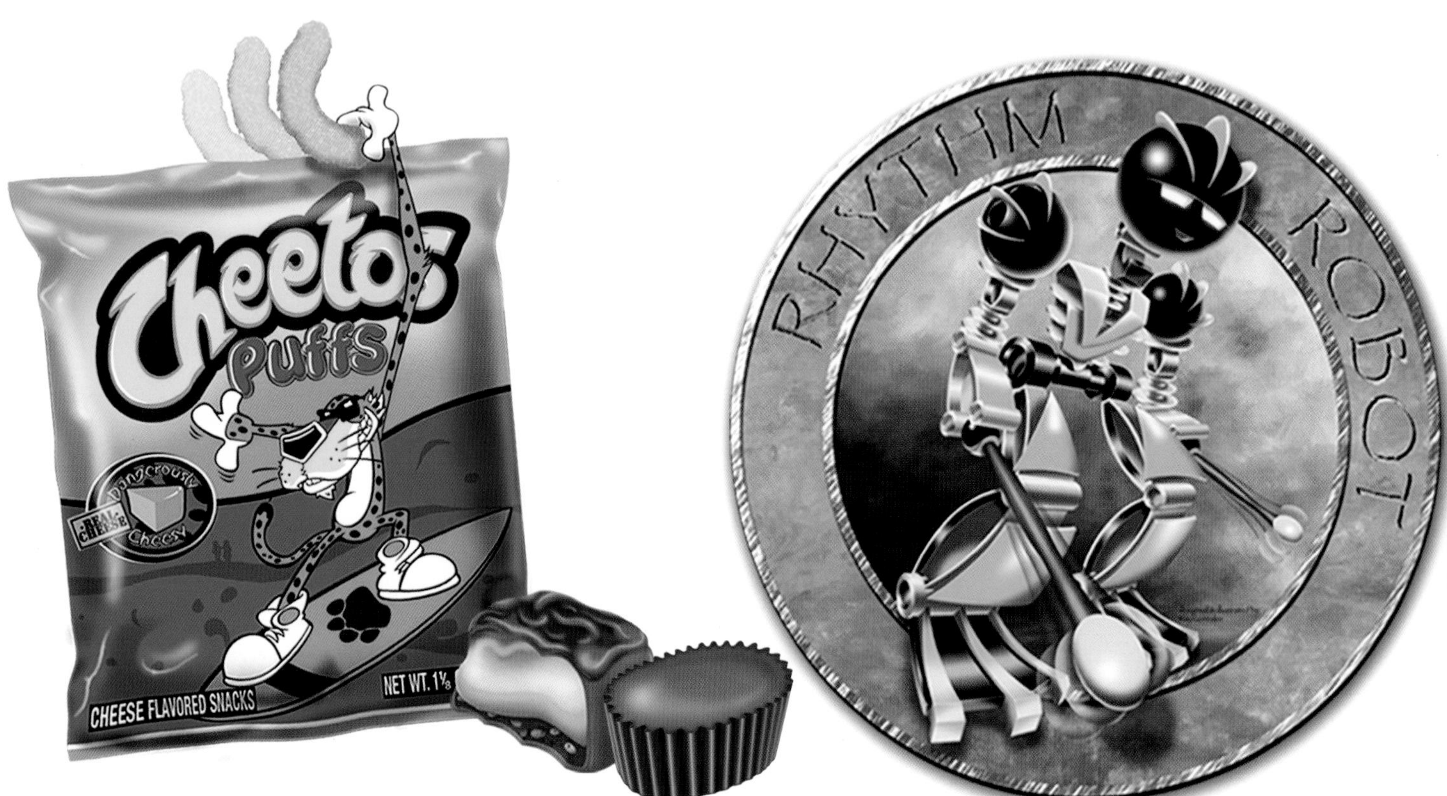
Cheetos
puffs
CHEESE FLAVORED SNACKS
NET WT. 1⅛
RHYTHM ROBOT

CLIENTS INCLUDE:
BLACK & DECKER, COTY BEAUTY, COCA-COLA, FRITO LAY, HOME DEPOT, KEEBLER, LOWE'S, MAYBELLINE, OSTEONICS, PEPSI-COLA, REEBOK, SCOTT'S, TOYS "R" US,

William Rieser
Illustration / Design
Telephone: 415.389.0332
E-Mail: wrieser@r2design.com
website: www.r2design.com
Stock Available

ReCHARGE!
NFL
Action for Healthy Kids

view online @: www.directoryofillustration.com/WilliamRieser www.theispot.com/artist/wrieser www.R2design.com

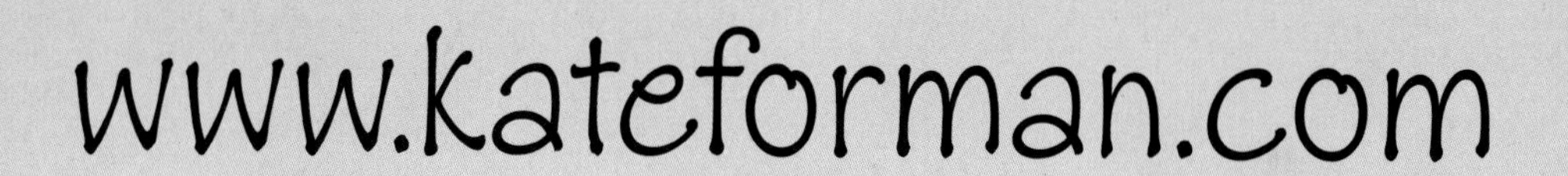
www.kateforman.com

Kate Forman

718-706-1599

917-623-0106

kateillustrate@aol.com

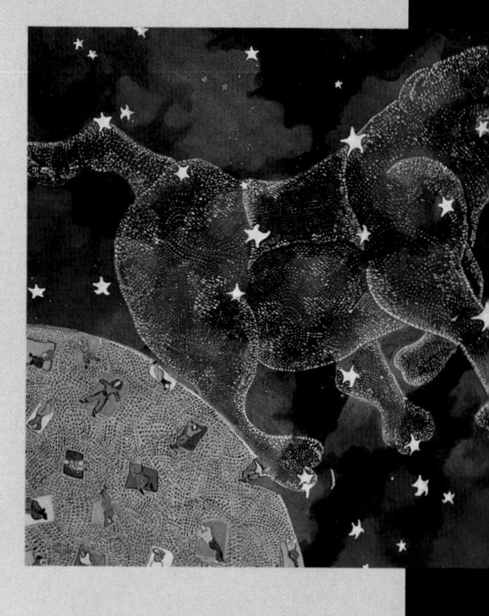

Kate Forman
ILLUSTRATION

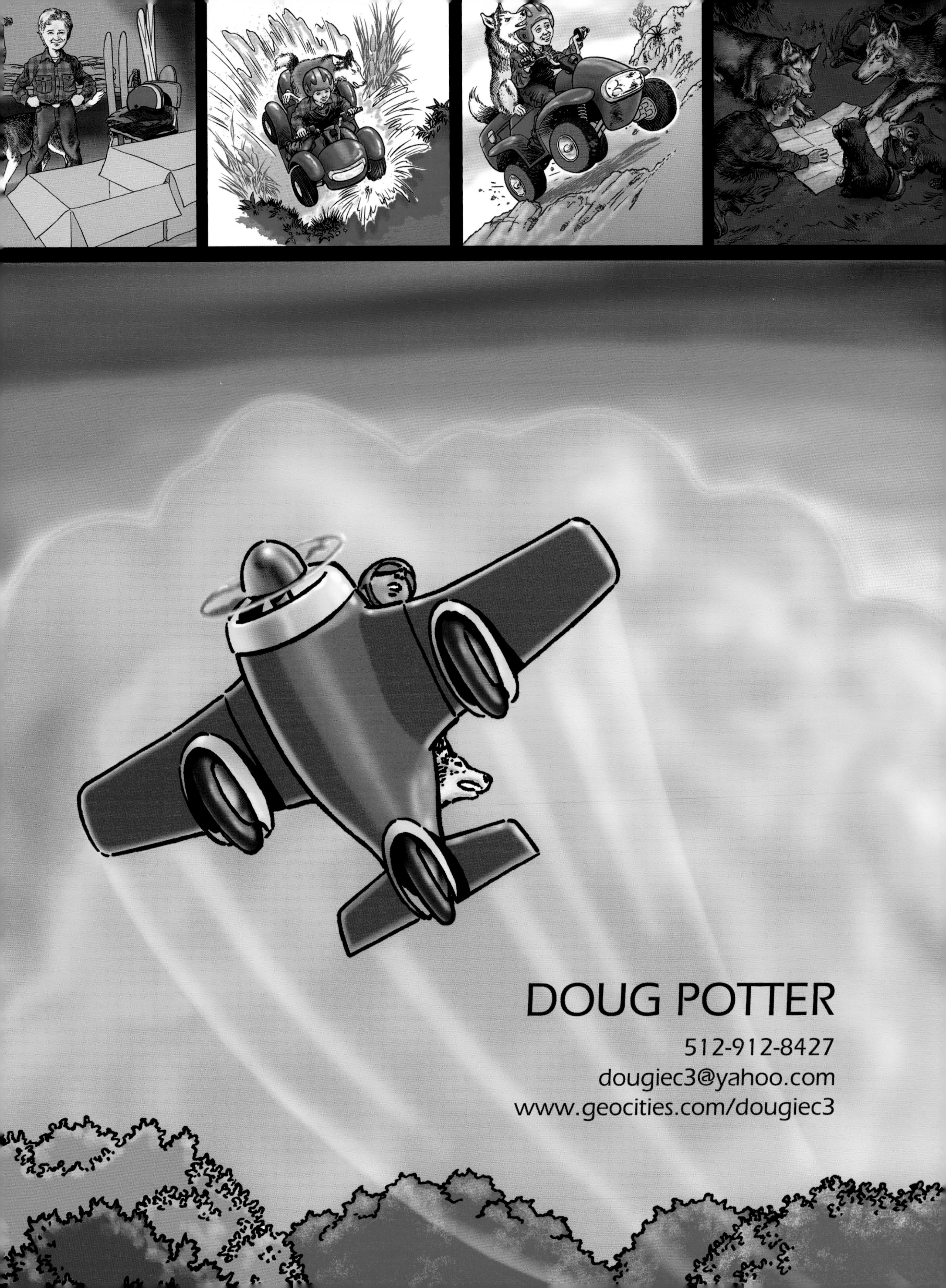
DOUG POTTER
512-912-8427
dougiec3@yahoo.com
www.geocities.com/dougiec3

ZAP!

09 37

CHRIS McARDLE
PO Box 398006
Cambridge, MA 02141
TEL: (617) 513-8307
e-mail: Artist88McArdle@yahoo.com
www.ChrisMcArdle.com

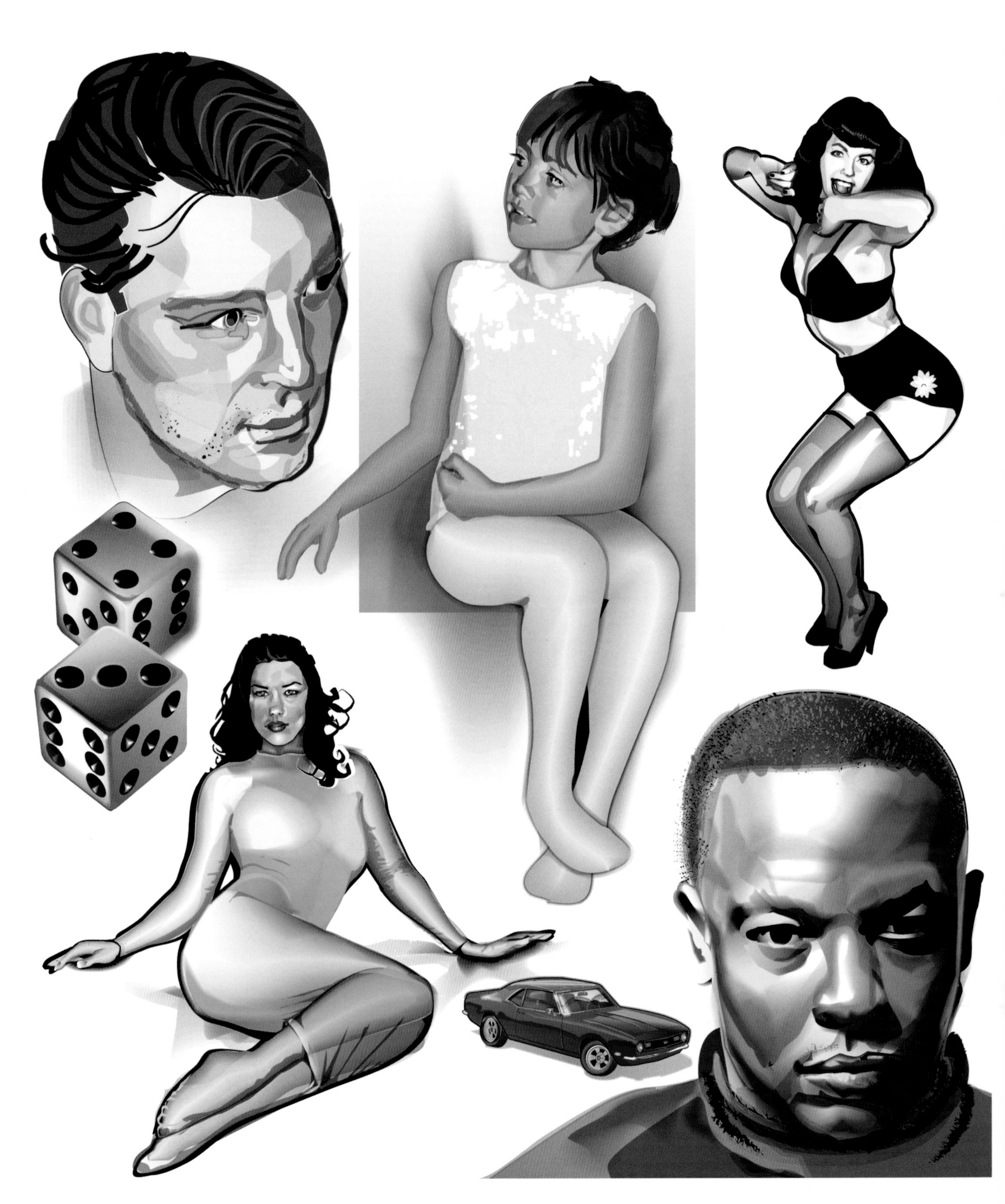

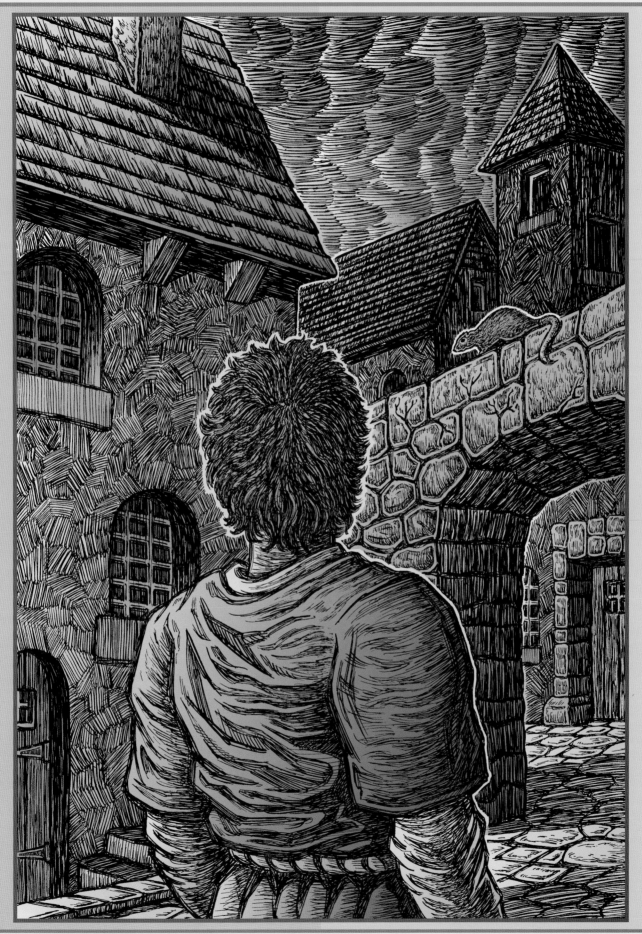

TOM DUNNE
e-mail: dunne@mindspring.com
www.tomdunneart.com

LISA FALKENSTERN

Califon Graphics

To view more work, see Graphics Artists Guild Directory of Illustration Vol. 12-21.

904 RAVINE ROAD, CALIFON, NJ 07830
Phone: (908) 832-5789 Fax: (908) 832-2445
Email: lisamilt@mindspring.com or lisa@lisafalkensternart.com

LISA FALKENSTERN

Califon Graphics

To view more work, see Graphics Artists Guild Directory of Illustration Vol. 12-21.

904 RAVINE ROAD, CALIFON, NJ 07830
Phone: (908) 832-5789 Fax: (908) 832-2445
Email: lisamilt@mindspring.com or lisa@lisafalkensternart.com

Hello!
ciao!
Liisa Chauncy Guida
...A Source of Whimsy with Children & More!
www.GuidaArt.com
Studio 970-845-0771
Liisa@GuidaArt.com
aloha!
hola!

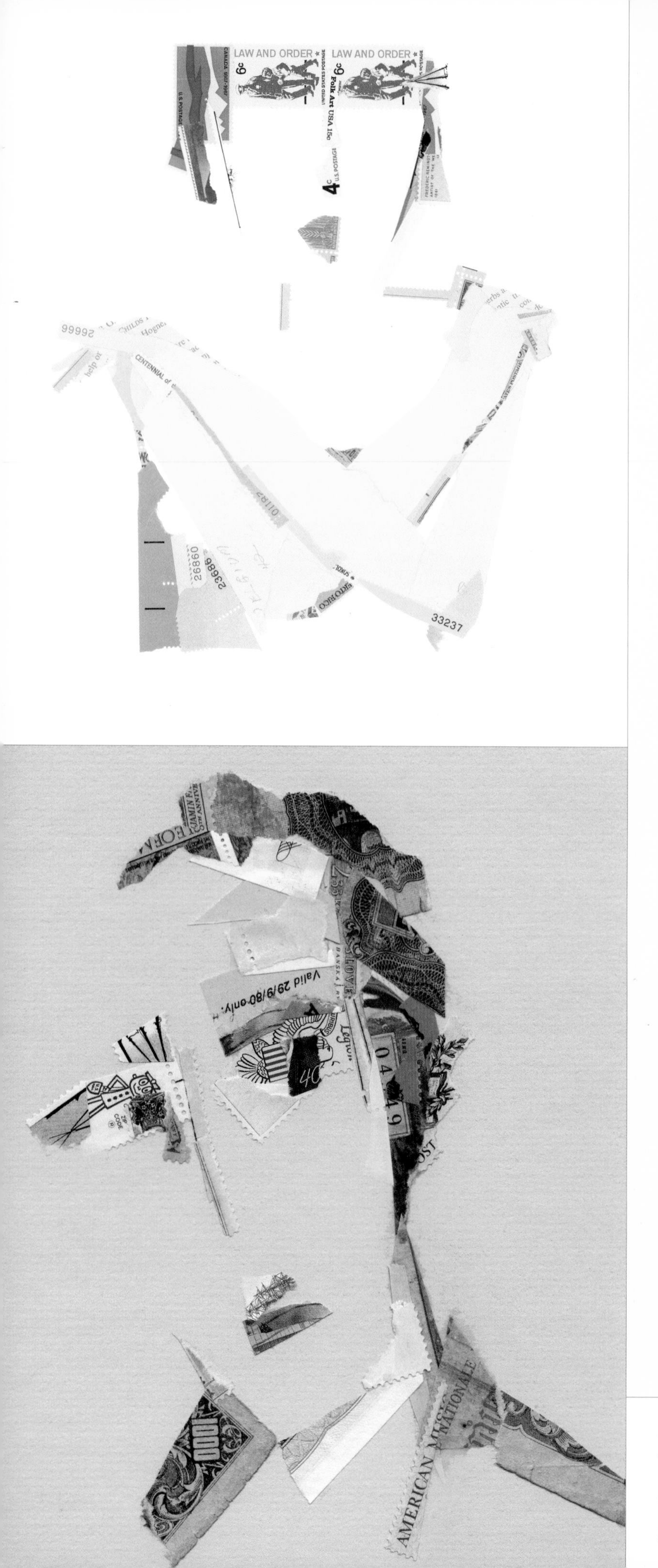

JULIE HELLER ROSENFELD
EMAIL: JULIE@JULIEHELLERROSENFELD.COM
&/OR JULIEHELLERROSENFELD@MAC.COM
ST.LOUIS [314] 574·6958

Jeremy Staub - Killustration, Ink
email: Killustration@yahoo.com
website: www.killustrationink.com
phone: 914.522.4822

Killustration, Ink.

MARCOS

ken orvidas
425 867 3072
orvidas.com

worth magazine. corporate directors and officers
are protected from litigation when another is sued.

ORVIDAS

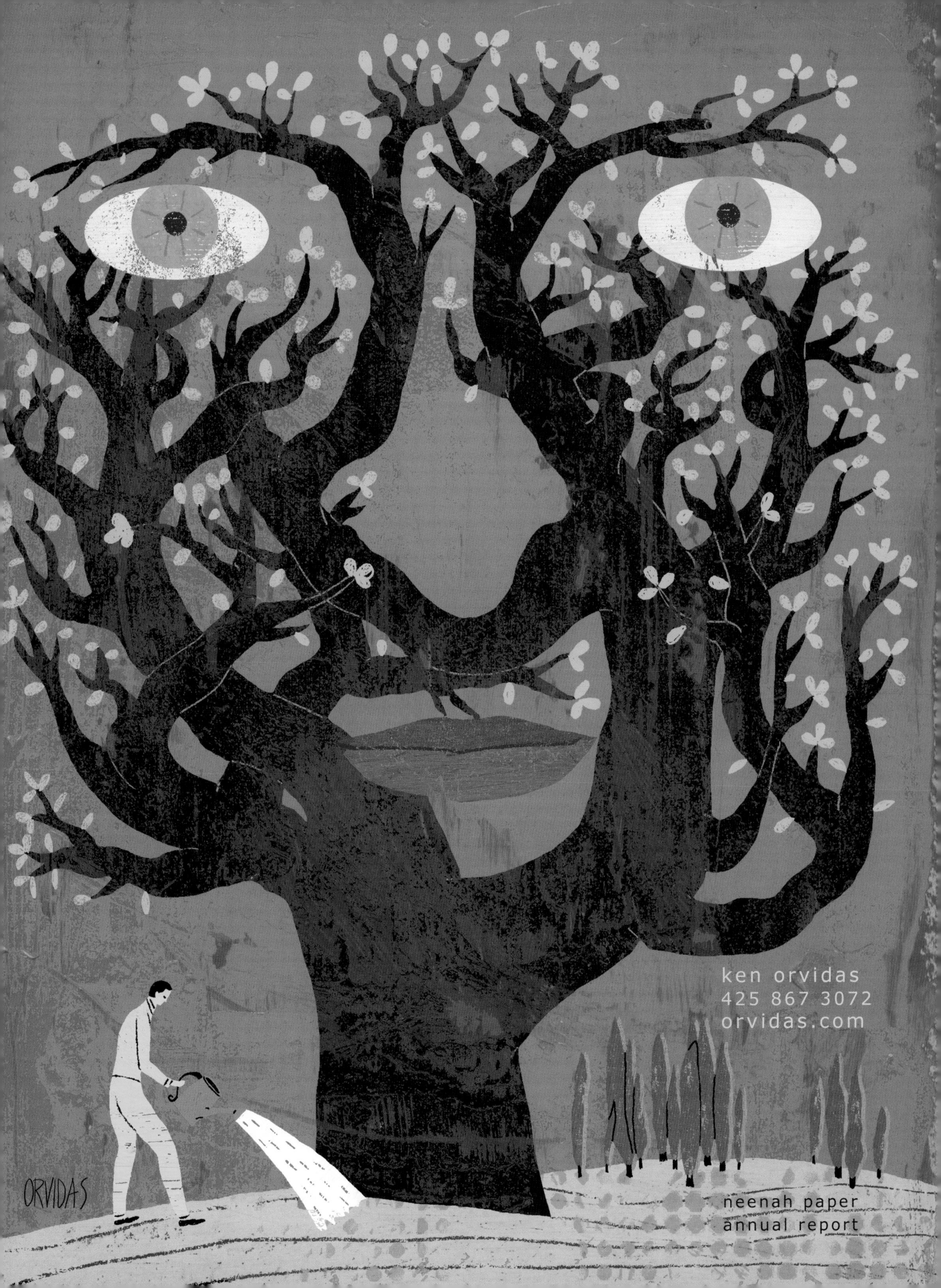

ORVIDAS
ken orvidas
425 867 3072
orvidas.com
neenah paper
annual report

beckyhearner.com

Becky Hearner
illustration

Cooking

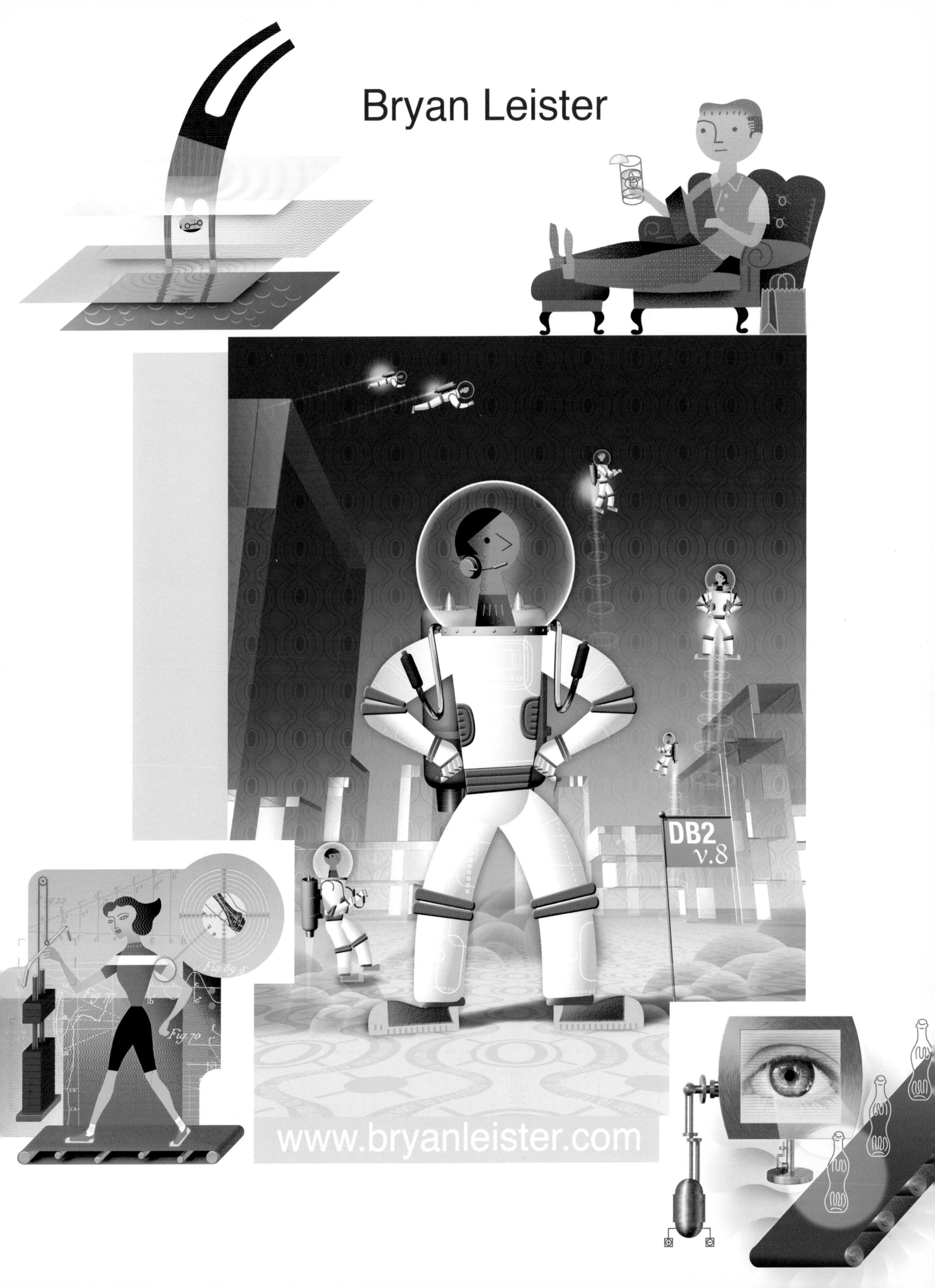
Bryan Leister
DB2
v.8
Fig 89
Fig 70
www.bryanleister.com

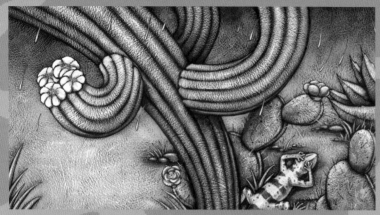

www.melissaturk.com

Joe LeMonnier

Desert
Lizah
ADRIA
Fangetall
ALBANY
Territory of Peace
Eastcliff
Albany Road
Map Legend
River
Road
Railroad
MONROVIA
SARUM
Field of the Kings
OMARUS
Old Judge's
GOTTHARD
Great Canyon
Kellen
Valley of the Rocks
Mines
N
W
E
S
Mining Camp
Muirk
King's Cottage
PALATIA
General's House
Caves of Laurel

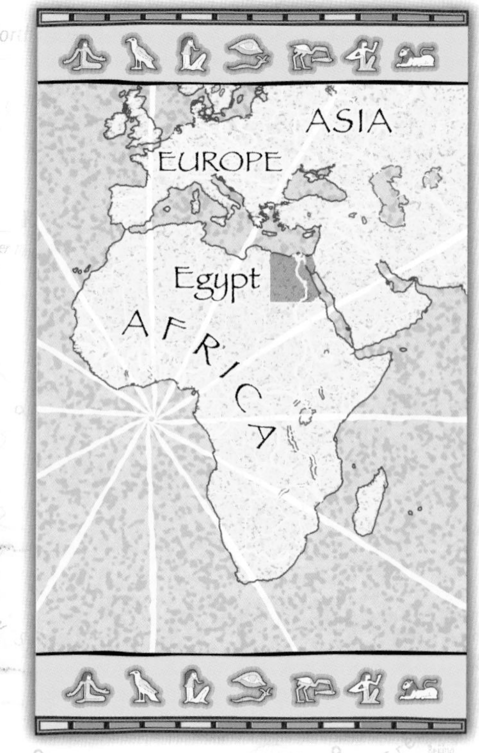
ASIA
EUROPE
Egypt
AFRICA

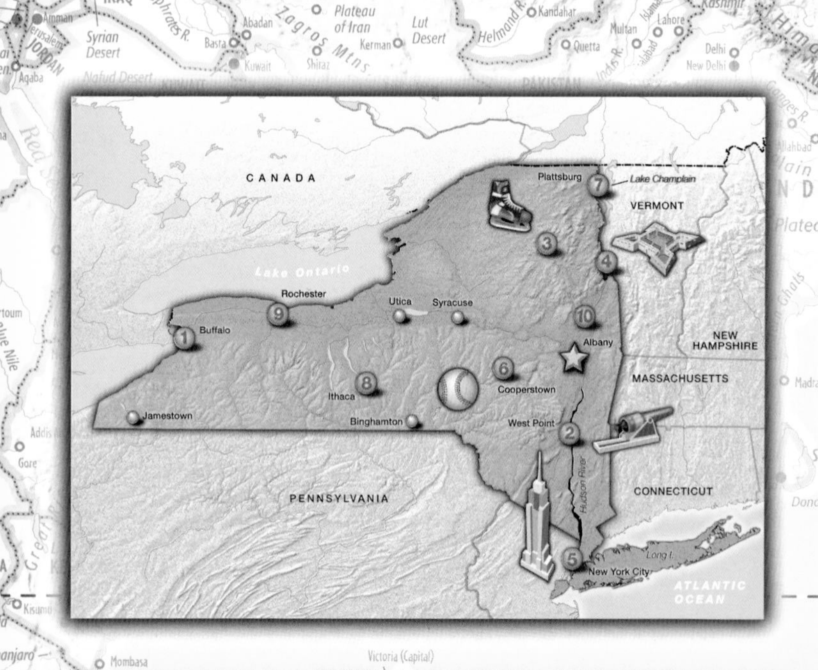
CANADA
Plattsburg
Lake Champlain
VERMONT
Lake Ontario
Rochester
Utica
Syracuse
Buffalo
Albany
NEW HAMPSHIRE
Cooperstown
MASSACHUSETTS
Ithaca
Jamestown
Binghamton
West Point
PENNSYLVANIA
CONNECTICUT
Hudson River
Long I.
New York City
ATLANTIC OCEAN

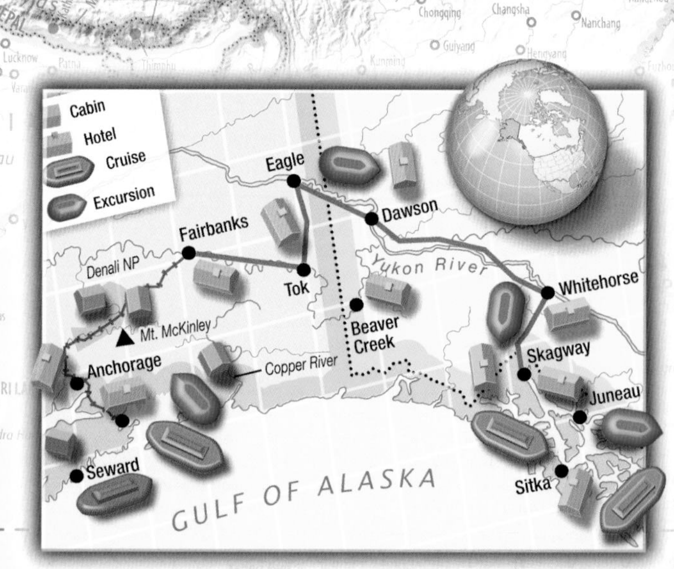
Cabin
Hotel
Cruise
Excursion
Eagle
Dawson
Fairbanks
Denali NP
Tok
Yukon River
Whitehorse
Beaver Creek
Mt. McKinley
Skagway
Anchorage
Copper River
Juneau
Seward
GULF OF ALASKA
Sitka

Melissa Turk
THE ARTIST NETWORK

(845) 368-8606 melissa@melissaturk.com www.melissaturk.com

Nancy Lane

Melissa Turk
THE ARTIST NETWORK

(845) 368-8606 melissa@melissaturk.com www.melissaturk.com

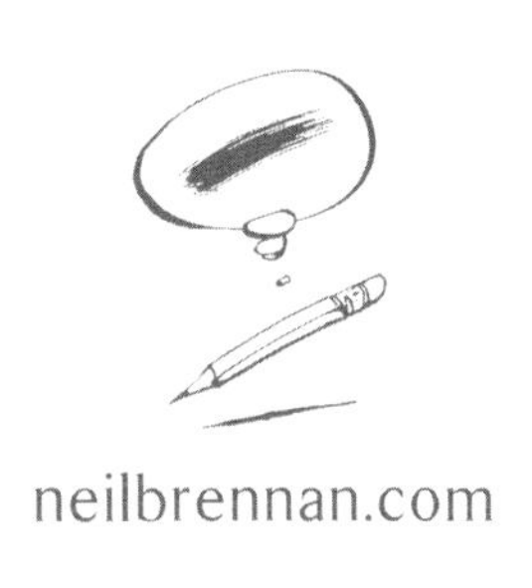

neilbrennan.com

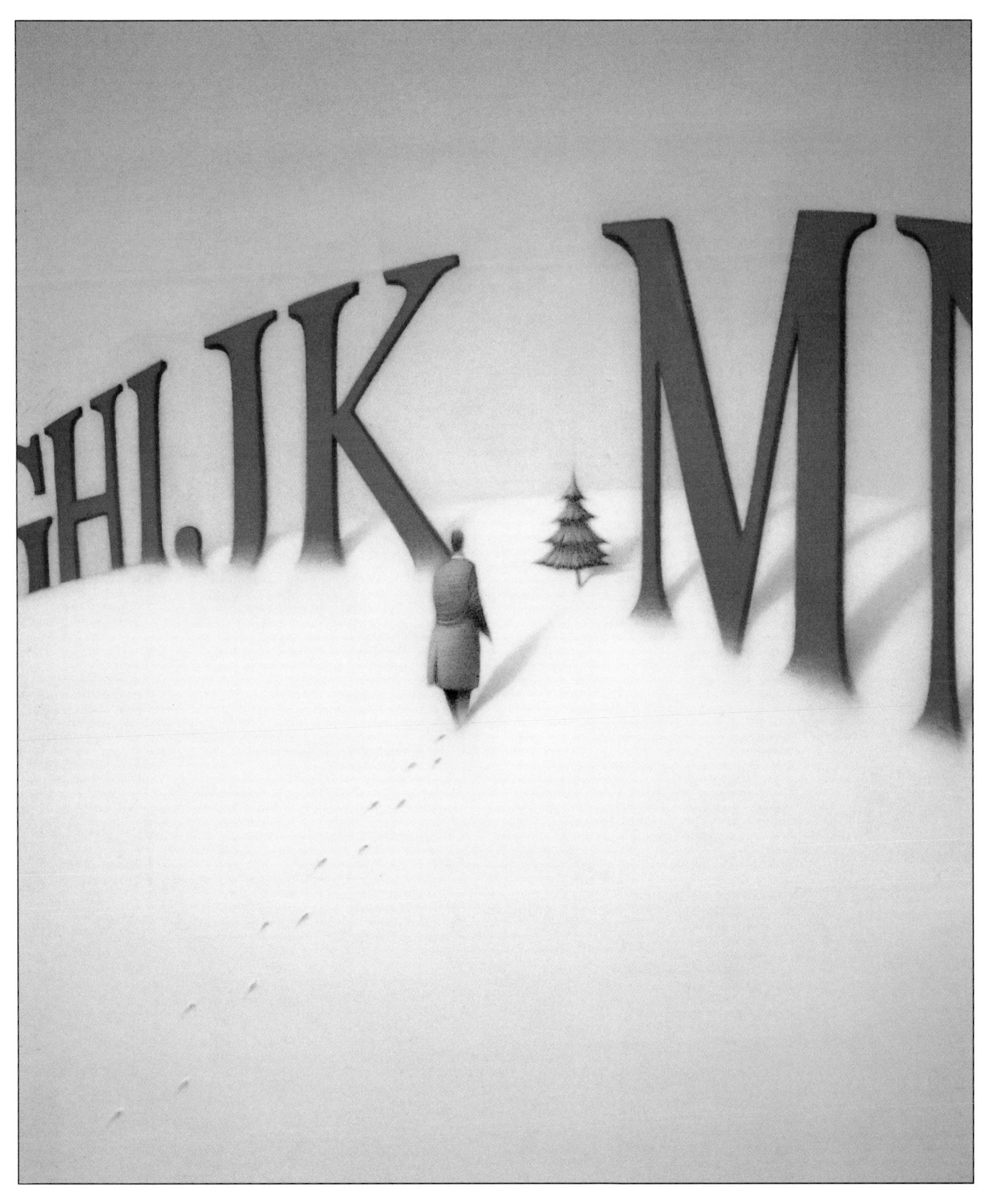
GHIJK
MN

"No L" ...(noel)

NEIL BRENNAN

757 875 0148

Jeffreydecoster.com
(415)-822-9430

Jui Ishida
DAS GRÜP
represented by:
Carrie Perlow 310. 540. 5958 www.dasgrup.com

THE CODE OF FAIR PRACTICE

FOR THE GRAPHIC COMMUNICATION INDUSTRY

The New Code of Fair Practice upholds existing laws and practices. A formally adopted Code of Fair Practice will serve to explain the manners and etiquette defining the professional relationships throughout the visual communications industries. It will serve as a standard of ethical practices between creators and clients. It will also help educate those entering the profession to accepted codes of behavior.

GRAPHIC ARTISTS GUILD

90 John Street, Suite 403
New York, NY 10038
212-791-3400
www.gag.org

RELATIONS BETWEEN ARTISTS AND BUYERS
The word "artist" should be understood to include creative people in the field of visual communications such as illustration, graphic design, photography, film and television. This code provides the graphic communications industry with an accepted standard of ethics and professional conduct. It presents guidelines for the voluntary conduct of persons in the industry, which may be modified by written agreement between the parties.

ARTICLE 1
Negotiations between an artist or the artist's representative and a client shall be conducted only through an authorized buyer.

ARTICLE 2
Orders or agreements between an artist or artist's representative and buyer should be in writing and shall include the specific rights which are being transferred, the specific fee arrangement agreed to by the parties, delivery date and a summarized description of the work.

ARTICLE 3
All changes or additions not due to the fault of the artist or artist's representative should be billed to the buyer as an additional and separate charge.

ARTICLE 4
There should be no charges to the buyer for revisions or retakes made necessary by errors on the part of the artist or the artist's representative.

ARTICLE 5
If work commissioned by a buyer is postponed or canceled, a "kill-fee" should be negotiated based on time allotted, effort expended and expenses incurred. In addition, other lost work shall be considered.

ARTICLE 6
Completed work shall be promptly paid for in full and the artwork shall be returned promptly to the artist. Payment due the artist shall not be contingent upon third-party approval or payment.

ARTICLE 7
Alterations shall not be made without consulting the artist. Where alterations or retakes are necessary, the artist shall be given the opportunity of making such changes.

ARTICLE 8
The artist shall notify the buyer of any anticipated delay in delivery. Should the artist fail to keep the contract through unreasonable delay or non-conformance with agreed specifications, it will be considered a breach of contract by the artist. Should the agreed timetable be delayed due to the buyer's failure, the artist should endeavor to adhere as closely as possible to the original schedule as other commitments permit.

ARTICLE 9 (new)
Whenever practical, the buyer of artwork shall provide the artist with samples of the reproduced artwork for self-promotion purposes.

ARTICLE 10
There shall be no undisclosed rebates, discounts, gifts, or bonuses requested by or given to buyers by the artist or representative.

ARTICLE 11
Artwork and copyright ownership are vested in the hands of the artist unless agreed to in writing. No works shall be duplicated, archived or scanned without the artist's prior authorization.

ARTICLE 12
Original artwork, and any material object used to store a computer file containing original artwork, remains the property of the artist unless it is specifically purchased. It is distinct from the purchase of any reproduction rights.* All transactions shall be in writing.

ARTICLE 13
In case of copyright transfers, only specified rights are transferred. All unspecified rights remain vested with the artist. All transactions shall be in writing.

ARTICLE 14
Commissioned artwork is not to be considered as "work for hire" unless agreed to in writing before work begins.

ARTICLE 15
When the price of work is based on limited use and later such work is used more extensively, the artist shall receive additional payment.

ARTICLE 16
Art or photography should not be copied for any use, including client presentation or "comping" without the artist's prior authorization. If exploratory work, comprehensives, or preliminary photographs from an assignment are subsequently chosen for reproduction, the artist's permission shall be secured and the artist shall receive fair additional payment.

ARTICLE 17
If exploratory work, comprehensives, or photographs are bought from an artist with the intention or possibility that another artist will be assigned to do the finished work, this shall be in writing at the time of placing the order.

ARTICLE 18 (new)
Electronic rights are separate from traditional media and shall be separately negotiated. In the absence of a total copyright transfer or a work-for-hire agreement, the right to reproduce artwork in media not yet discovered is subject to negotiation.

ARTICLE 19
All published illustrations and photographs should be accompanied by a line crediting the artist by name, unless otherwise agreed to in writing.

ARTICLE 20
The right of an illustrator to sign work and to have the signature appear in all reproductions should remain intact.

ARTICLE 21
There shall be no plagiarism of any artwork.

ARTICLE 22
If an artist is specifically requested to produce any artwork during unreasonable working hours, fair additional remuneration shall be paid.

ARTICLE 23
All artwork or photography submitted as samples to a buyer should bear the name of the artist or artists responsible for the work. An artist shall not claim authorship of another's work.

ARTICLE 24
All companies that receive artist portfolios, samples, etc. shall be responsible for the return of the portfolio to the artist in the same condition as received.

ARTICLE 25
An artist entering into an agreement with a representative for exclusive representation shall not accept an order from nor permit work to be shown by any other representative. Any agreement which is not intended to be exclusive should set forth the exact restrictions agreed upon between the parties.

ARTICLE 26
Severance of an association between artist and representative should be agreed to in writing. The agreement should take into consideration the length of time the parties have worked together as well as the representative's financial contribution to any ongoing advertising or promotion. No representative should continue to show an artist's samples after the termination of an association.

ARTICLE 27
Examples of an artist's work furnished to a representative or submitted to a prospective buyer shall remain the property of the artist, should not be duplicated without the artist's authorization and shall be returned promptly to the artist in good condition.

ARTICLE 28**
Interpretation of the Code for the purposes of arbitration shall be in the hands of the Joint Ethics Committee or other body designated to resolve the dispute, and is subject to changes and additions at the discretion of the parent organizations through their appointed representatives on the Committee. Arbitration by the Joint Ethics Committee or other designated body shall be binding among the parties, and decisions may be entered for judgment and execution.

ARTICLE 29
Work on speculation; Contests. Artists and designers who accept speculative assignments (whether directly from a client or be entering a contest or competition) risk anticipated fees, expenses, and the potential opportunity to pursue other, rewarding assignments. Each artist shall decide individually whether to enter art contests or design competitions, provide free services, work on speculation, or work on a contingency basis.

*Artwork ownership, copyright ownership and ownership and rights transferred after January 1, 1978 are to be in compliance with the Federal Copyright Revision Act of 1976. ** The original Article 28 has been deleted and replaced by Article 29.

A31654
© Jack Unruh, 2005

Let's draw the line on STOCK
illustration growers of AMERICA

DIRECTORY OF ILLUSTRATION INDEX

STYLE/TECHNIQUE/SUBJECT SPECIALTY

NO. 22

CREATIVE TALENT ORGANIZED IN

CREATIVE CATEGORIES

3D COLLAGE

3D COMPUTER

AIRBRUSH

ANIMATION

COLLAGE

CUT PAPER

FINE ART

GRAPHIC DESIGN

LINE ART

LOGO DESIGN

MULTIMEDIA

PAINTERLY

PAPER SCULPTURE

PASTEL/ COLORED PENCIL

PASTEL/ COLORED PENCIL

PEN & INK

PHOTO ILLUSTRATION

REALISM

STORYBOARDS & COMPS

TECHNICAL

WATERCOLOR

WEB DESIGN

WOODCUT & SCRATCHBOARD

ACTION/ADVENTURE

ADVERTISING

ANIMALS

ANUAL REPORTS

ARCHITECTURAL

BOOK COVERS

BOOK COVERS

CHARACTER DEVELOPMENT

CHARTS & MAPS

CHILDREN

CHILDREN'S BOOKS / PRODUCTS

CHILDREN'S BOOKS / PRODUCTS

COLLATERAL

COMIC BOOK

CONCEPTUAL

CORPORATE

EDITORIAL

EDITORIAL

FASHION & COSMETICS

FOOD

GREETING CARDS

HISTORICAL

LANDSCAPE

LICENSING

MEDICAL

MURALS

MYSTERY

PACKAGING

PORTRAIT

POSTERS

PRODUCT

ROMANCE

SCIENCE FICTION/ FANTASY

SCIENCE & NATURE

SCIENTIFIC

SPORTS

TOYS & GAMES

TOYS & GAMES

WEB SITE ILLUSTRATION

WILDLIFE

CREATIVE PEOPLE ARE LUCKY

CELEBRATE GREAT FORTUNE

No. 22

PROMOTING GREAT TALENT COAST TO COAST

EVERY HOUR, EVERY DAY, ALL YEAR

GRAPHIC ARTISTS GUILD'S

DIRECTORY OF ILLUSTRATION

MARKETING 365 DAYS A YEAR : BOOK RELEASE IN NOVEMBER 2006

NO. 23